MEDICAL JOURNALISM

The Writing, Design and Production of
Local Medical, Pharmaceutical and
Hospital Publications

Edited by
Craig D. Burrell, M.D.

SANDOZ CORPORATION

Library of Congress Catalog Card Number: 86-60059
ISBN: 0-913046-16-7

Printed in the United States of America

Published by Sandoz Corporation
608 Fifth Avenue, New York, N.Y. 10021

CONTENTS

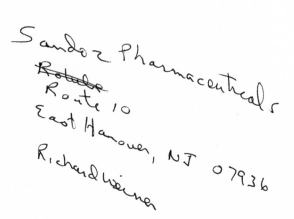

Sandoz Pharmaceuticals
~~Rotule~~
Route 10
East Hanover, NJ 07936
Richard Weiner

INTRODUCTION

Several thousand medical and pharmaceutical journals are published in the United States, ranging from such well known publications as the *Journal of the American Medical Association* and the *New England Journal of Medicine* to specialized archives, newsletters and magazines. In addition to the national journals, there are over 1000 small-circulation publications—published by state, county and city medical societies, state pharmaceutical associations, hospitals and other local groups.

Many of the editors of these publications are physicians and pharmacists who have had no journalism training. Since 1974, Sandoz Pharmaceuticals has provided a unique service to these editors with the Sandoz Medical Journalism Program. For example, over 30 one-day workshops for medical, pharmaceutical and hospital publication editors have been conducted in every part of the country. The editors provide their own transportation, and Sandoz conducts the program. The faculty consists of Professor Paul Fisher, a graphics specialist at the University of Missouri (the world's largest school of journalism), and other renowned experts in journalism.

Several hundred editors have attended these workshops, and also received other help from Sandoz, including a quarterly newsletter.

The Sandoz Medical Journalism Program has directly and indirectly resulted in major improvements in the design and writing of many health publications. Dozens of publications have made major changes, including totally new formats. Thus, the editors and their readers have benefited.

Perhaps the most exciting component is the award program. Sandoz presents four annual awards of $500 each to outstanding medical, pharmaceutical and hospital publications. The awards are presented by Sandoz executives at the annual conventions of medical, pharmaceutical and hospital associations, including the American Association of Medical Society Executives.

In several cases, award recipients used the prize money innovatively. *Atlanta Medicine* gave its award to three medical students for essays in its journal. The *Journal of the Indiana Medical Association* set up an award program for outstanding research papers. The Medical Center Hospitals of Norfolk, Virginia, donated the award to its building fund. The Worcester (Massachusetts) Medical Society used the award money to set up a fund to send each year's editor to the Sandoz Workshop.

At several annual meetings of the State Medical Journal Group, Sandoz was praised for being "the single biggest force in the revitalization of state medical journals."

The newsletter, called *Medical Journalism*, is designed to provide easy-to-use pragmatic advice, suggestions and tips on writing, editing, layout, graphics, design, production, and all the other elements that go into the making of a successful publication.

Medical Journalism is for the physician who devotes a few hours a week as editor of a medical society magazine or newsletter, the executive director who produces a publication as part of a medical society total program, and the full-time medical journal staffer. Many of these people have little or no journalism experience or training; others are quite skilled with backgrounds that well qualify them for what they are doing. In addition, the newsletter is sent to pharmacists who edit publications of state pharmaceutical associations, and editors of external publications of hospitals and a variety of specialized medical publications, such as newsletters of chapters of national medical societies.

This book is a compendium of articles that have appeared in *Medical Journalism*. In addition, several original articles were commissioned, and a few articles are reprinted from medical journals.

Some of the pieces are direct quotes. Others paraphrase what the authors said. Still others are combinations of these two types of articles or originated with the editorial staff of the *Medical Journalism* newsletter.

Of course, most of the prices quoted in the articles about budgets have risen over the years. Also, many of the contributors have changed jobs, some publications have changed addresses, and a few individuals—and publications—have died. However, the advice offered is still valuable and we thank all of the contributors to the Sandoz *Medical Journalism* newsletter, wherever they are. I also appreciate the key role of public relations counselor Richard Weiner, who has actively participated in the project since its inception.

For its part, Sandoz Pharmaceuticals has derived great pleasure from its sponsorship of a project that has helped to advance the cause of good medical journalism. I personally have been delighted at the difference the newsletters and other aspects of the program have made in the writing, editing, design and production of many publications.

We hope that this book is more than a memento of the program, and is useful to its readers. If the book is useful to other journalists, then we indeed have succeeded beyond our primary objective. The cover is based on a design by Sarah Burrell.

Craig D. Burrell, M.D.
Vice President, External Affairs,
Sandoz Corporation

WRITING

Advice from Professor Ranly

To begin this section, advice on good writing is offered by Don Ranly, professor of journalism at the University of Missouri and a lecturer at many Sandoz Medical Journalism workshops.

First, Professor Ranly presented the following example of what started as a good idea but turned into an example of bad writing.

To communicate effectively with the written word, it must be emphasized to the writer that clarity, conciseness, simplicity and consistency are the paths to take to good writing.

The sentence, Don Ranly noted, is too long and awkward. Starting with prepositional phrases often is convoluted. The passive voice ("it must be emphasized") rarely is as effective as the active tense. "The paths to take" is trite.

Professor Ranly reviewed lots of examples of this type of writing in medical and pharmaceutical publications. Here are a few excerpts from his fast-paced presentation about writing for publication, as well as correspondence.

You sit down to write a letter, and the words just seem to fail you. You give it a stab anyway.

"Pursuant to our conversation November 30, I would like to address the question as to why . . ."

Hmm. Sounds rather legal. But you're not quite sure what you want to say, and it's easy to hide that uncertainty with lots of high falutin words. The reader will never understand what you're talking about, but it *sounds* important, doesn't it?

That is one of the major failings of writing today, whether in letters, memos or articles, said Professor Ranly.

"Complicated words don't make you sound more intelligent," he warned. "You should write to express, not impress."

One of his chief complaints about writing is the use of the "ize" words—which he says are pretentious and hurt credibility. "If we don't stop *utilizing* the English language, we're going to *finalize* it," he cautioned, adding that the worst examples are "prioritize," "utilize" and even "conversationalize."

He said business letters and also articles should be personal, informal and conversational. "Use the word 'you' in your writing—it helps break down the formality. And use simple, familiar words."

3

He suggested first outlining to help you determine what is important. And then once you begin the writing process, remember the word "short" —short words, short sentences, short paragraphs.

"People aren't reading anymore," Ranly noted, "and they are comprehending less. So it's important that our writing be clear and easy to read."

Ranly listed his "Seven C's" to follow for basic good writing:

1. *Correct.* Information must be accurate, both factually and grammatically. Check for correctly spelled words, good grammar and proper punctuation.
2. *Consistent.* Use a good dictionary and stylebook for abbreviations, capitalizations and spellings.
3. *Clarity.* Be clear—don't garble the message with unnecessary words.
4. *Concise.* Brief is better. It will be more clear. More people will read it. Conciseness breeds clarity.
5. *Coherent.* Your writing should be logical. The single greatest fault in writing today is incoherence. Ask yourself if what you wrote makes sense.
6. *Complete.* Is all the information there? Are all the questions answered? "Never underestimate readers' intelligence, but never overestimate their knowledge."
7. *Creative.* Try to add some imagination to your writing. Don't be boring.

Dr. Ranly recommended cutting by one-third anything you write. Most of the time needless information is included, and by cutting it out, more people will read what you have written.

Readers must be helped along from one paragraph to the next, and that is called "transition." You can repeat words from the previous paragraph, or carry through an idea, but transitions must be written deliberately. "Moreover" and "nevertheless" are good transitions.

The journalism professor urged all writers to avoid the passive voice whenever possible. To see if you are using the passive voice (where the subject is being acted upon, rather than doing the acting), he offered three tests for the passive voice: 1) it always has a form of the verb "to be"; 2) the preposition "by" is always there, whether implied or direct; and 3) it is a past participle. Example: It is estimated that . . .

He also recommended avoiding the "his/her" problem by using the plural. Or try switching to the second person 'you.' "

Here are a few words and phrases to avoid: "pursuant to," "hopefully," "there was," "there is" and "recently."

Do you need to know why Don Ranly hates these words? We hope it's obvious If not, let us know!

The common-sense rule of good writing applies to correspondence, as well as journalism. Here are a few examples from Don Ranly of how you can cut unnecessary words and phrases from your correspondence.

Too Wordy	*Much Better*
We beg to acknowledge receipt of . . .	Many thanks for your letter.
We are attaching hereto a copy of . . .	Here is your copy of . . .
We are forwarding under separate cover . . .	You'll receive separately . . .
Enclosed please find . . .	Enclosed is/are . . .
We wish to take this opportunity to thank you . . .	Thank you for . . .
We ask you to kindly . . .	Please . . .
In the amount of $75 . . .	For $75; of $75
Under date of June 15	On June 15

Shephard on Style, Grammar and Word Usage

Medical and pharmaceutical journals have improved tremendously during the last few years, particularly in design, typography, layout and graphics. Writing improvements also have been demonstrated, but they generally have not been as dramatic. It's extremely difficult for an editor to change the writing of physicians and other contributors, though it often may be essential.

The trend is away from clinical reports and other scientific articles in local journals, and the current emphasis is on news and features. Editors thus now have a greater need for writing which is clear, colorful and correct. Similes, metaphors and other figures of speech; alliterations, repetition and other attention-getting devices, quotations and other personalizations are some of the tools of the editor's trade.

Graphics and writing have been the subjects of the Sandoz Medical Journalism Workshops. We are proud to note that many editors attribute improvements in their publications to advice they received from the Sandoz faculty.

Medical journalism workshops also are conducted by other organizations and are not restricted to the United States. David A. E. Shephard, M.D., of the Kellogg Centre for Advanced Studies in Primary Care in Montreal, Quebec, Canada, has conducted many writing courses throughout the world.

Following are major sections of an article on medical writing by Dr. Shephard, which is based on a workshop he conducted in Australia. The article appeared in the January 12, 1980, issue of *The Medical Journal of Australia* and was reprinted by permission of Dr. Shephard, who is an anesthesiologist, and the *Journal.*

(We have retained the British spelling and style . . . Dr. Shephard's advice is universal.)

Writing melds two elements—form and content. For most physicians, content is less a source of difficulty than form, for all physicians are trained to deal with content, or data, whereas few are trained to write—to be familiar with problems of form, or style. In the reporting of formal investigative work, what is reported is of primary importance, though how the findings are reported does demand an understanding of at least the rudiments of style. Indeed, the need for clarity in writing may be crucial; ambiguous writing has even led to fatality. Then style is of enormous concern.

Constructing good paragraphs requires judgment. There are different ways of writing paragraphs. One is to introduce a new thought in the first sentence (the thesis or topic sentence) and to develop the thought in succeeding sentences. Other ways are to ask and answer questions; to compare and contrast a series of items; to analyze a statement; to describe events or findings chronologically or systematically; and to discuss causes and effects. There are however, no rules for paragraph construction, except that a body of thought be developed. But each paragraph should develop the paragraph topic completely; as one paragraph is succeeded by another, a logical break in thought should be evident; and each paragraph should be integrated into the whole paper. Good writers have an unerring sense of paragraph construction. The paragraph becomes a stylistic device, each contributing to the effect a unit of thought should produce.

The sentence thus either introduces an idea within the paragraphed unit of thought or enables the unit of thought to be developed in a paragraph. The sentence is the smallest entity in a piece of writing that can stand alone; therefore it is of great structural importance. And it is within the sentence that the proper words can be placed in the proper places; the sentence thus is another stylistic device.

As is true of paragraphs, there are no rules for construction of sentences, but guides are useful. One guide is to vary the construction of a group of sentences—to vary particularly the words with which different sentences start, the order of words in different sentences, and the number of words in different sentences. (This cannot be a rule because at times it is desirable to preserve similarity of construction, or "parallelism," rather than variety, the purpose being to facilitate the flow of thought; but the overall objective is to avoid monotony.) If one were to choose a single useful guide, sentence length would likely be that guide, because one of the commonest faults in medical writing is excessive length of sentences.

A sentence carries an idea—preferably just the idea expressed in the number of words that can effectively transmit that idea without presenting to the brain material that overloads its short term memory capability. A sentence of 100 words is therefore likely to be more difficult to understand than one of 10. One might formulate a rule based on length, but it is not possible to draw the dividing line between what is reasonable and what is not. A long sentence, particularly if it contains short words and is punctuated well, may be easier to understand than a short sentence constructed of just a few long, perhaps technical, words. (The sentence "Ontogeny recapitulates phylogeny" is an example of a three-word sentence that may well be difficult to understand without recourse to a dictionary.)

Thus a guide is better than any rule, and, concerning sentence length, it is useful to ask yourself, in revising your manuscript in its early stages, whether it might be shortened either by omitting redundant words or, better still, by making out of single sentences, two, three or even four sentences. This last sentence contains 51 words. It is reasonable to suggest that the same material be presented in a different style, in four sentences, as follows:

A guide is therefore better than a rule. Here is a useful guide to sentence length. When revising your manuscript ask yourself whether you can omit redundant words. Better still, break a long sentence into two, three or even four sentences.

The point is this: What are the proper places for the words, and what circumstances do you, as author, judge appropriate in creating the effect that sentence length in a particular context should produce? This is a matter of individual judgment. It is clear, too, that rewarding flexibility in construction is available to the writer for whom style serves the needs of clarity and, at the same time, of individuality.

Grammar

The following passage is instructive with respect to grammar, syntax and punctuation:

"Injuries which are intrinsic to the wearing of seat belts are numerous, however, the overall benefit more than outweigh these when you consider that the injury from seat belts is an alternative to a more severe injury or even death. In a survey done by Volvo in Sweden of 28,000 accidents under 60 m.p.h. involving 37,000 occupants. In this survey there were no fatalities in the lap shoulder (3 point) belt wearers."

It is a simple passage but it lacks style. Several flaws prevent a ready flow of thought. None of the flaws, considered separately, is serious, but all taken together make a second or a third reading necessary before the meaning becomes clear. Grammar, syntax and punctuation are faulty and as a result the reader has to work at the passage because the author has put obstacles in the way. Let us consider it further.

Grammar is no more than the set of rules that govern the way words are placed in relation to each other so that meaning rather than obscurity results. In the first sentence the main fault is the lack of agreement between the noun "benefit" and the verb "outweigh." You cannot tell whether the noun should be plural (in view of the plurality of the verb) or whether the verb should be in the singular because the noun is in the singular. Agreement between the noun and the verb is essential to clarity; in its absence, clarity is obscured. The lack of subject-verb agreement is one reason it is necessary to read the passage more than once.

The passage is syntactically weak also, syntax simply consisting of rules that determine the meaningful construction of sentences. In reading the second sentence of the sample passage, on its own, you expect more to come after the word "occupants"; the sentence is incomplete. You must read the sentence more than once, likely then concluding that the probable solution is to join the second and third sentences by deleting the words "In this survey" from the third sentence. Again, a solution can be found, but an author should never make the reader work at reaching the solution.

Implicit in what has been said is that the punctuation also is faulty. One fault is the period after the word "occupants," for this period marks the end of a sentence at that point. Another is the pair of commas that enclose the word "however" in the first sentence; better would be a semicolon after the word "numerous" instead of a comma, for theoretically the coordinating conjunction "however" could modify the preceding or succeeding clause. (It is likely, though, that the conjunction is more closely related to the second of the two clauses.)

Grammar, syntax and punctuation may be abhorrent to medical writers, or concern with them may amount to just an irritant. The simple fact, however, is that they are of practical value in facilitating communication; when they are faulty they prevent one from communicating clearly. Style demands a sense of grammar, syntax and punctuation, and the wise writer seeks to understand their underlying rationale instead of rejecting them.

Word Usage

The essence of style is the choice and patterning of words. The right words give precision, clarity, conciseness and directness, especially desirable in medical writing. Moreover, an individual's words chosen and arranged as only that individual sees fit give a unique and therefore an interesting approach to a particular topic.

The use of words is too large a matter to be even summarized here, but two points must be made. First, much medical writing is of one unimaginative mold. Too often medical writing is characterized by excessive use of impersonal pronouns, preference for verbs in the passive voice, delight in abstract polysyllabic words of Latin and Greek origin, over-reliance on adverbs and adjectives called up to support weak verbs and nouns, and a lifeless miasma of jargon and cliches. Such writing is unnecessarily complex and fortuitously obscure; it is also impersonal, unimaginative and boring. Second, it is seldom understood how simple it is to convert grandiose and opaque prose into plain and direct language—the language that invigorates and distinguishes an individual's writing and so stamps it with uniqueness of style.

Two sentences will illustrate my points. Compare the following original with the succeeding revision:

Consent to take photographs of patients and informants was informally granted after I started data collection.

Patients and informants informally consented to being photographed after I began collecting data.

The meaning of these two sentences is the same but the style is different. A minor difference is the length: version 2 contains three less words. More notable is the more frequent use of the verb form in the revised version, as compared to the noun form. In the original, the words "consent," "photographs" and "collection" are nouns; in the revision, the verb form of these nouns has been used. Since verbs describe action, the revised version is more vigorous than the original. The sense of action is strengthened by the preference for the active voice in the revision instead of the passive form of "consent . . . was . . . granted"; the active form of "patients . . . consented" describes action on the part of a particular group of persons.

These differences are small, but when they are multiplied throughout a piece of writing the overall difference is considerable and worth striving for. They are relevant to style in that preference for the verb form and for the active voice contributes to vigor, one of the circumstances that contribute to the effect that is often desirable for a given thought to produce.

It is not easy to write well, but it is easier when one knows the elements of good writing. For many physicians the problem is to become aware of these elements and then to recognize the simple fact that by incorporating them into their writing they will make their communication more interesting, more vigorous and certainly more lucid. By doing so they will also save time. Underlying this problem is a more basic one: instruction in writing is not a part of medical curricula and consequently the elements of style, which were learned early in school, remain as indefinable and intangible as one's childhood memories. Such a lack of instruction is surprising, because writing is an integral part of the physician-author's work that gives rise to the writing.

Ogilvy & Mather Formulates
Ten Principles of Good Writing

Tips on how to write more effectively are published just about every day. Magazines for editors, such as *Medical Communications* (the Journal of the American Medical Writers Association), newsletters for editors (such as the *Ragan Report* in Chicago and *Editorial Eye* in Alexandria, Virginia), books, articles in magazines and dozens of other sources (including the Sandoz workshops and seminars of other organizations) are so plentiful as to be overwhelming.

Fortunately, many of these tipsters repeat the same theme—keep your writing as simple as possible. Readers of medical and pharmaceutical publications are highly educated and sophisticated. More important, they are very busy.

All of us—editors and our readers—would love to have a set of infallible rules. Perhaps someone will develop a computerized program for use on our word processors. Meanwhile, we're forced to rely on something as simple and old-fashioned as common sense. It's probably not possible to provide a "quick fix." From time to time, however, we come across a list of tips which bears repetition.

In past issues of this newsletter, we have noted that editors can learn from the creative design and writing of many of the pharmaceutical advertisements. One of the world's most famous advrtising copywriters is David Ogilvy. Perhaps you have seen his books which have had popular appeal because of his humor, candor and other qualities. His advertising agency, Ogilvy & Mather (one of the world's largest and most successful advertising agencies), has published a list of 20 principles of good writing. If you follow them faithfully, you should improve the editorial content of your publication considerably.

Here are the principles:

1. Keep in mind that the reader doesn't have much time. What you write must be clear on first reading.
2. Know where you are going. Start writing only after preparing an outline to organize your argument.
3. Make what you write easy to read. For extra emphasis, underline important sentences or phrases. You also should consider numbering your important points, putting them in indented paragraphs, or beginning each paragraph with one or two dashes.
4. Short sentences and short paragraphs are easier to read than long ones.

5. Make your writing vigorous and direct. Wherever possible, use active verbs and avoid the passive voice.
6. Avoid cliches. Find your own words.
   Cliche: Turn over every rock for a solution.
   Direct: Try hard.
7. Avoid vague modifiers.
   Vague: Slightly behind schedule.
   Precise: One day late.
8. Use specific, concrete language. Avoid technical jargon.

Jargon	*Plain English*
To impact	To affect
Resultful	Effective, to have results
Finalize	Complete

9. Find the right word. Know its precise meaning. Use your dictionary and thesaurus.
10. Avoid spelling mistakes. When in doubt, use your dictionary. If you are congenitally a bad speller, make sure your final draft gets checked by someone who isn't similarly impaired. If your writing is careless, the reader may doubt the clarity or precision of your thinking.
11. Don't overwrite or overstate. Use no more words than necessary. Remember: The Gettysburg Address consists of only 266 words.
12. Get to the point. Churchill could have said, "The position in regard to France is very serious." What he did say was, "The news from France is bad."
13. State things as simply as you can. Use familiar words and uncomplicated sentences.
14. Handle numbers consistently. Newspapers generally spell out numbers for nine and under, and use numerals for 10 and above.
15. Avoid needless words.

Cliche phrase	*Rewrite*
Have a discussion	Discuss
Hold a meeting	Meet
Consensus of opinion	Consensus
Until such times as	Until
For the purpose of	For
In the majority of instances	Usually

   Always go through your first draft once to delete unnecessary words, phrases and sentences.
16. Be concise, but readable. Terseness is a virtue, if not carried to an extreme. Don't leave out words. Write full sentences and make them count.

17. Be brief, simple and natural. Don't write, "The reasons are four-fold." Write, "There are four reasons."
18. Don't write like a lawyer or a bureaucrat. "Re" is legalese meaning "in the matter of" and is never necessary.

    The slash—as in "and/or"—is bureaucratese. Don't write, "We'll hold the meeting on Monday and/or Tuesday." Write, "We'll hold the meeting on Monday or Tuesday—or both days if necessary."
19. Never be content with your first draft. Rewrite with an eye toward simplifying and clarifying. Rearrange. Revise. Above all, cut. Mark Twain said that writers should strike out every third word on principle. "You have no idea what vigor it adds to your style."
20. Have somebody else look over your draft. It's always wise to get another person's point of view.

Rules from Blake Kellogg

The following rules for writing were offered by Blake Kellogg, associate professor of journalism at the University of Wisconsin, Madison.

Ten Rules for Writing

1. Use simple words, and use no more words than necessary.
2. Write short, direct sentences.
3. Start a new paragraph for each new idea or point.
4. Use the active voice.
   active voice: Harold edits the newsletter.
   passive voice: The newsletter is edited by Harold.
5. If two words convey a meaning equally well, choose the common one.
6. Explain technical terms in everyday words.
7. Check your facts. Be accurate.
8. Observe the rules of grammar and spelling. Refer to a usage dictionary such as "Watch Your Language" by Theodore Bernstein.
9. Write as you speak. Focus on the most interesting element just as you would tell the most interesting part of an event. (Sometimes writing should be slightly more formal than speech.)
10. Edit your copy. Delete all unnecessary material.

Mr. Kellogg continued: Good writing is clearly focused. Good writing uses simple, direct language. Good writing is easy to read and easy to understand.

Medical and pharmaceutical writing can be "good." Sometimes it's difficult to simplify writing when dealing with a highly technical field, but it can and should be done.

By its nature, medical writing frequently must use technical language. This is not only permissible, but necessary. Even the most technical terms, however, can be structured in simple direct sentences. What must be avoided in medical writing is the use of medicalese—pompous, pedantic terms designed to impress the reader at the expense of conveying the information clearly.

Usually, medical or scientific articles conform to the following format:

1. Abstract
2. Introduction
3. Materials and methods
4. Results
5. Discussion
6. References

It is helpful to your reader if you use boldface subheads designating these parts of the article.

Diagrams, charts, and photos should be numbered consecutively. They should be individually captioned and appear in the sequence they are mentioned in the article.

Your guiding rule in writing a medical or scientific article should be to make every step easy for the reader. Naturally one assumes that the material has already met the test of being "new, true, and important."

Paul Jacobi's Suggestions

Unity. Coherence. Emphasis. Style. These four basic elements of writing were discussed by Paul Jacobi at a Sandoz Medical Journalism Workshop in Los Angeles. At the time, he was professor of journalism at the Medical School at Northwestern University. He recommended the following ingredients to enliven narratives and eliminate dullness:

Competition. Conflict. Controversy. Consequence. Familiar or Famous Persons. Heartstring or Human Interest. Humor. Problem. Progress. Success. Unknown. Unusual.

He advised editors to be clear, complete, concise, constructive, credible, controversial and captivating.

Here are some other Jacobi maxims:

Don't leave creativity to the fiction writer. Use it.

Know your audience, for whom you are writing. Truly know. Fully know.

Be totally, 100 percent accurate. There is no substitute for absolute accuracy.

Clarity is essential—meaning logical structure and proper word choice.

Keep sentences short, or at least simple to follow.

Inject interest. Accuracy and clarity alone are not enough. Inject interest to win readers.

Observe the rules of good writing. Use proper grammar and spelling.

Write authoritatively. Use authority to make important points.

Good verbs and good nouns make for good writing. Avoid overuse of adjectives.

Don't try to be cute or funny if you can't be or shouldn't be.

Don't try to be overly clever.

Don't try to be pompous.

Supply adequate background in a story to make it understandable to the reader.

Ponder hard that first sentence, and that first section.

Be organized. The disorganized writer is the rambling and fuzzy writer.

Edit. Edit.

The magazine article is a moving van.

Remember focus.

Remember personality.

Avoid garbled language. Read it aloud to hear if it makes sense.

Remember Thurber's moral: "A word to the wise is not sufficient if it doesn't make any sense."

Approach your work with enjoyment or no one else will enjoy what you've been working at.

The AMA Stylebook
Guidelines from the American Medical Association

The AMA Stylebook recommends that all abbreviations should be used without periods, e.g., AMA, MD, Co, NIMH. Sorry, but we do not agree. Other stylebooks, such as *The New York Times, Associated Press* and *University of Chicago*, take a more moderate position, e.g., M.D. and Co., but acronyms and common abbreviations may omit the periods, e.g. AMA and USSR.

Whether you use MD or M.D., it will be clear to your readers, so that's not a problem. But will all of your readers know that US refers to our country, and, quick now, do you know what these abbreviations mean—SGOT, WBC, PHS, CNS, IUD, VA?

Of course, you know that these are abbreviations for serum glutamic oxaloacetic transaminase, white blood cell, Public Health Service, central nervous system, intrauterine device and Veterans Administration. Or did you think that VA refers to Virginia? And what about typos which often substitute a V for a U!

Admittedly, it's easier to decipher abbreviations within the context of an article. However, we wholeheartedly concur with the first paragraph of *The AMA Stylebook:*

"A current criticism of medical articles is the overuse of abbreviations. The medical writer should avoid such overuse; if several abbreviations are to be used in an article, care should be taken not to confuse the reader. A saving in space can never justify a loss in comprehension. If doubt arises, abbreviations may be spelled out several times in a given article."

Somehow, to us, St Louis looks incomplete, as compared to St. Louis, and, with or without a period, we still get confused about the location of Ga, La, Me and other states. As for Wyoming, we never can remember whether it's abbreviated as Wy. or Wyo., which is one reason we continue to use the full spelling.

Where there is a choice, we simply recommend that an editor use the style of spelling, punctuation, abbreviation and grammar which seems to be understandable to most readers. Once you establish the rules, make sure that you follow them and are consistent.

Every once in a while, regardless of your proficiency, it's a good idea to read a stylebook.

McGraw-Hill and other textbook, reference and technical publishers issue guidebooks for authors which also include valuable material about style for medical journal editors. One of the most comprehensive is the *Prentice-Hall Author's Guide*, which stresses the need for clear, precise language, as indicated by the following excerpt:

Most of the previous suggestions in this book concerning manuscript preparation apply as well to the technical manuscript. Nowhere are clarity and precision in the use of language more important—or more appropriate—than in a book concerned with science; a fuzzy scientific statement is worse than none at all.

Be brief; but in being brief do not be obscure. Cut away the deadwood from your sentences, and weed out the nonessential statements from your paragraphs to achieve conciseness; do not telescope the meaning. Write as simply as your subject will allow, using words from the general vocabulary wherever you can without sacrificing accuracy or practicing circumlocution.

Similarly, in the interest of clarity, avoid "dangling" constructions: "Using this factor, the velocity becomes . . ." (Does the "velocity" use the "factor"?). Be careful with the use of commas: they should be used for nonrestrictive but not for restrictive constructions. For example, there is a difference if you say "the radioactive element uranium" *or* "the radioactive element, uranium." The latter implies that there is only one radioactive element known. Avoid indefinite references such as "this," "that," "the above." The antecedent for each of these words should always be clear to the reader; if it is not clear, then the indefinite reference should be replaced by a more precise expression, or the sentence in which it appears should be recast.

Take a look at the *AMA Stylebook* (which is published by Lang Medical Publishers, P.O. Drawer L, Los Altos, CA 94022, and sells for $8.50.) As with other stylebooks, it's filled with comments about correct usage which are useful to just about every writer and editor. We especially enjoyed the discussion of misused or confused terms, such as acute and chronic, age and aged, aggravate and irritate, apt, likely and liable, case and patient, compose, comprise and consist . . . and so on.

American Usage and Style

Are the following sentences correct?
  1. *This is as insulting of a proposition as I have ever heard.*
  2. *The door was kept locked other than when the neighbors were at home.*
  3. *He has ambitions to be a bank president.*
  4. *He was the recipient of an award.*

All the above sentences are wrong.
Here are the correct, or preferable, versions.
  This is as insulting a proposition as I have ever heard.
  The door was kept locked except when the neighbors were at home.
  He has an ambition to be a bank president.
  He received an award.

The authority is Roy H. Copperud, professor of journalism at the University of California, who writes the Editorial Workshop column in *Editor & Publisher*, the weekly magazine of the newspaper industry. Professor Copperud is the author of *American Usage and Style: The Consensus.* Professor Copperud conducted the writing portion of a Sandoz Medical Journalism Workshop a few years ago in Los Angeles, so we have a special interest in his work.

American Usage and Style helps writers and other users of language attain greater precision, differentiate meanings, avoid misspellings and grammatical errors and set the proper tone.

Roy H. Copperud examines different levels of style and demolishes superstitions about what is right and wrong. With brevity, clarity, wit and humor, this book covers the broad range of common errors, including redundancy, ambiguity, verbiage, objectionable euphemisms, and pompous usages that often mislead the reader and destroy a precise and beautiful language.

American Usage and Style is $14.95 at bookstores or from the publisher, Van Nostrand Reinhold, 135 W. 50th Street, New York, NY 10020.

University of Chicago Has Its Own Stylebook

In a section on scientific terminology, the *University of Chicago Stylebook* recommends:

> Diseases and syndromes. The names of diseases, syndromes, signs, symptoms, tests, and the like should be lower-cased, except for proper names forming part of the term; e.g. infectious granuloma, Hodgkin's disease, Meniere's syndrome.

> Names of infectious organisms are treated like other taxonomic terms, but the names of diseases or pathological conditions based upon such names are lowercased and set in roman type.

> Laws, principles, etc. Only proper names attached to the names of laws, theorems, principles, etc., are capitalized; e.g., Boyle's law, Avogadro's theorem, Planck's constant, (Einstein's) general theory of relativity, the second law of thermodynamics, Newton's first law.

> Chemical symbols and names. Names of chemical elements and compounds are lowercased when written out; the chemical symbols, however, are capitalized and set without periods, e.g., sulfuric acid; H_2SO_4.

You may not agree with all of the stylebook rules. O.K. Use them as guidelines, and adopt your own style sheet. But be consistent. In fact, it's a good idea to put your style rules in writing, for your own guidance and to provide to all contributors.

Don't allow the rules to inhibit the flow of your writing juices. The linguists have been trying to eliminate the widespread incorrect usage of such words as hopefully. As long ago as 1970, *Webster's New World Dictionary* defined hopefully in this way:

> 1. in a hopeful manner. 2. it is to be hoped (that) [to leave early, hopefully by six]: regarded by some as loose usage, but widely current

So the "hopefully battle" probably has been lost, though the purists still are trying. What is more annoying is that words like hopefully currently are overused. The publication of overused words and cliches is more annoying to careful writers than use of the vernacular.

Incidentally, *Esquire* book reviewer, Jean Stafford, commented: "Although all but 79 persons in the English-speaking world now doggedly misuse the word 'hopefully,' and I have been told to quit hollering about it, I can't: I can no more control my rabid reaction to this solecism than my system can handle shellfish and penicillin."

And that, we hope, is our final word on hopefully.

In the first issue of this newsletter, we asked about your favorite words.

Dr. James W. Short, editor of the *Tarrant County Medical Society Bulletin* in Fort Worth, Texas, suggested abrasive as a strong adjective which is onomatopoeic.

Dr. Short noted, "Our *Bulletin* is going strong, although we probably break every rule of journalism. I challenge any bulletin editor when it comes to the nitty gritty. Our members love it."

We don't want to nit pick, but the problem with many medical journals is that what's nitty gritty to the editors and board of directors may not be nitty gritty to the readers.

In the *Dictionary of Problem Words and Expressions* (McGraw-Hill, $10.95), Harry Shaw discusses 1500 common errors and suggests remedies without thou-shalt-not commandments. For example, here's a sample from the section on wordiness.

Reduce these	*To these*
after the conclusion of	after
are (am) of the opinion	believe
at the present time	now
come in contact with	meet
during the time that	while
in the event that	if
in view of the fact that	since
I would appreciate if if	please
of great importance	important
provided that	if
the necessary funds	money
with the exception of	except

Many physicians are journal editors because of their long-time interest in writing. Quite a few of us were reporters on our high school and college newspapers. Others have developed an interest in writing as a result of their journal responsibilities.

For years, the authoritative reference book for writers, almost as indispensable as a dictionary, was the *Dictionary of Modern English Usage* by Henry Watson Fowler, first published in England in 1926. Fowler's American counterpart was a Baltimore journalist, H. L. Mencken. In both cases, their books were arranged like dictionaries, but the annotations were brilliantly written essays on language, generally with a mixture of terrifying admonitions and wry commentary.

It is not necessary to be a language scholar to function as a journal editor, though it can help in enjoyment, as well as skill. Here's one short cut: a *Dictionary of American-English Usage* has been compiled by Margaret Nicholson based on Fowler. The Signet paperback is only $1.25. However, the book still is British-oriented; for example, it criticizes the American tendency to drop hyphens and combine words, as in premed and percent.

All things considered, it's impossible to recommend a single language reference book for medical journal editors, though, if we had to rely on only one book, it probably would be the *The New York Times Stylebook*, which is currently out of print but is still available in some bookstores.

About Medical Writing

Dx and Rx: A Physician's Guide to Medical Writing is one of the best books of its type. It provides specific advice (and not entertaining generalizations) to the physician who wants to improve the accuracy, clarity and readability of his medical writing, and also is useful to medical journal editors.

The author is John H. Dirckx, M.D. (pronounced Dirks; don't be confused with all of the x's in the title and author's name), medical director of the Student Health Center at the University of Dayton. Perhaps you are familiar with his 1976 book, *The Language of Medicine.*

Dr. Dirckx's book was published by G. K. Hall & Co., Boston, but is currently out of print.

Following is an excerpt.

The ideal sentence comes quickly to the point. Though a brief introductory passage sometimes improves clarity or lends a pleasing variety, a sentence with a lengthy preamble seems top-heavy and long-winded. The serious and attentive reader does not need a running start to get into the core and substance of each sentence. If he did, the common practice of launching a statement in the realm of the abstract would not help much. "The most frequently observed difference between A and B is in particle size" not only starts off in the abstract, it stays there. Why not just say "A particles are usually bigger than B particles"?

Too often a writer employs a vague or hackneyed introductory formula to draw the unsuspecting reader into the midst of an absurdity or a non sequitur. Starting a sentence with "As everyone knows" or "It is generally agreed'' and finishing it with a highly dubious or controversial assertion is like putting blinders on a horse and backing it over a cliff.

The end of a sentence is no less crucial than the beginning. Even in sentences that are not laid out in periodic form—the great majority—the end position must be respected and handled with care. A sentence is not like a windup toy that proceeds steadily from a state of full energy at the start to one of inertia at the end. Each half of the sentence ought to bear an approximately equal burden of meaning, so that they balance neatly around an imaginary node or caesura near the middle. When properly poised, a sentence has a tail light, a last intellectual fillip to the reader. Ending with a prepositional phrase, as in the following example gives the reader a jolt of disappointment.

"Protective circulatory adjustments occur rapidly in acute blood loss, but they have a limited power of compensation, and they can usually correct losses of about 30% of the total blood volume at most."

In rhetoric, the term *climax* preserves its classical meaning (Greek, *ladder*) and refers to the whole of an ascending series, not just its highest point of culmination. A sense of climax is critical to the proper disposition of a series. Generally speaking, a series whose members vary in magnitude or importance should ascend steadily. If you write that the patient had "four fractured ribs, a ruptured spleen, a pneumothorax and an abrasion of the knee," you inflict an anticlimax on the reader. The abrupt drop in level lets him fall flat, and whether he reacts with amusement or annoyance the general result is a loss of effectiveness. Similarly, it is so natural to list drowsiness, confusion, delirium, stupor, coma and death in that order that any other would seem eccentric.

Sentences constructed without due attention to balance and climax cannot fail to induce malaise and indigestion. Much the same observation may be made about the design of paragraphs. Even when every sentence after the first one is a simple statement of fact, exemplifying or demonstrating what is set down in the first, the concluding words of a paragraph ought to round off the whole neatly instead of leaving the reader hanging. But beware of adorning the end of a paragraph with empty verbiage just to give it the right look on the page, or the right balance to the ear. The ideal is an intellectual as well as an auditory rounding off, not a final sentence composed entirely of inert ingredients.

"The incidence of murmurs in children between the ages of 11 and 19 ranges from 32 to 44%. Organic lesions account for a very small fraction of these murmurs. Most murmurs are the result of hemodynamic factors which produce sounds of sufficient intensity to be audible to the human ear."

Padding is tiresome enough in a novel, but in technical writing it is simply intolerable.

Another feature that is vital to a comfortable writing style is skillful phrasing. I refer here to a phrase not in its grammatical meaning but in the broader sense of any group of words, whether two or 32, which are meant to be taken together. Phrasing in music depends on the length of the violinist's bow (ultimately on the length of his arm) and on the vital capacity of the oboist's or the tenor's lungs. The amount of information which the mind can grasp at one time is also subject to physiologic limits. A sentence is a mental mouthful: if it is too short it will disappoint the reader, if too long it will choke him.

The beginning writer tends to write in short and simple sentences, just as he might dictate.

Medical Journals: Which Will Survive?

"Surviving journals must be those that give the physician-reader his information most effectively and with the least confusion," said journalist Byron Scott in a talk he gave some years ago. Mr. Scott predicted that medical writing in the future would be clearer, more purposeful and more "human." For the most part, it would seem that his predictions have proved valid. Here are some excerpts as they appeared in the *Medical Journalism* newsletter:

I have heard the complaint from many physician-readers that much of today's journal content is devoted to what might be called "bookkeeping articles." Examples of these are the reports of the last 50 kidney transplants at a major medical center, of the last 1,500 infections treated with streptomycin; the emphasis being on more-of-the-same confirmation with relatively minor deviations. Such reports could better go directly into a computer, where the practitioners' consensus could be most clearly apprehended. The rhetoric and the minor deviations and the handy tips could be recorded briefly in the journals, sans the usual bulky and often incomprehensible statistical footwork.

There are many who would argue that the clinician should have all the data in one spot so that he could make an individual judgment. The thoughtful reply must be that it is only the subspecialists, certainly not the busy practitioners in a non-university practice, who have the time and expertise to make such judgments. . . .

If I were forced to guess, and your chairman has asked me to do so, I would say that as many as one third of the journals we have today will not exist 10 years hence. The social and communication pressures already mentioned are a major part of the problem, but there is another awesome difficulty: cost. Postal rates, paper supplies, printing are yearly increasing in price at as much as from 15 to 20%. . . .

In addition to fewer journals, it is obvious to me that the surviving journals must be those that give the physician-reader his information most effectively and with least confusion. This speaks strongly for clearer and more purposeful medical writing than we have today. It also presages a significant change in content. Many if not most journals of a decade or so hence likely will be filled with "state of the art" essays, tips on practice management, and interesting observations about patient behavior as well as about social and political problems of the day. If you compare this editorial profile to *The Journal of the American Medical Association* or *The New England Journal of Medicine* of from 40 to 60 years ago, the resemblance is striking. In those publications the essence of the scientific method was evident in page after page, but the pleasing aura of humanism equally was present.

The EN Dash

State and county medical journals range from slick, sophisticated magazines with full-time, extremely capable professional staffs, to low-budget newsletters which are erratically produced by part-time personnel who often have other priorities.

Most of the physicians who are attracted to this field have had little or no journalism experience but do have an appreciation of good writing and effective communication. Some are semanticists and language purists, and others are not interested in style rules, which they consider nit-picking.

The following communication on the en dash, by Harry L. Arnold Jr., M.D., co-editor of *The Schock Letter* (formerly *Current News in Dermatology*) may therefore be considered of minor importance by some editors, while others will be entertained and delighted. We are in the latter category, so here it is.

An em is a printer's measure, originally defined as the width of a capital M in the typeface concerned. An en is half an em. A hyphen is about half as wide as an en.

The typewriter doesn't provide any handy way to distinguish between an en dash and a hyphen. One typewriter hyphen (or in more sophisticated practice one = sign) means a hyphen in print. Two means an em dash. The en dash is just nowhere unless the copy editor marks it, thus: $\frac{1}{N}$.

The result is that very few en dashes make their way into print; they remain as hyphens. This doesn't offend anything more serious than the eye in many cases. For example, "3—5 times a day" is perfectly intelligible; it just doesn't look as good as "3-5 times a day" does. Properly, an en dash and not a hyphen is the way to separate numbers.

Who Says Physicians Can't Write? Not This Doctor!

This article was excerpted from *Pennsylvania Medicine*. It was written by Naomi Bluestone, M.D., who was completing her residency in psychiatry. It addresses the inhibitions that prevent doctors (and other people) from producing a report, speech or journal article. Dr. Bluestone is the author of *So You Want to Be A Doctor*, a book published in 1981, and has written more than 100 articles on medicine and health.

She began the *Pennsylvania Medicine* article with a poem:

Breathes there a doc
with soul so dead
who never to himself
has said,
"This is a case I should write up,
I'll do it tonight, before I sup!
Tomorrow, well-known I shall be
They'll name a clinic after me!
Lectures I'll give
reprints in hand, I'll
circumnavigate the land!
A specialist in ars scribendi
They'll clamor for my Mss.'s Medendi!"

Dr. Bluestone then demolished the excuses many people offer for their failure to write. Here are excerpts:

To avoid facing and dealing with the free-floating anxiety associated with writing, physicians will assume a heavy burden of personal blame, most of it inappropriate, undeserved and not credible.

"Guess I just don't have what it takes" rings as false as it is demeaning. "Never find the time" is broad-based and meaningless. "Can't spell, never could" is parlor talk, not an explanation, and "You have to know somebody" is an antique pensee left over from the days of application to medical school.

"Tried it once, they sent it back"; "My wife was going to help me" and "Didn't know how to put the damn thing together" all ring hollow from professional people, each of whom once beat out 10 others for a residency.

Beneath all of these patent absurdities lurks "I'm scared, embarrassed, ashamed, helpless, inadequate, beyond my depth; I'm afraid I'll get cut up and I dread it."

The physician-author then notes that doctors need not write that important article themselves. They can hire an experienced freelance writer or make use of the services of their medical center's public relations or grant writing department. But if the individual wants to do the job, use a place with the right ambience and the necessary tools. This means a site "not contaminated by the noise and confusion of either home or office."

The "tools" should include a waste basket, paper, manila folders, large mailing envelopes, lots of sharpened pencils, several pens, an eraser, white tape, large and small paper clips, rubber bands, a stapler with refills, a postal weighing machine, a pair of scissors, several rolls of Scotch tape and several bottles of whitener.

Without all of these items, the author asserted, "you will be impeded and frustrated in your approach. Would a surgeon have to leave an appendectomy because he ran out of mosquitoes?"

The article deals only briefly with writer's block as such, recommending that if you have this problem, you read *Writing Without Teachers* by Peter Elbow and *How To Write and Publish a Scientific Paper*, by Robert Day, which the physician-author considers a "small masterpiece."

You also are urged not to get obsessed with punctuation, spelling or grammar. Leave the fine tuning to the journal or magazine editor, whose job it is to deal with such things.

Dr. Bluestone also recommended that you:

- let your article lie for a few days if you are having trouble with it, then go back to it with renewed vigor and clarity;
- know your audience;
- take care of all the administrative details of submitting a paper, no matter how tedious this may be;
- if you are thinking of writing an article for a lay magazine, or submitting a "think piece" to a scholarly journal, first send a letter querying the editor whether he would be interested in seeing the completed article;
- remember that writing a paper or article is not a matter of inspiration but of business and hard work.

The author concluded by reiterating that the basis of withdrawal from the writing desk usually is fear, "a fear that can be understood, exorcised and ground down to a shadow of its former self."

The physician is encouraged to approach writing as a skill that is valued, can be learned, yields many rewards and is within the realm of the "do-able," even for those haunted by the ghosts of English teachers past.

The Joy of Language

Pick a word that you like. It doesn't have to be esoteric, but it should be a word or phrase which you ordinarily would not use in your publication . . . sanguine, tickle, crunch, swarm, ferocious, feisty, splendid, gritty, gambit —there are so many colorful adjectives and adverbs; and then there are similes, metaphors, personifications and other figures of speech; and colors, like alabaster.

Now insert the word or phrase somewhere in your publication—properly, of course, but really just for fun. Language can be joyous. Do you agree?

Prepositions

President Carter's campaign to simplify the language of Government documents and speeches was laudable, of course, and undoubtedly was helpful to all organizations, including medical societies.

The Canadian Government has had a language simplification program for several years. A key part of it is a column, Readable Writing, which appears in the monthly newspaper for employees of the Department of Supply and Services.

Here's what the author, Sam Samuel, advises about prepositions.

Ground Rule 5: **Don't be afraid of ending sentences with prepositions.** Do I hear moans and groans out there?

Compare the inherent sense of strain of *"the clause I referred to"* against "the clause to which I referred." The first is more fluent.

It's been 50 years since Fowler tried to lay to rest the superstition of avoiding prepositions at the end of sentences.

Sir Ernest Gowers, updating Fowler about 40 years later, sadly reported that the superstition lingered on. Loads of examples from the Bible and Shakespeare, and from the best authors, end with prepositions.

Lumpy sentence: "It has been determined that new departmental employees are only introduced to those individuals with whom they are initially assigned." Smoother, though not perfect: "*We found that new employees in the department were introduced only to those people they're first assigned with.*"

MORE ON WRITING

This chapter consists of a few articles that do not exactly fit into the pattern we have set for this book. Indeed, none of them was published in the *Medical Journalism* newsletter. They appear here because of the interesting and informative things they have to say about writing and because they are themselves excellent examples of vigorous, clear and highly readable prose.

The first piece, composed specifically for this work, is by a distinguished science writer who was science editor of *The Associated Press* for many years.

The other articles, which are reprinted from a variety of medical journals, are by well-known physicians who have done considerable writing of their own and who, like innumerable medical colleagues, have been involved in the agonies and pleasures of "producing a product" for publication.

The Elements of Good Writing
ALTON BLAKESLEE

This clear, concise and beautifully written piece is by a former science editor of *The Associated Press*. A reporter and editor for over 40 years, Mr. Blakeslee has been honored for his contributions to science journalism by the American Psychiatric Association, American Chemical Society, Lasker Foundation, American Academy of Family Physicians, AAAS-George Westinghouse Science Writing Awards Program and other medical, scientific, academic and journalism organizations.

Good writing—heck, even bad writing—begins with some varying degree of terror from staring at a blank piece of paper in your typewriter, or a cursor winking disinterestedly in your word processor.

Nothing exists until something comes out of your brain. And how well it comes out, how effectively you tell your story to others, is always its own adventure.

But there are some guidelines to help steer the result. Here are some put together from years of medical-science writing:

— Push your enthusiasm button when you start writing. If YOU are not interested, or interesting, how can you expect to interest readers? If you approach your story as being just a chore, it shows—by being dull.

— THINK what your story means, and how best to say it. As all writers know, good thinking is the hard part. Distill and distill your facts and goal to the core of meaning.

— Regard your readers not as being ignorant, but more likely innocent of your topic and its technical terms. You may have learned the intricacies and significances of your article only hours or days ago, so don't succumb to arrogance.

— Explain technical terms instantly if you must use them with a general audience (and you often must), then you can use them again in that same story. But you can't glibly use them in your next story without again defining them—you may well not have the exact same audience.

Jerry Bishop, science writer of the *Wall Street Journal*, says the most technical stories he reads in newspapers are on the sports pages. They never explain technical terms, requiring the reader, even from abroad, to know them. Imagine if the sports writer had to explain "strike" and "first down" in every story. But it's a duty the medical writer often faces until terms like AIDS become common knowledge.

— Explain the unfamiliar by comparing it with something familiar. It may not be precise, but a good analogy can serve well. The analogy, of course, has to be in the age range or ranges of readers.

— Put yourself on the other side of your typewriter or word processor, and ask yourself and then answer all the questions that could occur to you if you had never heard of your topic before. This can avoid leaving readers puzzled or wondering.

— Don't put all the "logs" of attribution and identification into one place just to get rid of them. Be more solicitous of your readers, or you may lose them. If you begin with something interesting, and then flip to: "This was reported by Dr. James J. James, professor of biotechnology, department of pathology, at the Fairview Medical School of the University of Harwell in Peoria, Illinois, in studies supported by the National Science Foundation,"— two things happen. Your reader leaves you, or skips past all that information. Your source and other elements in the story do not receive proper credit. Spread out names, affiliations, sponsors so they do get attention.

— Look for gems of detail and quotes that can make a story sparkle with interest. Report and write with your ears as well as your eyes, attentive to phrases that say something extremely well and colloquially, in the language of the people interviewed, or others overheard.

— In interviewing and researching, there is no such thing as a dumb question when you want to understand something correctly in order to write about it accurately. Don't be embarrassed to ask. Who knows everything? Your interviewee likely will be favorably impressed by your honesty and desire to understand.

— Be not afraid to use periods liberally, otherwise sentences become cumbersome. And avoid putting two unfamiliar points in the same sentence.

— Look for different-from-ordinary ways of expression. This is the mark of the writer who prefers to fly rather than plod the old pathways.

— Give your story some focus, and a place to go. Then quit. The wandering story is distracting and confusing. So is the ambiguous or uncertain beginning or lead.

Sometimes the ambiguous lead is not the fault of the writer, but the source can't express his/her conclusion (or doesn't really have a point to make.) You then get into what I call the "wet watermelon story lead." You start writing, then discover the presumed point skips away, like trying to pick up a wet watermelon seed. Try again, the seed is off mark. The solution is to think more, or give up in belief the source doesn't know what he/she is talking about anyway.

— Wring out the "water" of excess verbiage and repetition. Is each phrase, even each word, really necessary?

— What you leave OUT of a story can be as important as what you put in. Otherwise the reader may feel he is drowning in non-essential detail, on the shores of boredom.

— *Never* let a story or article go without taking a second look. Is there some better or more accurate or more appealing lead or phrase, some livelier description, some sharper beginning? Likely there is.

— Avoid beginning a story with a question, except in unusual circumstances. Instead, answer the question.

— You don't have to worry about your second paragraph, unless your first paragraph hooks your reader's interest, as Mark Bloom, a science writer for magazines, points out. Your opening, whether dramatic or soft key, is critical to draw attention of busy readers in a world competing for their time and attention.

— In seeking how to begin, it is often helpful to tell someone verbally what your story is all about, what you think you want to or should do with it. The concept of the story is what counts, and the verbal telling may bring it forth or refine it.

— Remember your first draft is not written in concrete. Use it to put all your facts and descriptions into one account, so you can see it better in perspective. Later, you can change the order of presentation, find better analogies, and the like. So let that first draft flow. Don't interrupt when it is flowing to look up a name or spelling or detail that can be inserted later.

— Digest your material. Then relax and say what you want to say.

Rebound Articles in
"Hand-Me-Down" Journals
ALFRED SOFFER, M.D.

The author of several books and many articles on cardiology and chest medicine, Alfred Soffer, M.D., is a world-renowned medical writer and editor.

A former senior editor of the *Journal of the American Medical Association*, Dr. Soffer is now a member of the editorial board of that publication and, in addition, editor-in-chief of *Chest*, editor of *Heart and Lung*, chief editor of the *Archives of Internal Medicine* and, for many years, executive director of the American College of Chest Physicians.

The following three articles have been culled from among the hundreds of editorials, letters, reviews and articles that Dr. Soffer has written over the years in a variety of medical journals.

During a recent trip to a western state, I was invited to participate in a meeting of the publications committee of the state medical journal. The candid dialogue included these comments:

> "We are not going to get anybody to open our journal unless we have a lot more scientific material in it."

> "O.K., then, let's publish the talks given at some of our local medical meetings and research papers from some of our city hospitals."

> "We won't get good scientific articles unless we invite doctors to write for this journal. There are distinguished investigators in this state; let's invite them to give us some of their finest papers."

> "The *New England Journal of Medicine* started out as a local periodical. Why don't we try to become like that journal?"

> "I disagree. I do not believe the chief function of state or regional journals should be the publication of original studies. I think we have other opportunities and responsibilities."

When asked for my evaluation of these long-range goals, I suggested that there is one function which *should not* be undertaken by many regional journals. Original clinical investigation intended to establish new guidelines in diagnosis or therapy should be published only in periodicals with meticulous editorial peer review procedures.

The medical community cannot tolerate the existence of "hand-me-down" articles or second rate investigational journals. Scientific reports published after cursory review may confuse the investigator and bewilder the clinician. A sad succession of therapeutic fads has characterized our tortuous progression towards scientific truths in the twentieth century. Much of the responsibility for these evanescent and misdirected clinical trends must be attributed to editors who sanctioned publication of erroneous data or unjustified clinical conclusions. Thus, the existence of "B" or "C" medical research journals endangers health care as much as the existence of "B" and "C" medical schools.

Fewer than 50 percent of manuscripts submitted to leading research journals in the United States are accepted for publication. Priorities differ among journals of comparable quality and it is reasonable to encourage some authors to send their papers to other editorial boards after initial rejection. However, many of these articles contain fundamental defects in the investigational protocol and could not be salvaged even after extensive revision. It is not a service to medicine to provide an ultimate forum for documentation of these communications by supporting the thesis that, "It is probably good enough for a local journal." This attitude results in an ongoing quest by the disgruntled author who senses that there must be some journal somewhere which will accept his report. He is often correct in this presumption! As a result, our current genius for retrieval of data in the medical literature is occasionally a disservice because some of the data obtained would best remain buried in eternal anonymity! Aspiring authors should accept occasional negative verdicts with equanimity because the preparation of a formal manuscript (even if never published) is an important educational experience particularly if detailed referee's comments accompany the rejected manuscript.

"Rebound" research articles also appear far too frequently in national journals with controlled circulation and some national paid circulation publications. We must now challenge the right of every journal to publish original research without regard to the minimal publication safeguards that this entails. The scientific community has the right to ask each editor these questions: "To what degree do you ascertain the validity of the methodology in each report? Is each major paper reviewed by two out-of-office consultants? Are the services of a consultant in biostatistics available? Are detailed comments for revision returned to the author?" Obviously, not every manuscript requires evaluation by a clinical pharmacologist or biostatistician. It is, however, a rare manuscript which does not need modification after conscientious review by an investigator who has not been a participant in the clinical experiment described. These procedures are not luxuries, but rather fundamental necessities if publication mishaps are to be prevented.

These observations are not meant to denigrate county, state or regional periodicals. Why should their editorial boards accept inferior research reports when their pages can represent the very best of other journalistic formats (particularly when second best encompasses grave dangers)? Anecdotal clinical observations have their place in medical literature if authors emphasize the limitations of these studies. Review articles offer vital clinical guidance; however, such a task should not be assigned to the neophyte author or to the inexperienced researcher because the preparation of a balanced review is an intricate task. A carefully studied case report remains an important teaching device which should find a receptive readership in regional periodicals. Epidemiologic and communicable disease information of regional character is ideally suited for these periodicals. Feature articles on teaching centers and community hospitals in that area will be of interest to their heterogeneous medical constituency.

Some regional society periodicals may feature a combination of these departments and others may serve primarily as fraternal house organs. In either instance, it is far better to publish a superior feature story or imaginative news report than an inadequately reviewed communication which contains basic defects in the investigation or in the manuscript itself.

The written word remains perhaps the most important single method of continuing education in medicine. It is unfortunate that many professionals are not discriminatory readers. An understanding of the discipline of clinical research is still an unknown entity to many clinicians. We should begin to correct these deficiencies, but this does not absolve editorial boards from the responsibility of adequate editorial review.

Reprinted from *Chest*, February, 1976.

Flexibility in Medical Writing
ALFRED SOFFER, M.D.

"What format shall I use for the preparation of an article to be submitted to a medical journal?" This is a question frequently asked at workshops devoted to medical writing. To this inquiry we often respond, "Which journal and what department in that journal would be most appropriate for your communication?" The structure of an article is partially dependent upon the journal section for which it is intended, since this is a reflection of the purposes for which the report was written. The guidance provided by an editorial is significantly different from that of a review article. The review, in turn, has a different purpose than the original investigation. Even the neophyte author is cognizant of the major differences between the purposes of a case report and a book review.

Let us assume that the author is planning an article which describes a study of 50 patients who have received a new therapeutic regimen. One may begin by preparing an outline which identifies the major conclusions and the data needed to validate these conclusions. The author must formulate a title which is short but descriptive and which accurately identifies the thrust of his message. It is usually appropriate to prepare an introduction to the communication. These introductory sentences or paragraphs suggest why the study was undertaken, *i.e.*, what information was sought and the relevance of this information to scientific advancement. The author should provide a section on methodology which includes the tests and instruments used and a description of the patient population (or laboratory animals) used in the study. This section should be detailed enough so that, if indicated, other investigators can repeat the experiment. A results section may follow and herein is contained the "hard data" obtained in the study. The next section is the "discussion" which may contain an interpretation of the data and the investigator's evaluation of the clinical applicability of the observations. The discussion section provides an opportunity for comparison with the results obtained by others. This "formula" of introduction, methods, results and discussion is the most common format in current medical literature. The distinguished editor, Dr. Franz Ingelfinger, once rebuked clinical journals for their inflexible reliance upon this formula which he called "IMRAD." It is the author's privilege to offer a writing style uniquely his own, one that has not lost individuality because of rigid compliance upon any single formula. There is, however, considerable virtue in including the elements of this formula in most reports.

Some authors cite "conclusions" in the discussion. Others prepare a separate conclusions section which serves to interpret the data and the discussion in the context of the investigator's understanding of the outcome of his studies. He may define in these concluding comments the implications or the relevance of the observations. Whether or not conclusions are mentioned in the discussion or presented as a separate department, it is important to prepare, in addition, a synopsis or abstract. The summary has achieved a unique position in medical literature. Many editors prefer to place the synopsis in the front of each article, whereas other journals retain the more traditional position at the end of the communication. The position is not as important as the preparation of this vital element of each report. It must clarify the purposes for which the study was undertaken and it should contain the major conclusions. These meanings should be clear even to the reader who is not intimately conversant with the discipline which was the subject of the investigation. Not a word can be wasted if all this is to be accomplished in 150 words. We recently reviewed an abstract which stated "certain tests are discussed." The second sentence stated "previous studies are presented" and the third noted "an explanation of why some of these tests are inadequate is given." Such phraseology is appallingly noninformative. Abstract content must be factual: using a direct approach, the author should have supported his thesis with a brief listing of new facts.

Is there a place for the personal pronoun in a serious scientific communication? Fortunately, most authors are losing their prejudice against use of the first person. It is both forthright and illuminating to say "I noted that" or "I believe." The modesty of past decades in which this was frowned upon (except perhaps in editorials) has been abandoned. This change may be related to sociologic changes which have brought more candor and directness into personal communication. Compare the Victorian fashion of writing with the more terse modern style. Another virtue of using "I" or "we" from time to time is that it avoids the passive voice. Thus, instead of writing "this paper concerns itself with" one can state in a more forceful and interesting fashion "we wish to describe a case." I applaud the advice of King and Roland that the excessive use of the passive voice is dull writing. Instead of writing "catheterization was performed in each patient by the resident" why not note "the resident catheterized each patient" or better still (whenever applicable) "we catheterized." This approach is not synonymous with anecdotal or chatty writing, but rather it is a method of enlivening and strengthening scientific communication.

Several drafts of the paper should be written before submission of the final version for publication. Vital assistance may be obtained by permitting a colleague to review a later draft. It is astonishing how often sentences which seem entirely clear to the author require additional clarification. The writer is often "too close" to the manuscript to identify ambiguous areas without the help of a second party. A last critical step should be taken to be certain that all redundancy has been removed. Excess words are an imposition upon the reader and may be deleterious to understanding. We assume that excess verbiage has been removed with every draft of the manuscript. We refer now to specific revision of a late stage copy for the exclusive purpose of removing unnecessary words. This can be a very rewarding exercise in the quest for forceful writing. Be on the lookout for phrases which lengthen text and weaken writing style. A valuable clue to such defects is the presence of expressions beginning with the indefinite "it" followed by the verb "is." One should eliminate phrases beginning with "it is perfectly obvious that" or "it is entirely possible that" or "it is becoming increasingly apparent that." Read the sentence before and after these words have been deleted to identify how unnecessary they were!

We abuse the English language in daily conversation. Listen to the dialogue in the hospital corridors and wards with the thought of identifying cliches, jargon, sloppy sentence structure and poorly descriptive phraseology. This is a sad phenomenon which may explain some of the problems faced by medical editors. It is far more serious to permit such bad habits to confuse and weaken our medical periodicals. Fortunately, these are defects that can be corrected by frequent rewriting and the author's insistence that "this paper will not pass my hands if it contains words which are unnecessary to my message."   Written with Sylvan Lee Weinberg, M.D., and reprinted from *Heart and Lung*, January–February, 1975.

Beware the 200-Word Abstract!
ALFRED SOFFER, M.D.

A television commentator was on the telephone: "I am interested in writing a story about a recent report from a national medical convention. The claim was made that atherosclerosis can be reversed with the use of drastic dietary restriction of fat in combination with an exercise regimen." Acting upon his request, I investigated the study protocol of this so-called research. I learned to my dismay that the "researchers" were far more adept in public relations than they were in structuring an adequate clinical trial. The control group of subjects was grossly inadequate, and for this and many other reasons, the conclusions were suspect. Indeed, "suspect" is the kindest word that can be used to describe the interpretation of the data. The commentator received comparable opinions from a number of sources; and fortunately, these purveyors of a "miraculous breakthrough" in the treatment of atherosclerosis were denied a national forum on television. However, their skills at self-promotion did provide a harvest of articles in the press, and even some otherwise critical science writers publicized the unjustified conclusions of a grossly inadequate investigation.

How is it possible that such episodes can occur to delude the layman and bewilder the clinician? Perhaps some of these mishaps can be traced to a persistent gullibility on the part of science writers (and even some physicians) in their uncritical acceptance of reports from congresses and conventions and to a naive nondiscriminatory belief in published convention abstracts. The value of reports at scientific assemblies is directly proportional to the skills and responsibilities of the program committees; however, even in the most optimal circumstances, selection of reports is not invariably based upon criteria constituting a single standard of excellence. Frequently, planning committees consider the need to provide adequate interdisciplinary or geographic representation. Thus, an uneven caliber of reports does not imply that the planning has been inept or mischievous. However, more than any other factor, the 200-word abstract presents the greatest hazard to program committees. It is difficult to evaluate the true status of research from the brief abstracts that serve as the basis for acceptance of convention reports. Perhaps this is why many investigations that receive high rankings from scientific program committees (which do not have access to the detailed investigational protocols) receive very poor ratings when studied by editorial boards. Editorial peer review of formal manuscripts provides the best and ultimate judgment of the merits of an investigation.

An abstract and the presentation of the report should serve primarily as a stimulus for further dialogue. Thus, a convention report should be regarded as an initial effort to obtain the guidance and criticism of colleagues. The success of a medical convention should be judged not by the number of abstracts submitted or the number presented, but rather by the amount of time provided for discussion after each report. In the current rush to be a leader in the "numbers game," there is the temptation to encourage presentation of increasingly larger numbers of reports, at the expense of question-and-answer periods and panel discussions.

Such an orientation indicates that the researcher can obtain maximum benefit from his convention experiences if he considers his report as an investigation in progress. This perspective was the basis for an educational venture conducted at last year's annual convention of the American College of Chest Physicians. The "Research in Progress Forum" was a teaching session structured to provide assistance to the investigator who wished to obtain guidance in the presentation and publication of original data. The announcement of this event stated,

One of the deficiencies of large assemblies is the absence of dialogue between the investigator and the panelists or members of the audience with experience in these disciplines. The Research in Progress Forum has been organized to correct this deficiency—the discipline of research is not taught formally in most postgraduate programs. Therefore, these sessions may provide vital guidance for younger researchers; preceptors will comment on the research design, methodology, and hypotheses.

Time allotted for discussion was equal to the time provided for formal presentation of reports. Those in attendance stated that vigorous dialogue did indeed ensue and a rich learning experience was shared by both "teacher" and "student."

No investigator can be entirely objective about his own research, and one of the finest traditions of American medicine has been the concept of "peer review." In spite of the limitations of the system of reviewing abstracts, legitimate program committee scrutiny is a helpful first step in the evaluation process; unfortunately, however, it is relatively easy to circumvent such impartial review. Do editorial boards demand additional evidence to justify the conclusions in your report? Do scientific program committees of speciality societies neglect your medical gift to mankind? Well then, do what others are doing! Form a society that can then schedule a convention (or symposium) to publicize your miracle cure! This permits you to issue bulletins describing the spectacular effects of your drug or device. Of course, meticulous analysis of the "data" would disclose glaring deficiencies, but it is hard to criticize a formal manuscript when none has been offered. And it is difficult to contradict the contents of a speech when there is no time for rebuttal. Indeed, it is particularly clever to invite only those speakers whose point of view is comparable to your own; this is not difficult to arrange.

Let us consider a recent example of this method. The dangers attendant to the use of chelation therapy suggest that this form of therapy for cardiovascular disease could not be the subject of clinically oriented conventions or symposia. Unfortunately, the enthusiasm of the medical zealot knows no bounds, and a "national convention" has been presented with predominant emphasis on the glories of chelating drugs in the treatment of atherosclerosis. Evidently, invitations were carefully extended in accordance with the known biases of the speakers.

Conventions can offer an unique opportunity for peer criticism, but preconvention reports in news periodicals negate this check and balance. These promotional techniques are used not only for conventions, but also for smaller meetings and symposia. A shrewd science editor can vary this approach by providing full background coverage with in-depth interviews, photographs, and data hours after a scientific assembly has been presented. This manipulation decreases the publication lag to zero, but the end product, consisting essentially of individual interviews without rebuttal, destroys the very purpose for convening the meeting. Premature dissemination of scientific information of dubious value may result. These trends endanger the objectivity of scientific communication. Am I exaggerating the effects of inappropriate news reporting? I submit that the direction and magnitude of current medical research has frequently been modified by "purple prose reports" with prominent elements of personal aggrandizement. Resultant public pressure has caused significant sums of money to be shunted to certain research areas as a result of such publicity.

These abuses of scientific assemblies do not destroy the essential values of the fraternal and scientific activities which form the basis of our conventions. However, the critical limitations of the convention report and abstract must be understood by medical societies, the clinician, and the national press.

Reprinted from the Archives of Internal Medicine,
November, 1976.

Not So Friendly Enemas
THOMAS H. COLEMAN, M.D.

The following well-written editorial appeared originally in the *Bulletin of the Denver Medical Society*. Composed by Thomas H. Coleman, M.D., editor of the *Bulletin* at the time, the offbeat piece seems to start in a jocular vein but obviously carries a serious medical message.

Dr. Coleman practices internal medicine in the Denver area.

Are you temporarily tired of reading about HMOs, liability trusts and miscreant doctors? We are temporarily tired of writing about them, so let's all drag out East Colfax Avenue for some continuing education at the enematorium. That's where the simple folk go for relief right here in not-so-little old Denver. We have a professional obligation to know what happens to them there; some of them might be our patients, before or after.

One of our informants, still preoccupied with his experience, told us he had a girlfriend who worked in one of those places. She invited him out for a free treatment. She arranged him in a gown on a table in a booth and connected him via tubes to hanging reservoirs of tepid water. In mute consternation he watched his middle rise and subside, then rise again with the tide that flowed and sluiced through valves at the command of his former girlfriend, now transformed into Ms. Hydraulics Tech. When he was able to get up and escape, he said he felt "different."

We all have patients who are convinced that we are eager to hear, in mindless and indelicate detail, of their innermost workings. We are stupefied at their daily gulps of salts, herbs, bran and oils in doses that are usually eruptive. But they don't usually tell us about their enemas, perhaps because of television. TV commercials are not shy about bad breath, odors in other parts of the anatomy, nor about hemorrhoids or constipation, but they don't tout enemas. Yet hundreds of people take enemas at home or go get them for a fee, as casually as they floss their teeth or go to the hairdresser's.

No apes take enemas. They leave their beautifully automatic systems to themselves. But man, the intelligent one, tampers with his system daily.

Apparently all this sigmoidopathy and scatophobia originated, at least in America, in the Victorian ethic of clean minds in clean bodies. Then it became mixed up in ideas of Christian morality. All that corruption must be bad, and if it were not tended to, it would seep into the heart and brain causing illnesses, idiocy, and moral turpitude. These frights were passed along easily by the grandmothers, aunts and nursemaids to every defenseless child in the protected intimacy of the bathroom.

Into that set of obsessive fears came the Victorian doctors prescribing cathartics, or enemas of milk and molasses. The colon was the indolent villain and had to be cleaned out. Some doctors went into the business of making and selling laxatives. Perhaps they didn't know or didn't care that they were battling Lydia Pinkham and the obstipation of her laudanum tonic.

Devices were sold door to door. Lewis Thomas has a story about a lady ancestor of his on Long Island who was sold a ten-pound iron ball sheathed in leather. She was to lie on her back and roll the ball up and across and down the supposed course of the colon in the hope that the lazy organ would be thus encouraged and get on with it. Whether through success or failure, the ball was loaned to a neighbor and lost for two generations. A new owner of the neighbor's house started a backyard garden one spring and the ball was dug up. Without its leather cover, it looked like a cannonball and the DAR spent some excitement trying to calculate what trajectory from what Revolutonary battery may have brought it to bury itself on Long Island.

Enter the 20th century and the surgeons. Not content with the outside approaches, they began opening the abdomens of the afflicted to lay hold of the torpid colon in its lair. First, they hitched it up because it was too mobile, then they bypassed it because it was too long, then they took out a foot or two of it because it was redundant. Then they began to take out the whole thing. A technically brilliant surgeon named Arbuthnot Lane could do an entire colectomy in 45 minutes. He and his less skillful imitators, disciples of the autointoxication theory, and without antibiotics, combined to produce a horrendous incidence of peritonitis and a mortality of 16%. If you don't believe this, read J. Lacey Smith's historical account in the *Annals of Internal Medicine* of March 1982.

Supersititions die hard. There is still a fringe of practitioners today who actually believe that dangerous materials cling to our insides for years and threaten our health if they are not removed regularly by a "high colonic." Some Colorado chiropractors with this belief got themselves anonymously published in the *New England Journal of Medicine* one month because they don't believe in germs or antiseptics. In washing out "poisons" they washed amoebic dysentery into 36 people; six died.

We wonder whether other diseases less easy to trace, such as hepatitis with its long incubation period, might also originate in these enematoriums. Perhaps we should be a little more inquisitive into our patients' habits which they consider ordinary and we would consider bizarre.

The Value of Vigorous Writing
WILLIAM D. SNIVELY JR., M.D.

The following article, reprinted from *Medical Times*, stresses the benefits of vigorous writing. Dr. Snively defines vigorous writing as the kind that strikes the reader forcibly and prompts him to read what the author has written.

Dr. Snively is a past president of the American Medical Writers Association and professor emeritus of life sciences at the University of Evansville and Indiana University.

Why worry about "more vigorous prose"? Because vigorous prose exerts a powerful impact on the reader, increasing readership. Hilaire Belloc once said:

"When I am dead,
I hope it may be said:
'His sins were scarlet,
but his books were read.' "

Yet much writing—including much medical writing—actually *defies*
reading. For the hard working, perhaps jaded, practitioner, difficult medical communication is exactly what he does *not* need. Vigorous prose is one
means of crashing through that communication barrier.

Now what do we mean when we say we are going to write vigorous
prose? We mean we shall write in such a way that the writing strikes the
reader forcibly enough so that he will *read* the writing. All too frequently
writers do not write in such a way that maximal impact—or any impact at
all—is exerted on the reader. Why? Our writer may know his grammar, his
composition, his technical field. He may have done his research with meticulous care and insight, garnering a formidable array of useful information.
He may have thumped his typewriter night after night. Yet his cherished
brainchild fails to get read.

Such a debacle (really a tragedy for the writer) usually stems from one
or more of the follow acts or omissions: He may have failed to recognize the
importance, even the nature, of words—those basic units of language. He
may have mistaken the *word* for the *thing*, the *symbol* for the *object*. Foun-
dering in this he may have neglected to choose the familiar over the unfamiliar, the warm over the cold, the simple over the complex, the short
Anglo-Saxon-derived word over the long Latin term.

He may have used long complicated sentences; he may have paragraphed
unwisely or scarcely at all; he may have revealed himself as an addict of the
passive voice (proper in its place) and therefore *incapable* of vigorous writing. He may have forgotten—if he ever knew it—that brevity is the soul of
wit (in its original sense of *intellectual power*). He may have obeyed every
rule in every manual of grammar. But if he failed to write in an attractive,
interesting, vigorous style, he lost his readers on the first page—never to
regain their interest.

Now let's consider what makes for more vigorous prose, especially as it
applies to medical writing (although the principles apply, more or less, to all
writing). First off, I know of no slick tricks, sensational shortcuts, or pat
mechanical formulas. What is required is painstaking, intelligently directed
toil. Even Jonathan Swift, a master of English prose, didn't find writing
easy, for he said:

"Blot out, correct, insert, refine,
enlarge, diminish, interline.
Be mindful when invention fails
to scratch your head and bite your nails."

Now vigor in writing doesn't stand alone; writing that is vigorous must have all the other attributes of good writing, otherwise the vigor will soon pall and leave the reader jaded and dissatisfied. So, as we analyze what it takes to achieve maximal impact, we shall consider not only vigor but a cluster of closely related matters.

Here are a number of tips on how to write a better clinical paper, or any other kind of paper for that matter. Following each tip, or principle, are examples illustrating the point I am attempting to make.

- **Only rarely should there be more than 30 words per sentence.**

Poor: This liaison with one another and with the general practitioner and all other community agencies has to be organized to operate effectively and continuously from the domiciliary intervention at the first sign of need for geriatric help throughout the whole course of the breakdown and its aftercare.

The above sentence, in addition to being much too long, lacks vigor and clarity as well. Like some other examples I shall present, here it is from a journal indexed by the Index Medicus. It might be reworded in this manner:

Better: Thoughtful planning is a must, if the elderly are to receive optimal medical care, starting with the initial need at home and extending through aftercare. In short, family physicians and all involved community agencies must be organized for effective action.

Poor: In Illinois, for example, Social Security says Continental Casualty, which serves all the state except the Chicago area, had just over four weeks' work on hand as of May 1970, but that Blue Shield, serving the Chicago area, was a full 18 weeks behind during that same month.

Better: The Department of Social Security reported recently on the sickness insurance backlog for Illinois as of May 1970. Continental Casualty, serving all the state except Chicago, was four weeks behind; but Blue Shield, serving Chicago, had an 18-week backlog.

- **Originally, there should not be more than 20 words per verb.**

Poor: The development of modern surgical technique, with its emphasis on leisurely and meticulous tissue dissection followed by layer-by-layer anatomical reconstruction, performed with no particular regard for the time required for the surgical procedure, rests entirely upon that dramatic and indeed epoch-making discovery, namely that of anesthesia.

Better: Modern surgical technique requires anatomical dissection and reconstruction of tissues, without time restriction; without the boon of anesthesia, this would be impossible.

Poor: The study of the low-sodium diet, time-honored dietetic approach to the management of diverse clinical states characterized by damaging retention of sodium, presents knotty problems, with particular reference to assessment of the actual sodium content of the diet, as well as its true clinical efficacy.

Better: The low sodium diet has long proved effective in certain conditions characterized by sodium retention. But be sure you answer these questions when you use it: 1) How much sodium is the patient really receiving? and 2) is the diet indicated for the clinical condition in question?

• **Modifiers such as adjectives and adverbs should be restricted in use.** (Strunk says: "Write with nouns and verbs.")

Poor: The cold, cyanotic, dehydrated comatose patients, lying pulseless and almost lifeless, became animated after the subcutaneous infusion of warm salt water.

Better: The patients, in advanced shock, revived after subcutaneous infusion of warm salt water.

• **Unnecessary words detract greatly from vigor.**

Poor: The great improvement in the mortality statistics of prostatectomy in recent years is due to several causes. As the operation becomes more widely known and more popular, patients seek relief at an earlier period, while their condition is good and with much greater prospects of success.

Better: Why has the mortality from prostatectomy decreased greatly in recent years? Because patients are generally aware of the success of the operation and seek help earlier, before the lesion has reached an advanced state.

• **Vary sentence length.** (Otherwise you'll put your reader to sleep.)

Poor: Hypothyroidism was formerly present in the Great Lakes area. It was due to lack of iodine in the diet. Supplementing the diet with iodine relieved the problem. Now hypothyroidism is infrequently seen.

Better: Hypothyroidism caused by iodine deficiency was formerly prevalent in the Great Lakes region. When iodine was added to the diet, the condition almost entirely disappeared.

• **Vary sentence type, using simple, complex, and compound sentences.**

Poor: Typhoid fever was formerly a deadly ailment. This was due in large part to lack of understanding of the pathologic processes involved in infection of Peyer's patches and of their tendency to rupture. Achievement of understanding of this matter led to dietary therapy designed to prevent rupture of infected Peyer's patches.

Better: The deadly nature of typhoid fever in past years resulted from failure to understand the involvment of Peyer's patches and their tendency to rupture. With recognition of the nature of these lesions, dietary therapy designed to minimize rupture was adopted.

• **Vary the initial words of sentences.**

Poor: The child was well until 5 P.M. The child then developed a high fever. The child vomited repeatedly and became cyanotic.

Better: At 5 P.M., the previously well child developed a high fever, vomited, and became cyanotic.

- **Begin some sentences with other than the subject.**

Poor: Bubonic plague was one of the great medieval decimaters of mankind. Asiatic cholera also caused an enormous number of deaths over the centuries. Typhoid fever likewise rates considerable attention as an ailment that brought death to millions in widely varying areas of the world.

Better: One of the great medieval decimaters of Mankind was the bubonic plague. Other deadly plagues—responsible for the deaths of millions—were Asiatic cholera and typhus fever.

- **Keep subject and object close to the verb.**

Poor: The government indicted the harried, preoccupied, research-oriented delinquent surgeon.

Better: The government indicted the surgeon—who was harried, preoccupied, research-oriented, and delinquent.

- **Choose words precisely.** Careless word choice detracts from vigor as well as from meaning.

Poor: The patient had in general a sickly appearance, thus manifesting a disease of long duration.

Better: The patient's pronounced pallor indicated that he had been ill for a long time.

- **Use the concrete rather than the abstract, the graphic rather than the obscure.** Vigor is, of course, helped by pictures but also by *word pictures*— similes, metaphors, personifications; look them up and *use* them.

Poor: The impoundment of the financial resources of the merged clinic, eventuated in high-level perturbation.

Better: After the merger, the purchasing clinic group took over the cash reserves of the purchased clinic, deeply disturbing the latter's management.

- **Keep thought development orderly.**

Poor: This state of affairs is usually gradual in its development and occurs because of physical, psychiatric or social ideologic factors or through combinations of two or all three of them.

Better: This state of affairs results from varying combinations of physical, psychiatric and social factors; it usually develops gradually.

- **Make sure that the passage is clear on first reading.** It should be!

Poor: All speculation as to the cause of endemic goiter and cretinism must be regarded as absolutely misredirected, which leaves out of sight the fact that both diseases have the marked character of local maladies confined within quite narrow circuits and which seeks in disregard of this fact to find the diseases factors in such influences as, so to speak, of cosmopolitan kind.

Better: Endemic goiter and cretinism appear to result from factors arising within a circumscribed region; they do not stem from national or even regional phenomena. To discover the causes of these ailments, one must consider the geographical incidence.

• Again, as William Strunk urges (in *The Elements of Style*), **write with nouns and verbs.**

Poor: The incompetent, money-mad, poorly trained bronchoscopist was lowly regarded.

Better: The bronchoscopist had had inadequate training and his work revealed his incompetence. Nevertheless he sought money madly. Not surprisingly, he was lowly regarded.

You will note, in presenting these No-No's and Do's, that I have not emphasized the proper use of grammar, assuming (rightly?) that you know this already.

You Gotta Have Style

Now let's talk about *style*, since it plays an essential role in imparting vigor to writing. Webster defines tyle in his *New Collegiate Dictionary* thus: "Mode of expressing thought in language, especially such use of language as exhibits the spirit and personality of an artist. Quality which gives distinctive character and excellence to artistic expression, as 'his writing lacks style.' "

Perhaps most writers agree that one acquires a writing style gradually and subconsciously through reading the authors he enjoys and of whom he approves. Gradually, elements of these styles become his, as they subconsciously contribute to what will ultimately become his writing style. One does not (in my opinion, at least) deliberately set out to develop a style.

While style may be difficult to define precisely, all of us recognize when this quality is attractive and winning or when it is dull and pedestrian. So the final phase of our workshop will be to rewrite some uninteresting and colorless passages.

• A regional woman's magazine wants you to write a short story or filler expounding on sunbathing. The information furnished is in the form of a chart compiled in the dermatology department of a local medical school:

Solar Radiation Exposure Time	Predicted Effect (90% of Population)
Under 15 minutes	None
15–30 minutes	Increased skin temperature
30–45 minutes	Erythema
45–60 minutes	Erythema, pain, scaling
Over 60 minutes	Erythema, pain, scaling, toxic reaction

Dull: The foregoing is accurate, but dull. Rewrite it in terms that will be familiar to the readers and that will attract and hold their attention. Humor might help.

Bright: This problem (and correction) are courtesy of S.A. Sanchez, M.D., of the Scott and White Clinic of Temple, Texas. Here's how Dr. Sanchez changed the style from vapid to vigorous:

Sun Bather's Cooking Guide

Sun Time (minutes)	Suntan
under 15	No change
15–30	Rare
30–45	Medium
45–60	Ouch! Well done
over 60	Burned to a crisp! Call your doctor!

• Your institutional magazine has requested a humorous story. You select the following item:

Dull: The Phi Ki fraternity played a joke on students in the ward at Midwestern Memorial Hospital. They substituted dribble glasses for medicine cups at the nurses' station on April 1. The most commonly prescribed medicine was Kaopectate for an epidemic of intestinal flu. The effect was devastating: Kaopectate on the patients' gowns and in their beards, on their linens, and so forth.

Rewrite this in the form of a lively and humorous short short story.

Bright: An unforgettable sight struck Dr. _____ when he walked into the medical ward of Midwestern Memorial Hospital last evening. All through the ward patients were dripping a white gooey substance from their beards, their gowns, even from their sheets! Nurses and patients alike were almost frantically bewildered: surely all the patients weren't *that* messy. Only next day did the explanation surface: students of the Phi Ki fraternity, beguiled by an April Fool's elf, had substituted dribble glasses for medicine cups at the nurses' stations on the eve of April 1, knowing full well that Kaopectate was being widely ordered because of a flu epidemic.

This problem was presented by Dr. S. A. Sanchez. The suggested rewrite is the author's.

• *Dull:* The Saxons who lived in England realized that their ancestors had come from northwestern Europe, where the fogs shrouded the landscape. So they didn't view the people from Scandinavia as enemies but as brave overseas cousins. The Anglo-Saxon *Beowulf* portrays the Scandinavians as heroes, people who fought alongside the ancestors of the English. The Vikings appeared almost divine to the English. The latter were in for an extremely unpleasant, indeed a murderous, surprise for the Vikings turned out to be skilled but merciless killers.

Bright: The Saxons of England realized that their ancestral homeland lay toward the rising sun along the fog-shrouded coasts of northwestern Europe. They, therefore, viewed the Norsemen who hailed from that general area not as potential enemies, but as brave cousins from over the sea. The Anglo-Saxon poem, *Beowulf*, pictures the Scandinavians as heroes, companions in arms with the ancestors of the English, almost demigods. The English were in for perhaps the most monstrous awakening in history.

• *Dull:* Since 1946, Greely's comrade, Brainard, has been buried alongside him on the hill. So they are as close dead as they were when they lived during that long hard winter when they were left to freeze at Sabine.

   Bright: Since 1946 his (Greely's) comrade Brainard has been near him on that same hill, as close now in final sleep as in their long winter of trial, abandoned at Sabine. (Problem, paraphrased from *Abandoned* by Alden Todd, New York, McGraw-Hill Book Company, 1961; answer, quote from *Abandoned*)

• *Dull:* Night is over and the stars have disappeared: a joyous dawn lights up the faintly foggy top of the mountain.

   Rewrite this sentence using figures of speech such as metaphors and personification. Be as poetic as you like.

   Bright: Night's candles are burnt out, and jocund day stands tiptoe on the misty mountaintops. (Problem, paraphrased from William Shakespeare. Answer, William Shakespeare. Note how Shakespeare used a metaphor and three personifications, splendid figures of speech in this context.)

   Go ye, therefore, and do likewise!

Remember: Active is Stronger than Passive

• **Use the active and passive voice properly. In general, the active voice promotes vigor.** This topic deserves particular emphasis. The verb is in the active voice when the subject performs the action or is in the condition described by the verb. Thus, the boy caught the fish. When the subject of the verb receives the action, the verb is in the passive voice: The boy was caught by the fish (perhaps "Jaws"?). Passive verbs consist of a form of the verb *to be* or *to get* or *to become*, plus a past participle, as in the above unhappy example.

   Although the active voice is usually preferable to the passive, passive verbs do have several legitimate uses. When, for example, the recipient of the action is more important in the writer's mind than the doer of the action, one should use the passive: The author's first novel was universally panned by the critics. In indefinite statements one may use the passive voice when the doers are unknown, or when they are not to be named (for one reason or another.) In medical case reports and experiments the passive is often used: The animal was injected with ethanol. Many writers (including the author) would prefer: We (or I) injected the animal with ethanol. Dr. Charles Roland has suggested, not entirely facetiously, that there is a tendency to use the passive for unfavorable results and the active for successes.

For some reason, many writers find it easier to write in the passive voice than in the active; first drafts, therefore, tend to reveal excessive employment of the passive voice. Many a manuscript that was weak, verbose, and lacking vigor became strong, terse, and vigorous when its passive verbs were largely changed to actives. Such transformation also shortens most manuscripts by 20% to 25%. This, too, contributes to vigor.

William Shakespeare owes much of his effectiveness to his inspired use of active transitive verbs. (A transitive verb is one that takes an object.) Note these examples of his "active, kicking verbs" (provided by Louana Losee):

From Richard III:
> The tiger now hath *seiz'd* the gently hind;
> Insulting tyranny begins to *jet*
> Upon the innocent and aweless throne . . .

From Much Ado About Nothing:
> . . . boys
> That *lie* and *cog* and *flout, deprave* and *slander*

From Romeo and Juliet:
> *Arise*, fair sun, and *kill* the envious moon . . .
> . . . he *bestrides* the lazy-pacing clouds,
> And *sails* upon the bosom of the air.

From Macbeth:
> But *screw* your courage to the sticking place,
> And we'll not *fail*.

Perhaps most sparkling of all, from King Lear:
> *Blow*, winds, and *crack* your cheeks! *rage! blow!*
> You cataracts and hurricanes, *spout*
> Till you have *drench'd* our steeples,
> *drown'd* the cocks!

Now try your hand at rewriting the following:

Poor: Typhoid fever was contracted by the boy after drinking contaminated water.

Better: The boy contracted typhoid fever from drinking contaminated water.

The History of Medical Journalism in New Jersey
ARTHUR KROSNICK, M.D.

Dr. Krosnick is Editor of the *Journal of the Medical Society of New Jersey*. This article appeared in the September 1984 issue of the *Journal*.

The history of medical journalism in New Jersey is rich and illustrious. Linked by the practitioner's eagerness to transfer information to others, journals and periodicals have become a storehouse of interesting and stimulating material.

Although journalism is the business of managing, editing, or writing for journals or newspapers, the distillation of this concept is the communication of ideas. From Hippocrates to the present, physicians and teachers have been obliged to share their knowledge and experience with students and peers. The transition from word-of-mouth and show-and-tell to electronic communication has been less a change in concept than an advance in technology. Emphasis has moved from description and empiricism to pathogenesis, laboratory and clinical testing, classification, and specific therapy over the past two-and-a-half centuries in New Jersey, but practitioners of medicine—from the barely trained novices and apprentices of the first half of the 18th century in New Jersey to the present scholarly scientists who manipulate DNA—are linked by their eagerness to transfer information to others.

Letters, Oral Communication, Journals, and Diaries: 1623 to 1766

Because of the development of language and the use of symbols to communicate ideas, man has distinguished himself from lesser creatures and has made giant strides from the cave to the computer. The spoken word was the bridge from practitioner to apprentice, even as it is today. Present-day medical and scientific meetings are based on a foundation of lectures and workshops—albeit supported by slides—but these differ mainly as to the size of the audience.

Colonial practitioners, who were few in number, used their senses for observation, palpation, and olfaction and auscultation (before and after the invention of the stethoscope) to make diagnoses and used their experience and instincts to make therapeutic decisions since the primitive state of medicine and medical education offered few alternatives. During the colonial and pre-Medical Society periods the majority of "physicians" had not received any formal training. The "practice of the healing art was chiefly in the care of the clergy" who were intelligent and well educated: "Many of them were distinguished for their knowledge in medicine, and were authors of some of the earliest medical papers printed in America. In some instances the schoolmaster also was the physician and surgeon of the neighborhood. When the literature of the profession was confined to the few writers of those early days, it was easy for the student in literature and science to furnish himself with the theories of medicine and practice."[1]

In the more sparsely settled regions of the colonies, women cared for the sick; being untrained, they turned to "medicinal recipes" in their family record books, many examples of which are stored in the manuscript collections of the New Jersey Historical Society.

During the colonial period, physicians kept journals and diaries in which they recorded the dates, services (house call, phlebotomy, extraction of tooth, and medicines), and fees. This fascinating material points out the limitation of treatments (bleeding, purging, dressing, and reduction of fractures) and the regular dependence on empirical medicinals with modest concepts of dietary manipulation.

During the slow transition from observation, empiricism, and trial-and-error to a "medical science" in colonial New Jersey, the "doctor's" major resource for information was the spoken word. One can imagine the discussions about the first epidemic in the province, which virtually annihilated the Swedes and English in Salem Creek, about the first recognition of malaria at the end of the 17th century, and the initial cases of smallpox in 1715 and yellow fever in 1743 in Burlington. Diphtheria and scarlet fever were New Jersey scourges in 1735 and 1736, although they were not recognized as such.

Medical information was published in newspapers and in other non-medical publications. A newspaper at the time carried the following item: "In July 1751, was committed to the care of Dr. Peter Billings, an experienced physician and man-midwife, and formerly in the King's service, the most extraordinary and remarkable cure that was ever performed in the world upon one Mary Smith, single woman. She had been upwards of 18 years out of her senses (most of the time raving mad), eating her own excrements, and was completely cured by him in two months—contrary to the opinion of all who knew her."

Modest communications in the form of descriptive letters probably were the first example of formal medical writing in those days. An early record of such a letter, written in 1738 and 1739, and later published as a pamphlet in Boston, was the handiwork of Rev. Jonathan Dickinson.

This publication, "Observations on that Terrible Disease Vulgarly Called the Throat Distemper with Advices as to the Method of Cure," was published in 1740 and doubtlessly represents the first published case report from a New Jersey physician, Jonathan Dickinson, a clergyman, theologian, physician, author, and first president of the College of New Jersey (Princeton University), wrote his first medical publication when asked about his experiences in New Jersey with the throat distemper in 1738. At the behest of a publisher he agreed to describe his observations and treatment. His paper contained a remarkable epidemiological and clinical description of "that extraordinary disease, which has made such awful desolations in the country, commonly called the throat distemper." Ultimately the deadly infection was called diphtheria (1826). Dickinson wrote "in the most plain and familiar manner" in order to "communicate to you some of my experiences in this distemper" and "to contribute what I can towards the relief of the afflicted and miserable." What an auspicious beginning by a clinician-writer for New Jersey journalism![1]

Transactions of the New Jersey Medical Society

America's first medical society was formed at Duff's Tavern in New Brunswick on Wednesday, July 23, 1766, and was called the New Jersey Medical Society. The Secretary took minutes at this and each subsequent meeting by hand, and these were carefully preserved. At its Annual Meeting, May 25, 1875, the Society voted to examine and publish the old records. Stephen Wickes edited the *Transactions* from 1766 to 1859, which then were printed in a single volume. The title page, *The Rise, Minutes, and Proceedings of the New Jersey Medical Society*, from the original document, is held in the manuscript collection of the New Jersey Historical Society.[3]

The *Transactions* represented the proceedings of the Annual Meeting and were highlighted by the President's address; they represent a gold mine of interesting and important medical, social, public health, and governmental and legislative issues. The inaugural address of the president often contained clinical material, e.g. the first tumor conference. In the 1785 *Transactions*, a 17-year-old boy was presented to the assembly by the physician, who discussed the removal of a tumor from the patient's forearm. In 1787, Dr. William Burnet, who was the second president of the Society, delivered the first scientific paper by a member of the organization, "On the Nature and Importance of the Healing Art," which later was published.

The New Jersey Medical Reporter

Unlike the *Transactions of the New Jersey Medical Society*, the *New Jersey Medical Reporter* was the first professional journal "devoted to the interests of medical science generally." It was published quarterly by a very business-like editor, Joseph Parrish, M.D., of Burlington, who charged $2 per annum, payable in advance, or $10 for six copies to be sent to one address. Parrish warned that "those who wish to be placed on our subscription list will please make their remittances without delay." Volume I, No. 1, was dated October 1847 and included proceedings of the New Jersey Medical Society, committee reports, a rather testy commentary against the system of medicine started by Samuel Hahnemann, called homeopathy, and proceedings of the National Medical Convention held in New York in 1846 and in Philadelphia in 1847 (New Jersey was not officially represented by action of the State Society). There is an editorial explaining the reasons for publishing the *New Jersey Medical Reporter:* "To provide the proceedings of meetings of the Society, to reproduce papers presented to District Societies, to lay before the subscribers a general summary of medical science such as may be obtained from the various kindred periodicals of this country and Europe, and to publish editorials, biographical notices, and other items depending on available space."

Parrish also wrote an editorial on the new scientific breakthrough, "Application of the Vapour of Sulphuric Ether in Practical Medicine and Obstetrics." There also were articles on splints, a case report (placenta praevia), book reviews, and so on.[4]

In 1850, Dr. Samuel W. Butler, a new graduate from the Medical Department of the University of Pennsylvania, commenced practice in Burlington and was appointed assistant editor of the *Reporter*. In 1854, Parrish retired and Butler became the editor and proprietor of the *Reporter* which he changed to a monthly publication. He was so successful as an editor that "in 1858 he determined to remove from the somewhat provincial quiet of Burlington to Philadelphia, at that time, and largely still the professional metropolis of the country."[5] He then made another daring change, altering the journal to a national weekly publication (10¢ a copy, $3 per annum) and retitling it, *The Weekly Medical and Surgical Reporter*. According to a subsequent editor, D.G. Brinton, Butler continued to publish the *Reporter* during the Civil War, "when nearly every other medical periodical in the country was obliged to succumb."

The Journal of the Medical Society of New Jersey

H. Genet Taylor first suggested a monthly journal in his presidential address in 1889. In September 1904, Volume 1, No. 1 of *The Journal* commenced publication under the direction of the Committee on Publication, as ordered by the Board of Trustees in July of that year. Richard C. Newton, M.D., of Montclair, was appointed the first editor.

Some of the reasons for becoming a monthly were: 1) to enlist the interest (and membership in the Society) of younger New Jersey physicians; 2) to provide a better means of communication among the members; 3) to make the members better acquainted with each other, to induce them to attend and participate in meetings, and to promote a higher grade of scientific work; 4) to collect and print excellent addresses and papers; 5) to induce the hospitals and asylums in New Jersey to prepare and publish better scientific and clinical reports; and 6) to aid collateral organizations, e.g. state and municipal health boards, the Sanitary Association, and the State Board of Medical Examiners.[6]

It appears that the reasons have been fulfilled and continue to be valid. During the last 80 years, there have been seven editors of *The Journal:* Richard Cole Newton (1904 to 1906); David C. English (1906 to 1924); Henry O. Reik (1925 to 1933); Alfred E. Shipley (1934); Frank Overton (1935 to 1940); Henry A. Davidson (1941 to 1973;) and Arthur Krosnick (1973 to present).

The Journal has remained the mouthpiece of the State Society, but its editors have functioned with independence and honesty. While the character of *The Journal* has changed very little, its style has varied with the times, reflecting advances in medicine and science, changes in socioeconomic and legislative circumstances, and the needs of the members of the Society.

Older issues are a storehouse of exciting medical facts that link practitioners through many aspects of health and science but especially at the moments of great discoveries or worldly events. Four wars have intervened during the life of *The Journal,* and the scientific discoveries have been so numerous as to defy tabulation in this essay. Names like Ehrlich and Mayo, items like paper milk bottles and the roentgen ray, and drugs like sulfa and recombinant DNA insulin, are in the pages of *The Journal.*

A number of significant changes have characterized our present award-winning magazine: 1) an active, participatory Committee on Publication; 2) appointment of a highly competent Editorial Board, manuscript reviewers, and book reviewers; 3) an up-beat, positive approach to covers, graphics, typography, readability, and editing; 4) a strong participation by university-affiliated authors and contributors to special departments; 5) emphasis on current and future trends in health, economics, professional liability, governmental and regulatory influences, and the role of the physician and organized medicine in New Jersey's health care system; 6) a staff with publication skills at the cutting-edge of the craft; and 7) special issues.

In 1947, MSNJ started a *Periodic Newsletter* during the presidency of Royal A. Schaaf of Newark with Richard I. Nevin, emeritus executive director and editor; this became the *Membership Newsletter* with a change from a special-subject publication to a more diverse, 4-page periodical published under the direction of the Council on Public Relations with Vincent A. Maressa, executive director, as the editor. In July 1983, the *Membership Newsletter* was terminated as an independent publication and was incorporated in *The Journal.*

Publications and Health-Related Journals

State Board of Medical Examiners of New Jersey Annual Report. The First annual Report of the State Board was published in 1891. The Board was appointed July 8, 1890, under "an act to regulate the practice of medicine and surgery," which was known as the Medical Law and was approved March 12, 1881. The first published report "To His Excellency Leon Abbett, Governor of New Jersey," was submitted by Wm. Perry Watson, M.D., Secretary. It concerned itself mainly with the imperfection of the law and the ease with which individuals with bogus credentials become legalized physicians in this state.[7]

The first state examination was given on October 10, 1890, to 11 candidates for licensure to practice medicine; 10 passed and were granted certificates. Each report thereafter contained the scores of the examinees and the institution at which their medical education was obtained. The Ninth Annual Report indicated that 121 candidates were examined for license to practice medicine and surgery and 97 passed.[7]

Bulletin of the Academy of Medicine of New Jersey. The Academy, founded in 1911, did not establish a journal until April 15, 1955. The first *Bulletin* had James E. Gardam as acting editor, and served to provide to the Fellows of the Academy the proceedings of a symposium on heparin which was given at the Academy of Medicine on December 16, 1954. The President was Asher Yaguda, M.D. Some very illustrious scientific speakers and writers were represented in the *Bulletin*, which dealt with such timely subjects as corticotropin (Philips S. Hench, Nobel Prize recipient addressed this symposium), alcoholism, highway safety, and fluoridation. The *Bulletin* ceased publication in December 1970.[9]

Public Health News: New Jersey State Department of Health. MSNJ President George T. Welch's prediction in 1893 that a cabinet-level Secretary of Health would be appointed early in the 20th century came true. In 1865, the Legislature appointed a State Sanitary Commission, and in 1873 created the State Board of Health. In 1903, New Jersey became the first state to license municipal health officers and sanitary inspectors. In 1915, legislation established the State Department of Health to replace the Board and following this, a monthly publication, *Public Health News* appeared. This periodical still exists and reports current public health data, advice, and statistics.

New Jersey Journal of Pharmacy. The New Jersey Pharmaceutical Association was the first such organization in the United States when it was founded in 1870. The origin of the Association was a conference with members of the Essex County Medical Society. The *New Jersey Journal of Pharmacy* succeeded the *Proceedings* of the Association in 1927 and is published monthly.[12,13]

The Country Practitioner **or** *New Jersey Journal of Medical and Surgical Practice.* Published 1879 to 1881 by Dr. E.P. Townsend at Beverly.[11]

New Jersey Eclectic Medical and Surgical Journal. Published in New Jersey from 1874 to 1876; then moved to New York.[11]

New Jersey State Homeopathic Medical Society. Published *Transactions* or *Proceedings* from 1855 to 1911.[11]

The Fountain **or** *Hydropathic Journal.* Published at Morristown in 1846.[11]

The New Jersey Association of Osteopathic Physicians and Surgeons. The Association was organized in 1901. It published a *Bulletin* from 1901 to 1963 when it became the *Journal* of the Association.[11]

The New Jersey State Dental Society. The Society has published *Transactions* or *Proceedings* since 1870. Their journal was called the *New Jersey Dental Journal* from 1912 to 1919; in 1929, the current monthly *Journal of the New Jersey State Dental Society* started.[11]

Auxiliary of the Medical Society of New Jersey. The Women's Auxiliary to the Medical Society of New Jersey was organized at the Annual Meeting in Atlantic City on June 17 to 19, 1926; the name later was changed by dropping "Women's." Although the Auxiliary did not publish a journal, their Primer (*The Blue Book*) encouraged the members to read *The Journal* of the Medical Society of New Jersey and the official organ of the Women's Auxiliary to the American Medical Association called *The Journal* and published since 1928. They also were encouraged to read the AMA magazine *Hygeia* (now called *Today's Health*).[13] In September 1948, the Auxiliary *Newsletter* was initiated and has been published ever since. Presently titled *The Shingle*, it is published three times a year; its editor is Mrs. Thomas H. McGlade, and associate editor is Mrs. Ralph Fioretti.

Health Hints; Junior Health Hints. These publications were prepared as a public service by the Subcommittee on Public Relations of the Medical Society of New Jersey under the editorship of Richard I. Nevin, Executive Officer. Each issue contained papers intended for classroom presentation.

Summary

The history of medicine, medical education, medical organizations, and the history of medical journalism in New Jersey is rich and illustrious. Our oldest journals and periodicals are a storehouse of interesting and stimulating material which spans two-and-half centuries.

References

1. Wickes S: *History of Medicine in New Jersey and Its Medical Men.* Newark, NJ, Martin R. Dennis & Co., 1879, pp. 14–15, p. 37, pp. 89–98, p. 234.

2. McClenahan RL: New Jersey medical history in the colonial period. *Proceedings New Jersey Historical Society*, pp. 362–374.

3. *Transactions, Med Soc NJ* 1776, pp. 3–4, p. 9, 1847, 1859, 1861, 1893.

4. New Jersey Medical Reporter and Transactions of the New Jersey Medical Society. Burlington, NJ, 1848.

5. *The Medical and Surgical Reporter.* D.G. Brinton, M.D. (ed). Philadelphia, PA, December 1873 to July 1874, p. 60.

6. *J Med Soc NJ* Vol. 1. Richard Cole Newton (ed). Newark, NJ, September 1904–June 1905.

7. First Annual Report of the State Board of Medical Examiners of New Jersey. Trenton, 1891.

8. Saffron MH: *A History of the Academy of Medicine of New Jersey, 1911–1981.* Lawrenceville, NJ 1981, p. 3.

9. Bulletin, AMNJ, 1955–1970.

10. Benson DS: Highlights of the history of public health in New Jersey: *Public Health News* 45:165–169, 1964.

11. Cowen DL: *Medicine and Health in New Jersey: A History.* Princeton, NJ, D. Van Nostrand Company, Inc., 1964.

12. Cowen DL: Fifty years of the New Jersey journal of pharmacy. *New Jersey Journal of Pharmacy* 50:14–17, 1977.

13. Rogers F, Sayre AR: *The Healing Art.* Trenton, NJ, Medical Society of New Jersey, 1966.

Special Report

Journal editors rarely have the time to research and write an in-depth investigative report of the type published by major daily newspapers and general magazines. In addition to the time, this genre of news reporting requires considerable journalistic skill.

Ann Gray, the long-time Executive Editor of *Virginia Medical*, has written many special reports which are equal in quality to those which appear in America's top newspapers and magazines. For example, the November 1983 issue of the monthly publication of The Medical Society of Virginia, included a nine-page article about freestanding ambulatory surgery centers. Ms. Gray focused on a specific facility in Roanoke and chronicled the saga of how they obtained a certificate of need (CON). The provocative title, *CON Artist* was questionable, but the article itself indeed was a blend of careful research and creative writing. Within the article, Ms. Gray included three boxed inserts, one of which we include at the end of this chapter, headlined Footprints on the Sands of Certified Need.

Among the many examples of excellent writing, note the following:

Frequent use of short sentences, sometimes an entire paragraph consisting of only a few words.

Good mixture of past and present tenses to tell the story as it happened.

Interviews which make the reader see and hear the person. For example: . . . the lawyer "wanted $10,000 for starters. *For starters,*' he repeats incredulously. "And what did it cost Dr. Nelson?" He shrugs. "$25. For parking fees and photocopies."

CON Artist

Gone forever, no doubt, are the days when doctors ran their own hospitals, but two groups of Virginia physicians are recapturing some of that lost entrepreneurial ground by launching their own freestanding ambulatory surgery centers (ASCs).

Pioneering the two facilities are an association of seven Richmond urologists headed by Dr. C. M. Kinloch Nelson and the sixty-six physicians who own the multispecialty Lewis-Gale Clinic in Roanoke.

Freestanding ambulatory surgery centers exemplify the new wave of outpatient service designed to bypass the high cost of hospitalization. They accommodate "in-and-out" surgery, which is a cut above office treatment but not serious enough to necessitate hospital admission. Many Virginia hospitals have installed ASCs in the recent past. These were categorized according to system, i.e., respiratory, nervous, digestive, musculoskeletal and so on, and each category was divided into four payment groups. Thus for a cystourethroscopy with retrograde pyelogram, the program offered $231. In contrast, the urologist said, at a Richmond hospital whose charges were neither highest nor lowest but somewhere in between, the charge for this procedure was $460. "That's comparing apples and apples," he emphasized. "Same procedure, same quality."

And these listed payments are the facility fees one conventionally associates with hospitals, correct? asked the interviewer. Correct, said Dr. Nelson. But in this case they would go to the urologists' ambulatory surgery center, and the physicians fees would also be billed as usual, correct? "Sure," Dr. Nelson answered swiftly, "we stand to make more money, but I'm not hiding that and I'm not ashamed of it." Although, he added, his face clouding over, some people seemed to find something wrong with it.

What urologic procedures would you perform in an ASC that could not be done in an office? the interviewer inquired.

"About 40% of our cystoscopies with retrograde pyelograms are now performed in the hospital, because the patients need sedation." Dr. Nelson replied. "We'd do those in the ambulatory surgery center. Some urologists perform vasectomies and circumcisions in the office, but we don't think the office is safe enough for those; the ambulatory surgery center would be, however. We're now doing prostate and bladder biopsies in the hospital, too, partly for sedation, partly for after-care; those could be done in the ASC.

"We specifically would not want to shift office treatment into the ambulatory surgery center," he asserted, "and we'll have rigid internal controls to see that that is not done."

Like everyone else who undertakes the certificate of need course, Dr. Nelson began with a little warm-up protocol. For the application form he got in touch with Mrs. Marilyn West, director of the Division of Resources

Development at the Virginia Department of Health. Once he'd mastered the form's marathon 19 pages, he took both the application and himself to the director of the nearest health systems agency, who was Michael Osorio of the Central Virginia HSA. Osorio pronounced the petition fit. Back it went to West. When she accepted it for review, it became Osorio's task to set up three hearings.

All three of these hearings would be open to the public and duly advertised in the local newspapers, but the first one is the designated public hearing. It amounts customarily to a small, friendly rehearsal for the petitioner's future appearances before two reviewing bodies, and such was the case with Dr. Nelson's public hearing on March 24.

Some questions were asked by Larry D. Jones, a provider-member of CAHAC and its chairman, who would not be able to attend the coming review by that group. Jones is a senior marketing representative for Pru-Care, a Richmond health maintenance organization.

Would the proposed office-located ambulatory surgery center so shift patients away from hospitals that it would lead to an increase in hospital costs? he asked. Dr. Nelson responded that the effect on hospitals would be insignificant, that prospective payment was going to change the costs picture in any event.

How did the proposed freestanding ASC fit into such developments as "emergicenters"? Ambulatory surgery centers are part of the same big trend to lower-cost settings for patient care, was the response.

What ancillary services would be available? Jones continued. X-ray and renal scan, Dr. Nelson said, and of course the requisite pathology lab.

Support for Dr. Nelson's application was offered by John N. Simpson, president of Richmond Memorial Hospital. The proposed ambulatory surgery center might well be in competition with his hospital, Simpson said, but if the urologists could provide less costly treatment, then they should be allowed to do so.

Hearing adjourned. Dr. Nelson's application would go forward.

More precisely, it would go upward, for the road to a certificate of need ascends through the local health advisory council, the regional health systems agency, and the Statewide Health Coordinating Council (SHCC) to the top, where sits Dr. James B. Kenley, Virginia's Commissioner of Health. For Dr. Nelson, the first stop would be Planning District 15's review body, the very Capital Area Health Advisory Council of which he is a member.

As do its counterparts in each of Virginia's 21 other planning districts, the Capital Area Health Advisory Council has 30 members, of whom 16 are consumers, 14 are providers. All serve without honoraria. Eight of the consumer-members are appointed by the counties within the planning district, and eight are elected by the Council.

Of the provider-members, 12 are appointed by provider organizations.

In PD 15, these organizations are The Medical Society of Virginia; Medical College of Virginia; South Central PSRO; Central Virginia Hospital Council; Virginia Nurses Association; Blue Cross Blue Shield of Virginia; Virginia Health Care Association (long-term care facilities); Virginia Association of Allied Health Professions; Neuropsychiatric Society of Virginia; and Region IV Consortium Mental Health/Mental Retardation/Substance Abuse. The other two provider-members are elected by the Council.

Ten days before each of its monthly meetings, members of the Council receive from the staff an analysis of each application to be considered at the coming session, with the staff's recommendations as to the application's disposition. On this staff report, Dr. Nelson's proposed ASC stubbed its toe.

Certain aspects of the application were "commendable," the report admitted, but there were other considerations. The regional Health Systems Plan clearly states, the staff noted, that free-standing ambulatory services should be established only when hospital-based surgical suites in the planning district equal or exceed 80% of the Plan's stated minimum utilization figure of 1,000 operations per room per year. A 1981 survey of the 11 hospitals in PD 15, however, yielded an average usage rate of 768.51 procedures per OR per year, well below the 80% specification.

Moreover, the contention that the proposed ASC would be more cost-effective was "probably a moot one," in the staff's opinion, because prospective payment was coming to hospitals, too, and there were four hospital-based ASCs with dedicated operating rooms already doing business in the planning district, and another was under construction.

The staff expressed grave concerns about shifts that could rock the health-care boat—shifts of costs in hospitals due to loss of revenue, shifts of patients from office treatment to ambulatory surgery, also cost-inflationary.

In summary, the staff recommended denial of Dr. Nelson's application for a certificate of need.

Copies of the staff report had been sent to CAHAC members before they convened on March 28. Dr. Nelson was there as both Council member and applicant. When the agenda proceeded to consideration of his application, he was asked to describe the project for which he was requesting a certificate of public need.

Available to him nearby were a podium, flip chart, audio-visual equipment and overhead projectors. Many CON applicants need these props for the copious graphic material with which they buttress their pleas. Dr. Nelson's material, however, was "all in his head," as one observer recalls, and he stayed seated at the table and talked from there.

He practiced urology with six other physicians, Dr. Nelson began: Austin I. Dodson, Jr.; J. Edward Hill; G. Bryan Duck; Frank N. Pole; William H. Atwill; and Gary B. Bokinsky. They wanted to install in their office building an ambulatory surgery center with two operating rooms, plus X-ray and renal scan. Their lab was entirely adequate to meet pathology needs. The facility would have a staff of four, led by a registered nurse. There would be appropriate medical review. No capital expenditures were required; the urologists had recently bought an office building, it had been renovated to suit the doctor's office practice, the ASC installation would be part of the renovation costs.

He emphasized the convenience to patients of the proposed ASC and wound up with a description of the HCFA's prospective payment program for Medicare patients. He had sent all details of the proposed surgical center to the HCFA people in Washington, and they had responded that all systems were go.

The acting chairman, David W. Pentico, Richmond statistician and consumer-member of the Council, entertained questions.

What about safety precautions for patients? one Council member asked. The urologists had set up an agreement with Richmond Memorial Hospital for backup in case of emergency, Dr. Nelson answered.

Was it to be closed staffing? No, Dr. Nelson replied, it would be open staffing; there are 16 other urologists in the area who are not associated with hospitals, and they would be free to use the center.

Would the Medicare program cover charges for X-ray and renal scan? No, those would not be covered, the urologist explained, but they would be charged at rates lower than those of existing facilities. How would they be billed? Separately.

There were a few other questions, then a vote was solicited. Dr. Nelson abstained. The 14 other members present voted unanimously to approve the application because 1) "the proposal appears to be cost-effective" and 2) "the free-standing ambulatory surgery center offers the provision of alternative medical care."

Next hurdle: The board of directors of the Central Virginia Health Systems Agency.

Like the subsidiary health advisory councils, the boards of each of Virginia's five HSAs are comprised of 16 providers and 14 consumers. They are appointed and elected in much the same way, except that HSA directors are drawn from the region rather than the locality; thus consumer-directors are appointed not by counties but by the planning districts of the region. The directors are volunteers; there is no honorarium.

The meetings of both council and board are similar, too. The CON petitioner appears to answer questions. The directors receive for study the same staff report that was submitted to the council.

On April 6, 1983, the board of directors of the Central Virginia Health Systems Agency met in the Blue Cross Blue Shield building in Richmond. Introducing Dr. Nelson's application for discussion, Mrs. W. Hamilton

Crockford III, consumer board member and its chairwoman, noted that the health advisory council had forwarded its recommendation for approval of the application.

But the staff's report recommended denial, a board member observed to Jack V. Quigley, HSA health planning specialist. What aspects of the application warranted approval?

The proposal to provide outpatient surgery procedures, the staff man returned, is definitely in the direction of cost-effective delivery of health care.

Have any hospitals raised any objections to your proposal? No, he'd had no objections from hospitals, Dr. Nelson related, and from one hospital had come a positive response.

Would Dr. Nelson comment on the relative costs? He cited the $460 hospital charge versus the $231 of the Medicare fee schedule.

One person couldn't understand about the absence of capital expenditures. Dr. Nelson assured the questioner that installation costs would be subsumed by the renovation budget.

"I'm in favor of the application myself," volunteered James L. Gore, vice president of provider services for Blue Cross Blue Shield of Virginia. "Sure, it may hurt hospitals for a while, but I think it's a legitimate form of competition, and unless we allow some legitimate competition in this area, we're not going to answer all the questions regarding the cost of health care."

Dr. Wyatt S. Beazley III, Richmond surgeon who is one of The Medical Society of Virginia's representatives to the Central Virginia HSA board, joined Gore's affirmative position.

"We've been searching for ways to save money," Dr. Beazley said, "and this is a new way to approach things. My concern is why you even have to have a certificate of need for it, because every doctor who wants to do something like this is going to have to apply. The quality of service is going to be just as good as it is in the hospital, I think, and the people who are going to benefit are the patients."

Whereupon there was a motion to approve for the reasons of 1) cost containment and 2) convenience to the public. The motion carried by a roll-call vote of 15 ayes and two nays.

Onward and upward to SHCC.

The national network of health systems agencies sprang up in response to legislation passed by Congress in 1974 and calling for oversight of certain aspects of American medical care, including accessibility, quality and costs. Each regional HSA is a non-profit, non-stock corporation funded by the United States Treasury.

The State of Virginia contributes to this apparatus through the State-wide Coordinating Council, which is a creature of the State and is funded equally by the State and the federal government.

Virginia's governor appoints the 31 members of the Statewide Council
—two consumers and two providers from each of the five HSA regions and
11 members appointed at large. Consumers dominate the at-large appoint-
ments; the ratio at present is eight consumers to three providers. Virginia's
physicians are always represented on the Statewide Council. Dr. George E.
Broman, Culpeper, was SHCC chairman for the recent 1979–1981 term.

Each SHCC member must belong to one of two committees. The Planning and Policy Analysis Committee works on the State Health Plan and
the State Medical Facilities Plan; in these two plans are contained the basic
criteria and standards for medical care in Virginia and projections for
future medical needs. The Health Facilities and Services Review Committee
considers certificates of need.

The Review Committee meets once a month, usually in Richmond but
sometimes in other cities of the state. Its members are paid $50 per diem and
travel expenses. Before each meeting, each committee member receives a
dossier on every CON petition to be considered at the coming session; this
includes information on all that has gone before in the review process and
recommendations from the Division of Resources Development for disposition of each application.

The state staff's appraisal of Dr. Nelson's application sang the same
song, second verse of the earlier HSA staff report. According to current
standards in Virginia's two Plans, "there is no need for additional surgical
facilities in PD 15," nor has the applicant "demonstrated that the need for
surgical services can be accommodated by existing facilities." The proposal
"could increase health systems costs" through the same cost-shifting that
had worried the HSA staff, the report continued, and although ambulatory
surgery can be considered "a less costly and more efficient alternative to inpatient surgery, prospective reimbursement should encourage more effective utilization of existing facilities."

The state staff recommended denial.

The SHCC review committee met on April 20 to consider five applications for certificates of public need—for a home health agency, a rehabilitation service, the purchase of a used CAT head scanner, more beds for a
psychiatric hospital, and Dr. Nelson's freestanding ambulatory surgery
center.

First the committee turned down the petition for the home health agency.
Then it gave its attention to the urologists' project. The acting chairman,
Carroll I. Leith, Jr., Alexandria, asked Dr. Nelson to outline his proposed
ASC. Leith, a consumer member of SHCC, is a retired federal employee.

Dr. Nelson complied, speaking extemporaneously and citing the support for the project of the Health Care Finance Administration, Richmond
Memorial Hospital and Blue Cross–Blue Shield of Virginia.

Then HSA staff man Quigley reported that the board of directors of the Central Virginia Health Systems Agency had unanimously approved Dr. Nelson's application because the proposed facility was viewed as an effective approach to cost containment.

Next, as the minutes of the meeting relate, came the questions.

To Dr. Nelson: How many other urologists are associated with this project? Dr. Nelson went into his opening-staffing routine.

To Quigley: Why isn't the St. Mary's ambulatory surgery center in operation yet?

This questioner was recalling the committee's recent approval of an application for installation of an ASC at St. Mary's Hospital in Richmond; the new service was then being built on the hospital's seventh floor at a cost of almost $2 million. St. Mary's Hospital and Dr. Nelson's office building are both in Planning District 15. They are, in fact, only a few blocks away from each other.

Quigley replied that the St. Mary's facility was still under construction and staff was being searched for it.

"It's my feeling," commented a committee member, "that if this project goes into an area where the same services are offered, it will increase costs. We must be concerned about the existing facilities, and not approve a service that would shift patients away from them."

The HSA board did not feel, Quigley countered, that Dr. Nelson's facility would cause anyone to raise costs, and Dr. Nelson himself asserted that a facility of the type he was proposing might even encourage hospitals to lower their costs.

Do the urologists have any relationship to the medical school? another committee member wanted to know, referring to the Medical College of Virginia. Only in that three of them are on MCV's clinical staff, the urologist replied.

Another committee member observed that the committee seemed to be overlooking the fact that the State Medical Facilities Plan has standards and guidelines that must be adhered to, and the state staff had pointed to existing surgical capacity in PD 15.

So saying, he moved to recommend denial of the application for the reasons given by the staff. The motion was promptly seconded and passed on a vote of 7 to 5. Exit Dr. Nelson, in pain.

"It was a terrible meeting," the urologist recalls. "I knew I was in trouble. They were so . . . adversarial."

Quigley does not remember the Review Committee as adversarial. There were a lot of new SHCC members at that hearing, he notes. They were fresh from studying the State Plan and were taking their duties very seriously.

In any event, the committee at that hearing refused all five CON applications set before them, but the company of these fellow rejects was small comfort to the urologist, who could only pin his hopes on a reprieve from the final arbiter, Commissioner Kenley.

The word from Dr. Kenley arrived in Dr. Nelson's mail two weeks after the SHCC hearing.

After "considering all factors," the Commissioner wrote, he was denying the application because 1) no more operating rooms, either outpatient or inpatient, were needed to accommodate the patient population in the area in question; 2) the State Plan says that no operating rooms should be added in an area until the existing ORs average 1000–1400 per year; and 3) the anticipated lower costs of the proposed freestanding ASC would not offset the costs generated by creating unneeded surgical capacity.

Dr. Nelson was entitled to appeal the decision if he wanted to, Dr. Kenley added.

Dr. Nelson definitely wanted to and duly showed up for the appeal on June 21 at the James Madison Building, home of the Department of Health in Virginia's capital city. Appointed by Dr. Kenley to conduct the appeal was Dr. Bedford E. Berrey, Assistant State Health Commissioner. Mrs. West and an assistant were on hand as staff. With Dr. Nelson came Dr. Richardson Grinan, vice president for medical affairs, Blue Cross–Blue Shield of Virginia, who was there to pledge the insurance carrier's support for the urologists' surgical center.

Two appeals, one informal, one formal, are open to an applicant whose request for a certificate of public need has been denied. This was the informal appeal. The three men and two women talked pleasantly for about an hour and a half, but the truth was that Dr. Nelson had his dander up, as revealed by the typewritten plea he left with Dr. Berrey.

First he took aim at the assertion that there was enough surgical capacity in PD 15 to accommodate the available patients. He cited the Maryland Health Plan, which says that when a hospital begins operating at 80% or higher efficiency, scheduling difficulties become severe, in-house procedures are delayed, and elective surgical admissions are postponed or cancelled. All add costs to the system and also increase patient anxiety, destroy work plans, and leave families and baby-sitters hanging.

The Commissioner's assertion that his project would not save the system money was Dr. Nelson's next target.

"This is pure and total conjecture by the Commissioner," he said, "and is erroneous in this new era of competition and prospective payment." Who are the parties most concerned with the system's cost? the urologist's plea asked. "Those that pay for it directly; in our area, this is primarily Medicare and Blue Cross–Blue Shield. This project was created because of the stimulus of the Health Care Financing Administration's new prospective payment program for Medicare and has received continuing encouragement and support from the HCFA. Blue Cross and Blue Shield have also strongly supported the project.''

Appended to Dr. Nelson's statement was a letter from Margaret Van Amringe, acting director of HCFA's Office of Survey and Certification.

"The HCFA assumes," she wrote, "that Medicare reimbursement for services provided in freestanding ambulatory surgery centers will result in a $2 million savings in fiscal year 1983 alone. . . . There is some evidence that the establishment of a freestanding surgical center in close proximity to a hospital has resulted in lower hospital fees for the same procedures. All in all, we are of the opinion that ASCs promote competition and thereby benefit both the Medicare program and its beneficiaries.''

Then Dr. Nelson shot some holes in the State Medical Facilities Plan, on which Dr. Kenley had based his decision.

"We live in a fluid, flexible and innovative society," Dr. Nelson wrote, "and to hold in the year 1983 to a Plan written in 1979 is absurd and unAmerican. It was clearly the legislative intent that the Plan be updated appropriately, and this responsibility was clearly accepted by the Department of Health. The Department has been woefully neglectful . . .

"Physicians have been asked to do something about the high cost of medical care. We are trying. We are attempting to obtain a certificate of need for a facility that would significantly reduce the cost for many surgical and diagnostic procedures.''

The appeal officer's verdict was handed down one month later. Documenting his decision with six pages of pros and cons, Dr. Berrey found for the urologist's proposed surgery center. His reasons: 1) Cost savings "argue overwhelmingly in its favor.'' 2) The State Medical Facilities Plan's guidelines to determining the need for additional ORs "does not consider efficiency of operation.'' 3) The Plan "has not been updated to reflect recent changes in the reimbursement system, so that innovation and creativity are inhibited.'' 4) Blue Cross–Blue Shield supports the proposed freestanding ASC because it has the potential for lower costs.

Altogether, Dr. Berrey concluded, the project' may well bring greater efficiency to the system, foster competition and lower costs, and he asked the Commissioner of Health to set aside his denial.

In a covering letter, the Commissioner did just that, and he enclosed the object of Dr. Nelson's campaign—the official certificate of need for the urologists' freestanding ambulatory surgery center.

He remained concerned, Dr. Kenley noted, about the impact of the project on the existing operating room capacity in PD 15, but since third-party payers were encouraging the development of these ASCs, his approval of this pilot project might provide "an opportunity for the study of its effect on the health care system.''

Dr. Nelson promptly began making his way through the sticky wickets of licensure for the Urology Center. He figured he'd get his hands on the necessary piece of paper without too much difficulty, and maybe the ASC could open for business in mid-December or thereabouts.

Up the street, construction finally ended on the new ambulatory surgery center at St. Mary's Hospital, and patients began to be scheduled in August. There are two dedicated operating rooms; St. Mary's had asked for four ORs, but the reviewers halved that number.

In Roanoke, the three operating rooms of the Lewis-Gale Clinic's ambulatory surgery center are being built into the third floor of a big new addition now under construction, with completion expected in the summer of 1984. The clinic is adjacent to Lewis-Gale Hospital, which was founded by physicians in 1908; today the clinic owns the emergency room and Hospital Corporation of America owns the hospital.

There's an outpatient surgery program at Lewis-Gale Hospital; the procedures are scheduled into a regular operating room. A spokesman was asked if the hospital intended to install a full-fledged ambulatory surgery center. "No, I don't think so," he said, "not now that the clinic is putting one in. I wish we'd gotten there first, because that's the way the business is going."

The author appreciates the generous assistance of the following persons: at St. Mary's Hospital, Christopher M. Carney; at the Lewis-Gale Clinic, Darrell D. Whitt; at Lewis-Gale Hospital, Robert D. Anderson; at the Central Virginia Health Systems Agency, Michael Osorio, Jack Quigley, Julie White and Anita Flint; at the Virginia Department of Health, Marilyn West, Elizabeth Taylor, Sue Rhodes and Steve Sorin of the Division of Resources Development, and May Fox and Deborah Blackburn of the Division of Health Planning.

Footprints on the sands of certified need

Remember the tug of war five years ago when the prototype CAT scanner tangled with Virginia's certificate of public need process? The health planners, from whom all permits flow, were alarmed by the new machine's price tag; those applying for the technology contended that it would save money in the long run. The providers prevailed, and scanning became a routine diagnostic procedure.

Today, applications to buy the second generation of CATs are proceeding quietly through the certificate of need system, accompanied by a growing market in second-hand scanners. Controversy now centers on higher tech at even higher cost, nuclear magnetic resonance.

Thus is history written in the certificate of public need program. At the program's outset, ten years ago, most of the applications were for bed-intensive projects. Today, the addition of hospital beds is frowned on in most localities, and nursing home beds reached such a peak of proliferation recently that a moratorium was placed on their construction. When the moratorium was lifted in July, a few nursing homes made haste to apply for new beds, but it is not expected that the reviewers will make haste to grant them.

Most certificates of need today have to do with new equipment and new service. In the equipment category, two technologies are challenging the CAT scanner activity: laser-ophthalmology, for which five Virginia hospitals were given CONs in the year ending July 1983, and digital vascular imaging, approved for six hospitals in the same period.

The costliest equipment yet is nuclear magnetic resonance. Richmond's Chippenham Hospital applied to spend $3.5 million to install Virginia's first NMR scanner, but the application was denied; until its clinical usefulness is known, said the Commissioner of Health, these new scanners should be placed in research-teaching hospitals. We'll appeal, retorted Chippenham officials.

As for new services, home health care is at flood tide. Of the 245 requests for CON application forms in the year ending July, 68 were for home health projects. A lot of these suppliants lost heart when they saw the form, a grueling document 19 pages long. Many who persevered were denied. Ten were granted certificates—five commercial firms, four hospitals and one clinic. The expansion of three existing home health agencies was also approved.

In the same 12-month period a flurry of hospitals asked to install cardiac catheterization laboratories, this rush occurring when the CC labs already in business began exceeding the official highwater usage mark of 500 procedures per year. Six new CC labs were approved and two hospitals were given permission to add second ones. Whereupon the planners allowed as how they'd better damp down this enthusiasm by raising the usage quotient.

Definitely a comer in the new services category is hospice care. In the same 12-month period, five new hospice programs were granted certificates of public need in Virginia: three independent operations, one hospital-based, one in a retirement complex. A surge of hospice activity is expected when the new Medicare reimbursement program for hospice care gets into gear.

Ambulatory surgery centers have been touted as a new medical service with big growth potential, and the 12-month record shows receipt at the Department of Health of more than a dozen letters of intent to apply for freestanding ASCs. Some of these letters have come from individual physicians, and since corporate entities overwhelmingly dominate certificate of need records, their names surprise the reader—a vascular surgeon in Virginia Beach; two general practitioners, one in Bristol, one in Norfolk; a plastic surgeon in Richmond; an ophthalmologist in Danville.

But as this was written only two certificates of need had been granted for physician-owned ambulatory surgery centers. The story is told in these pages.

Transatlantic Medical English
A.S.D. SPIERS, M.D.

Our language, American English, is spoken and understood throughout the world. Some of our British colleagues believe that American writers are lax in rules of grammar. Though their criticisms sometimes are valid, they generally forget the basic objective of all journalists, which is to communicate effectively. American writers have made substantial contributions by stressing *simplicity.*

Alexander S.D. Spiers, M.D., Ph.D., a British physician who now is professor of medicine at The Albany Medical College, Albany, NY, is an expert on British and American medical journalism. A 1960 graduate of the University of Melbourne in Australia, he has written over 200 articles, mostly on hematology and oncology.

The following article appeared in the December 22-29, 1984 issue of *The Lancet*, the distinguished British medical journal, and is reprinted by permission of *The Lancet*.

It has become trite to say that the United Kingdom and the United States are two countries divided by a common language. Indeed, they show signs of developing two distinct languages, and problems in communication that already exist promise to multiply. This is particularly apparent in rapidly evolving disciplines such as medicine.

It is not widely known that the rules of correct English usage are virtually identical in the US and the UK. The idea that there are major differences in correct usage has arisen because in the US there is very little respect for the rules, probably as a result of the (now declining) liberality of the educational system. The resulting variations of style suggest to the outsider that there is a special system of US usage with exceedingly complex rules—a pardonable error, but still an error. It is permissible to write correct English, but the writer should be aware that this will always identify him as a foreigner.

Professional Pomposity

Goethe made an excellent point when he made Mephistopheles say, ''A pompous word will stand you in stead, for that which will not go into the head": the tag should be more widely known. In the US, sick patients are diaphoretic, vasoconstricted, tachycardic, and have decreased mentation; when they are better, they ambulate. To suggest that they might be sweaty, pale, with a fast pulse and confusion, and able to walk when improved, is almost considered professional misconduct. Indeed, a student may be corrected for saying "bruise" instead of ecchymosis or "yellow" instead of xanthochromic. A senior individual may not be openly corrected but is sure to be thought a crude fellow for using such basic terms.

Yet the Trade Name!

Despite the passion for using words of learned length and thundering sound to describe symptoms and bodily functions, there is an overwhelming tendency to describe all drugs by proprietary names. Pharmacologists in US medical schools are most punctilious in their use of generic and chemical names, but this desirable influence is speedily overwhelmed by the effect of clinical teachers. All drugs are ordered by trade name, and writing a treatment order using generic names provokes a flurry on the ward, with much consulting of reference books until the trade name is located. It is not unknown for the patient eventually to receive the wrong drug, so there is some moral pressure to forsake one's good habits and to descend to the language of the marketplace when prescribing.

Abbreviations and Acronyms

Medical abbreviations are used on both sides of the Atlantic, but on the western shore they are a highly developed art form. Witness the patient with ASHD and PHMI, SPCABG, who PTA for ERCP had an episode of BRBPR. This is a quotation from a case presentation. It requires some years of residence to apprehend at once that this patient with atherosclerotic heart disease and past history of myocardial infarction, status post-coronary-artery-bypass graft, had an episode of bright red blood per rectum prior to admission for endoscopic retrograde choledochopancreatography. When one recovers from the cultural shock, it is apparent that this is a wonderful way of communicating information rapidly, and doubtless will prove very useful in working (sorry, interacting) with the computer. Unfortunately, there is no counterpart here of the useful Australian abbreviation, BND, for an overall assessment of certain patients (bloody nearly dead).

Many of the abbreviations used in general medicine are acronyms, but this branch of semantics has attained its finest flowering in my specialty, oncology. The popularity of a chemotherapy regimen may depend almost as much on the possession of a catchy acronym as on its clinical efficacy. Almost the only good feature of proprietary names for drugs is that they enrich the possibilities for creation of acronyms. Regional loyalties may also be invoked by chemotherapeutic acronyms. What New England oncologist could resist COD? And how many Oregon oncologists use the CHOP regimen? Culinary delights are suggested by M-BACOD, and horticultural pleasures by BVCCP (usually known as buttercup). But what would Senator McCarthy have thought of the intensive regimens known as PRAVDA and COMLA? The American cancer chemotherapist is truly enriching the language.

Euphemisms

The euphemism—a cardinal feature of "non-U" phraseology—thrives in transatlantic English. It began in a small way: patients expired and nobody ever died. Much progress has been made since: no one is dismissed from a job, they are "let go," implying that the motivation was theirs. A patient who abuses the doctor is "adopting an adversarial relationship." The best example comes from a Government document in which, after careful research, it could be shown that "adverse patient outcome" meant death. Who said that understatement was a British talent?

Governmentese

The language of rulers has always been a special part of their isolation and mystique. The Normans seldom communicated in Saxon. The US Government rarely communicates in English. Examples are myriad, but the one I like best is "portable reusable hand-held inscribing device." This is Pentagon-speak for "pencil."

Language and the Law

It is well known that legal considerations have an impact on US medical practice that approaches the grotesque (eg, a computed tomography scan of the brain and the administration of tetanus toxoid for a facial abrasion). There has also been a major impact upon the use of language. Thus, instructions state "to *assist* in avoiding injury, wear gloves when opening the vial." The statement "to avoid injury" could be incriminating by being too confident and implying a guarantee of safety. The phrase "assist in avoiding injury" occurs forty-six times in the owner's manual for my new car. Naturally, I am now afraid to use it.

Misprints

The rising costs of proofreading and resetting of type have led to a world-wide increase in misprints, even in the most august publications. In the US, they are found even in Government documents that are printed in millions of copies (eg, "list principle places of employment"). The finest example I have seen lately is the (printed) bill from the company that towed my car: "John Smith. 24 hour Towing and Wenching. 2 way Radio Service. Light & Heavy Duty." Even an eighteenth-century rake might be impressed by the vigour thus implied. But think not that the area in which I live is sunk in moral turpitude. One of our largest hospitals sends out notices about a function held on Friday afternoons and described (in every notice) as the "Morbidity and Morality Conference." Not everyone is wenching 24 hours a day.

The Prolific Apostrophe

Use of inappropriate apostrophes is a national passion. One becomes inured to signs offering to sell tomatoe's and potatoe's, but it is still traumatic when a patient is admitted with renal stone's. However, the UK is also afflicted: witness the sign in London requesting us to place our rubbish "in the bin's."

Demise of the Adverb

This useful part of speech is almost dead (expired). The prime example is that nothing is ever done regularly, only on a regular basis. And patients are no longer seen in the clinic, but on an ambulatory outpatient basis. Some miracles of healing undoubtedly occur, since even paraplegic patients are seen on this ambulatory basis—or so the referring letters say. The letters do not mention whether they are carrying their beds.

Mutations of the Noun

The master formula is to take a noun, turn it into a verb, form a noun from that, and then complete the circle. Thus a problem has a particular priority. When several problems are listed, they must be prioritised. The process is prioritisation. We then begin to assign prioritisations rather than priorities. We then need an extra secretary.

Signing Off

Complex conventions govern the signing of letters. I like the rule (well illustrated by Dickens' Mr Podsnap) that the more offensive the letter, the more abject should be the concluding phrase above the signature. In the US there is a charming convention that the more difficult, quarrelsome, or litigious the patient who is referred may be, the more effusive must be the end of the letter. Thus, "Thank you for the great privilege of collaborating with you in the care of this charming and interesting gentleman," may mean that the consultant barely restrained himself from throwing the patient out of his office.

Stock Phrases

The lure of the stock phrase seems stronger on the western Atlantic shore. We have survived the terrible era of "at this moment in time," and the phrase has gone to an unhallowed grave. But we have "collective interpersonal verbalisation" for "talking." Nothing is ever begun, it is always initiated. The word "before" has succumbed completely to "prior to." There are no men in medical writing; in correspondence they are all gentlemen, and in journals they are all males. A stock phrase always seems to beat a short concrete noun.

Medical Communication

Communication between doctors in the US is superb by any standards. The proliferation of pocket dictaphones, central dictation banks that can be reached by telephone from anywhere in the country, personal computers, photocopying machines, and now electronic mailing systems, makes possible the rapid exchange of clinical information. A single office visit may produce a two-page dictated note with carbon copies to seven other doctors concerned in the patient's care. Some of the motivation is less than altruistic—private practice requires excellent communication to survive—but the end result is excellent. The legal aspects of medical practice also have a major effect, and this is particularly apparent in the care and attention to detail displayed in reports of operations. Where else could the operative report of avulsion of a toenail be expanded to three pages?

Evolution

Language, like all living things, is fascinating. Like other life forms, it is subject to the pressures of mutation, natural selection, and evolution. Languages evolving in different environments show the divergences and convergences and evolutionary survivals that Darwin noted among animal species. It remains to be seen whether English can survive as a single species on the two sides of the Atlantic. As with animals, the ultimate test of preservation as a single species remains the ability to cross-fertilise.

PS

Many general magazines feature a page or section with late-breaking news. The format often is across-the-page typewriter copy, which saves time and money and actually increases readability. Several medical and pharmaceutical journals use this same format. Sometimes the page appears upfront, though this is not essential, and it often is used as the centerfold or elsewhere in the publication.

For example, *Alabama Pharmacy*, the monthly magazine of the Alabama Pharmaceutical Association, has a single page, called Post Scripts, with a brief typed letter simply blown up to fill the 8½ × 11 sheet.

The November 1984 Post Scripts page announced the election of an Alabama Pharmaceutical Association Board of Trustees.

The December 1984 Post Scripts provided details of a February 1 conference of the Alabama Medicaid Agency.

SPECIAL ARTICLES

Since the start of the *Medical Journalism* project, the medical, pharmaceutical and hospital publications with which it is concerned have changed in many ways—they have become livelier, better integrated, graphically compelling and generally more interesting to read. A number have become distinctive by publishing special articles—articles off the beaten medical or health-related path. Following are a few special pieces that have appeared in recent years:

History

One of the most popular features of medical and pharmaceutical journals is the historical article. Old-timers and youngsters enjoy the reviews of medical events in their areas, and these articles seem to bring out the best writing and design skills of journal editors.

The Journal of the Florida Medical Association has been publishing an annual Historical Issue since 1966. The July 1984 issue was edited by William M. Straight, M.D., who is Historical Editor of the *Journal.* Here is Dr. Straight's summary of the issue.

This, the nineteenth Historical Issue of *The Journal of the Florida Medical Association*, begins with a previously unpublished manuscript on yellow fever written by the distinguished Cuban physician, author, poet and intellect, Dr. Thomas Romay Chacon, in 1804. This manuscript, which came to light about ten years ago, has been translated and edited by the distinguished professors of history, Dr. William S. Coker and Dr. John R. McNeill.

The second article describes medical care in Spanish West Florida and is the work of the distinguished retired Professor of History of the University of Alabama and Caballero in the Order of Isabel la Catolica, Sir Jack D. L. Holmes, Ph.D. The recognized authority on the Spanish period of the lower Mississippi Valley and the Gulf Coast, Sir Jack was knighted by Juan Carlos I for his many contributions to the understanding of Spain's dominion in North America.

The next two articles of this issue are by Dr. Rabun H. Williams of Eustis, Florida. Dr. Williams gives us his observations of medical care in the

Golden Triangle of Central Florida and an account of the origin and development of the Waterman Medical Center.

The fifth article in this issue is by Dr. H. L. Harrell, of Ocala. Dr. Harrell records the medical history of Marion County during the past fifty years.

The final article deals with the medical beliefs and practices and the diseases of the Florida Indians who occupied our state before and during the first Spanish Period (1513–1763). This paper represents a vigorous two year search on the part of your Historical Editor in French, Spanish and English accounts and of the literature on Florida paleopathology and anthropology to assemble the scant information available.

We hope you find this issue both entertaining and informative.

Indeed, the issue was as Dr. Straight hoped!

One of the outstanding features of *The Journal of the Florida Medical Association* is its covers, which generally are produced by a physician. For example, the November 1982 cover was a humorous drawing depicting the lead article, "The Meal Ticket Syndrome," drawn by Andre Renard, M.D., a plastic surgeon in Jacksonville.

The staff and contributors all deserve credit, but for the annual historical issue, the spotlight is on Dr. Straight. As one of the editors stated in an editorial:

"Once again, we are indebted to Bill Straight, an exact storyteller, who thoroughly comprehending history, interestingly furnishes something of the experiences he has acquired by being a contemporary of all ages and a fellow citizen of all peoples."

To conclude this PAEN to Florida, the following article by Edward Pedrero Jr., M.D., of Tampa, appeared in the July 1984 issue of the *Journal of the Florida Medical Association.*

The medical writer yearns to pass to others what his imagination creates and he does so through the medium of the written word. He needs the ability to see more than facts: to look beyond them; to hypothesize about them; to draw conclusions from them. The medical writer's criterion is never art for art's sake—always it is art for others' sake. He writes because he likes to—needs or has to write, there is no other valid reason. Just what is the nature of the need to write, precisely? The answer, put briefly, is this: all writers are persons who seek a larger world and when they find it, they pass it along to others.

A medical writer is driven by a need to escape the limits of a too-small world, the medical world, that is. It is in his blood to range farther than life can ever let him. The impossible intrigues him. So do the unattainable, the forbidden, the disastrous. The medical writer wants to help guide the hand of fate, to somehow help mold the forces that shape the destiny of medicine.

Writing is not a logical process. Consistency is the hobgoblin of petty minds. The writer follows his feelings, sorts out the variables, rejects the false, catches glimpses of the larger pattern and draws confidences from knowledge. A good writer keeps grammar rules in proper perspective and violates them by design only. He will take sentence fragments, non-punctuation, stream of consciousness and one-word paragraphs and make them tools for manipulation of his reader's emotions.

Feeling is very important to a writer. Feeling springs from the human heart. A writer seeks a reawakening, a heightened pulse and a richer awareness in his readers. Intellectualization of art is alien to a true writer's thinking. First, last and all the time the writer deals with what he feels. A medical writer is subjective more than objective, his inner world appears to be more important to him than the external one. A good writer must separate logic from emotion and critical judgement from creation. A writer knows that simplicity and brevity in the wrong place can destroy his work. He knows that the heart of any writing is vividness.

A medical writer uses his facts as stimuli to feeling. He emotionalizes the facts and gives them a unique private life. In writing more than almost any other field initiative is the key. Sensitivity, drive, facility with language all linked with knowledge are translated into a literary process.

To be a medical writer, a creative person must retain his ability to react uniquely. His feelings must remain his own. The day a medical writer mutes himself or moderates himself or represses his proneness to get excited or ecstatic or angry or emotionally involved—that day he dies as a writer.

Many other state medical journals, notably Maryland and New Jersey, devote extensive space to biographies of prominent physicians and other historical articles.

In September 1984 *The Journal of the Medical Society of New Jersey* published a special issue titled *300 Years of Medicine in New Jersey.* Here is part of the introduction, which was signed by Morris H. Saffron, M.D., Guest Editor, (Archivist-Historian, Medical Society of New Jersey and The Academy of Medicine of New Jersey); Stuart Sammis, Project Director, (Archivist, University of Medicine and Dentistry); Arthur Krosnick, M.D., Editor, and Geraldine Hunter, Managing Editor, of *The Journal of the Medical Society of New Jersey.*

Financial support for the issue was provided by several sources, including Sandoz.

The Journal of the Medical Society of New Jersey with this special issue is honoring the knowledge and sophistication of its medical community.

"One measure of a civilized community could well be the extent of its acquired medical knowledge and sophistication.'' So states eminent New Jersey historian and author, David Cowen.

This issue of *The Journal* was conceived as a means of presenting to the citizens of New Jersey, both physician and layman, a history of the "healing art" in our state; for to understand where one is going, one must understand where one has been. The history of medicine often is viewed as the history of scientific misconceptions and quackery—that health professionals and their work are isolated from the rest of society. This issue we hope will dispel many of these erroneous myths as we present articles covering a broad spectrum of the "healing art." Articles reveal the contributions made to society by physicians outside of medicine, physicians who were involved in the political and military fight for independence, women who helped open the doors to equal opportunity in medicine, and crusaders for the rights, health, and safety of industrial workers and sailors.

In the realm of medical contributions, there are articles which discuss the early acquisition of medical knowledge by the Lenape Indians, the founding of our medical society (the oldest in the nation), the growth of the various aspects of health care, and some of the leading medical associations and personalities. Of particular use to researchers is the extensive bibliography of publications on the history of medicine in New Jersey.

The photographic section highlights the exhibits produced by the Middlesex County Cultural and Heritage Commission, the University of Medicine and Dentistry of New Jersey-Rutgers Medical School, and the Middlesex General/University Hospital, celebrating 300 years of medicine in New Jersey.

Hobbies

A local medical society publication that takes advantage of the writing ability of many of the society's members is the *Bulletin of the Camden County Medical Society*, published bimonthly in southern New Jersey.

The *Bulletin* features articles by Camden-area physicians on clinical subjects, socioeconomic matters and delightful personal pieces such as recent articles on skating, playing the banjo with a string band and the joys of sailing.

The piece on string bands, by Phil Lo Presti, M.D., started this way:

"When I began playing banjo in the late 1960's, I never thought that I would join one of the Philadelphia String Bands. However, while playing at my home, my mailman overheard my banjo and he invited me to join the Ukranian-American String Band (he was president). I explained that I really only had Sundays off and it was impossible for me to march in a string band; however, he assured me that they could help me with the drills and music. This was in mid-November and my experiences in the string band were quickly underway.''

After recounting what happened over the next few years and noting that his son also learned how to play the banjo as a member of a string band, the physician-author declared:

"It is certainly most exhilirating to march down Broad Street on New Year's Day with people lined up on the sidewalk eight to ten deep cheering the band and hearing their reception of your presentation. Also, the Fourth of July parade in Haddonfield and some of our presentations in neighboring towns are equally exciting and, of course, presented under much better weather conditions as a rule.

"Equally as important, being in the string band forces me to set time aside to be with my son on these special days when we can be together for a reasonable period of time, which might not be the case if we were not involved in this type of activity.''

In another issue of the Camden *Bulletin*, Nils G. Herdelin Jr., M.D., described his experiences as a sailor:

"Last summer, while gently reaching across Long Island Sound on the way from Essex, Connecticut, to Block Island, I found myself mentally as well as physically aglow in the pleasure of sailing. Sitting in the cockpit, one hand on the helm, the other holding a cold jug of gazpacho, in the company of my wife and two good freinds, I found us making an effortless six knots in the clear August sun, with no sound other than the hull knifing through the water. Absent were the hum of an engine, diesel fumes, traffic and the telephone.''

After describing his adventures as a novice sailor, Dr. Herdelin commented on cruising with his sailboat.

"Cruising is a great way to involve the whole family in sailing. There's a chore or two for everyone aboard, regardless of age or ability. Teamwork develops unconsciously. And with time, sailing skill seems to be acquired by osmosis. My wife and I enjoy sailing with the kids along, putting into an interesting port such as St. Michaels on the Miles River for their diversion at the Chesapeake Bay Maritime Museum. Or the magic of arriving in Nantucket Harbor for several days' layover to visit that island . . .''

The magazine also reports on local activities, listing society membership and executive committee meetings and continuing medical education programs at area hospitals. Other features are a "From Our Past" series and articles on Auxiliary doings.

The editor, William V. Harrer, M.D., discusses a variety of medical issues, from DRG's to corporate medicine, in a column called "Editor's Comments.''

The art editor, Marvin E. Herring, M.D., does an amusing cartoon, usually on a medical topic, for almost every issue.

Ardith R. Lane is the magazine's managing editor.

The Camden County Medical Society Bulletin packs a lot into its small package. The narrow page size is unusual, 8½ × 5½, and the total number of pages ranges from 32 to 40. The magazine has many outstanding qualities and it fulfills its objectives, which are to inform, educate and entertain.

The hobbies features indeed satisfy these goals. In a recent issue, Marvin E. Herring, M.D., described his experiences both as a competitive figure skater and as a doctor for skaters. Here is one excerpt.

"I asked my skaters what they wanted most from their doctor, and what they disliked most about doctoring for injuries. Often, I'd hear, 'I'd like to know what my problem is in my language; what my medicines and treatments do; I'd like to be comfortable about asking questions.' What they disliked most, of course, was not being able to skate when they got 'too hurt.' The common 'pet peeve,' not surprisingly, was, 'lots of doctors don't understand figure skaters . . . you can't just say, don't skate till it feels better.'

"It was sinful for me to see a competitor with a first degree ankle sprain 10 days after his injury, in an Ace bandage, on crutches, with no weight bearing for 10 days . . . no ice, no therapy, no follow-up."

Following the article was a cartoon by Dr. Herring showing a skater with a bandaged leg, using a crutch on a skate.

Computers and the Disabled

A young resident physician who developed a word processing program for disabled individuals described the project in a recent issue of the *Berks County Medical Record* (Reading, PA). At that time, the author, Margaret Stineman, M.D., was a first-year resident in internal medicine at Reading Hospital. Dr. Stineman, who received a B.A. degree in art from Temple University and an M.D. from Hahnemann Medical College, is physically disabled. She now is a resident in physical medicine and rehabilitation at the University of Pennsylvania.

She noted in her article, however, that she was actually inspired to write the computer program, for use with the IBM personal computer, by the courage of a patient who was in the terminal stages of amyotrophic lateral sclerosis but wanted to finish a book he was working on. The program, which involves use of two keys and various keyboard simulators, compensates for the patient's limited motor activity.

The passionate tone in which the article is written, as well as the detailed knowledge it imparts, exemplifies the concern that this physician has for people with severe disabilities.

Using a keyboard simulator, Dr. Stineman asserts, enables the individual to transfer input into the computer via the two keys. She adds: "Communicating this way is a meticulously slow process, for to type one letter takes up to five signals, yet for the severely motor-disabled, non-verbal, highly-motivated individual, programs like this, used in conjunction with a keyboard simulator, could be the only rational link with the outside world. It may form the basis for complex communications systems and environmental control and even allows computer programming. It is a tragedy that the thoughts and needs of such disabled patients in chronic care hospitals today are largely left uncommunicated."

Dr. Stineman then describes how keyboard simulators permit the use of a computer by the disabled person by translating the wide variety of motor responses into a small series of simpler ones.

She notes that there are several different types of simulators, including those with sensitivity to muscle contraction, "puff-and-suck" devices and simulators that activate the computer by voice. A simulator now under development, according to Dr. Stineman, would be activated by eye motion.

Expressing strong feelings about the help she can give severely handicapped patients, Dr. Stineman declares that "The finest rehabilitation medicine physician is the one who can inspire in his patients the courage to remain functional in a world designed for people who can walk, hear, think and see normally."

"The adaptive devices I have described to you," Dr. Stineman states in her article, "have little to do with inspiration. The most miraculous and ingenious equipment remains meaningless if the individual for whom it was designed lacks the courage to use it. Yet for the motivated and innovative individual, it can make a remarkable difference in terms of the person's ability to function independently. Even a severely disabled individual may now reach levels of achievement and quality of life which, up to now, have been unheard of."

Dr. Stineman concludes by noting that the technology to improve the quality of people's lives already exists but that its potential has not yet been fully tapped by the medical community.

"This small review," the author comments, "barely even touches the surface. I can only whet your appetite and share with you a few of the devices I have come across. There is no challenge greater than that of reaching one's full potential as a human being, whether one is able-bodied or disabled."

In addition to her medicine and writing, Dr. Stineman designed several of the covers of the *Berks County Medical Record*. According to Barton L. Smith, M.D., editor of the publication, Dr. Stineman is an extremely talented artist who has contributed much to the *Medical Record* by her illustrations. The cover for the March issue was related to Dr. Stineman's article. It consisted of fragments of a history and physical examination program written in the computer language "basic."

"Superimposed on the computer printout," Dr. Stineman says in a note in the magazine, "is the human element of art, something I hope we never lose as our society becomes increasingly mechanized."

Lori Jaffe
From the 1983 Annual Report of
Saint Joseph Medical Center
(Burbank, California)

The worst part was the loneliness.

Lori Jaffe was bed-bound for six months after an accident sent her car careening 500 feet over a cliff. Doctors feared she would never walk again.

"I got lots of visitors at the house in the beginning, but one by one people stopped coming over or calling. It becomes depressing for people when you progress so slowly. What do you have to talk about? 'Gee, I was able to get up and go the bathroom today.' The first time I dangled my legs, it was such a milestone that everyone in my family cried."

After the accident, Saint Joseph Medical Center emergency surgeons worked from 1 a.m. until 10 o'clock the next morning to save her legs, patching, sewing, hoping. Her knee was dislocated in two places and vascular damage nearly caused her to lose her leg. Lori spent six weeks at the Medical Center undergoing knee surgery, two skin grafts on her foot, a bone graft, insertion of a metal plate and eight screws to hold the pieces of bone in place.

"The whole situation was incredibly difficult for my mother," she remembers. "One day I was going to college, dating, looking forward to my whole life. The next day it was all gone."

Enter Randy.

Assistant head nurse on the intensive care unit, he understood the need for Lori to focus on new goals. "Instead of looking at all the negatives, it's important for a patient whose lifestyle must change to have something new to look forward to," says Randy, who has worked at the Medical Center for 10 years.

He began to visit Lori regularly in the hospital to teach her about careers that required little walking. Their relationship flourished and Lori encouraged him to visit her and her family when she went home.

"He would always be there when I was lonely and in pain," says Lori.

"I used to say that if I had my dose of Randy, I wouldn't need a pain pill."

As she grew stronger, so did their relationship, and the couple soon married. Now their baby Kimberly shares their time, along with a German Shepherd pup and a sky-full of hot air balloons that daily fly over their Moorpark home.

"Randy and I have shared so much together. He's been my nurse, my friend, my husband. We know each other completely. So much good has come out of the accident. I have more than I could have dreamed of having."

William Carlos Williams, M.D.

The September 1983 issue of the *Journal of the Medical Society of New Jersey* has become a collector's item, treasured by physicians, librarians and others. On the occasion of the 100th anniversary of the birth of William Carlos Williams, M.D., America's first medical society (founded July 23, 1766) published a commemorative issue about the physician-poet who lived in Rutherford, New Jersey. (Sandoz was one of the financial supporters of this project.) Avrum L. Katcher, M.D. was guest editor.

In addition to printing 10 poems and selections from fiction by Dr. Williams, the *Journal* featured an article by his eldest son, William Eric Williams, M.D. who also is a pediatrician in Rutherford. Other original articles were by several physicians and historians and also such scholars as poet John Ciardi, Ph.D.

Also reprinted was the *Journal's* obituary from its May 1963 issue:

In some respects, William Carlos Williams, M.D., was one of the best-known physicians in New Jersey. He was one of the few with a truly international reputation—in his case, world-wide acclaim as a poet. Williams was born in Rutherford in 1883 and he died there in his sleep on March 4, 1963. He received his medical degree at the University of Pennsylvania in 1906. He was a pioneer in pediatrics, one of the first men in the United States to make it a specialty. He did graduate work in pediatrics in Germany and in Switzerland in 1907 and 1908 when practically no such teaching was available here.

Dr. Williams first became known as a poet in 1909 when a slim volume won a national prize. Since then, blue ribbons in poetry and literature came his way in a regular procession. The list of awards and prizes and famous poems and odes is a long one. So is the list of honorary degrees and fellowships. But to the people of Bergen County, he was known chiefly as a pediatrician—and a good one.

Nuclear Warfare

For many years, medical journals have published articles about nuclear warfare, ranging from clinical descriptions of the patients in Hiroshima to emotional editorials about the moral and political issues. The Physicians for Social Responsibility is one of the organizations active in the battle to control the nuclear arms race. Recently, several medical journals editorialized about the ABC-TV network program on the consequences of nuclear bombs dropped in Kansas. More important than how you evaluated Jason Robards as the physician, is the tremendous importance of the subject to all health professionals.

Recent issues of the *Worcester Medical News* (published bimonthly by the Worcester Medical Society in Massachusetts) included several relevant items. Chairman of the publications committee and editor of the magazine is the Rev.Robert W. Bain, M.D., an Episcopalian priest and a practicing pathologist. The July–August issue featured on the cover a quotation from Maimonides:

"It is the duty of man to associate himself with the community."

Dr. Bain noted that this is the guiding principle of Maimonides' social outlook. This extraordinary man was born in Cordova in 1135 and forced to wander for years by the persecutors of the day until he and his family settled in Fostat, the old capital of Egypt, where he became the physician to the Sultan's court. His knowledge and wisdom as a philosopher-rabbi had already made him famous. He stated: It is both the greatness and the glory of man that he is interdependent, that neither in his physical or in his moral existence can he live alone without the support of his fellow human beings.

"We too must look at our community or rather communities for we have family, hospital, city, state, country and world," Dr. Bain said.

In the same issue, Dr. Bain excerpted from a booklet, "The Nuclear Arms Race: Countdown to Disaster," by the Rev. William W. Rankin. Here's Dr. Bain's introduction.

"The world begins at our fingertips and articles in this issue about WASAHC (Worcester Area Systems for Affordable Health Care) and the Worcester EMT service attest to our concern. We need to recognize our part in escalating costs and make every cut that can be made while protecting the patient from inadequate diagnosis and treatment.

"Sometimes a song reminds us of other parts of our life, and an old song 'What nature doesn't do to us, will be done by our fellowman' and 'They are rioting in Africa,' etc., came by my memory bank and caused me to look at some nuclear age data that will not allow me to put all my thoughts on cost control alone; after all, if we are all blown away, the issues we agonize over in Worcester will be solved and our disintegration or death from burns will change our perspective.''

Miami Medicine

The lay midwife law: is it necessary?
Learning to say no
Who's defending the good guys?
The gay patient

These are the titles of recent articles in *Miami Medicine*, the monthly magazine of the Dade County Medical Association, Miami, Florida. The titles are indicative of the publication's orientation, which is to stress general interest features, with a medical orientation but no clinical or scientific articles. Editor Richard J. Feinstein, M.D., and Managing Editor Paula M. Vogel worked closely with physicians and other authors to develop topics that combine human interest and news information. An indication of their success are these blurbs from 1982 contents pages.

Ivory Towers

The UM-School of Medicine has been plagued by a "town-gown" syndrome. Editor *Richard J. Feinstein, M.D.* maintains the schism still exists.

Subpoenas For Trial

What should you do when the court summons you? DCMA Legal Counsel *Roger Welcher* explains the do's and don't's.

Learning to Say "No"

Why do some physicians let ego and greed interfere with good judgment? What or who is intimidating them?

Hospice – Intensive Care With A Difference

For the terminally ill patient, his soul, as well as his body, needs "Total Care." That concept drives a special interdisciplinary team to offer a program of renewed spiritual and emotional health to the dying patient.

The Lay Midwife Law: Is It Necessary?

Are lay midwives behind the times, or is it the law?

Our Medical Center Is Alive and Well

The author takes a somewhat nostalgic look at the coming of age of the UM-School of Medicine—from its humble beginnings thirty years ago, to its present status as a nationally acclaimed medical center.

Stress in the Medical Marriage

For the physician's spouse, the daily pressures inherent in the practice of medicine often eclipse the romance and aura of marriage. Learning to cope with these pressures has now become an ongoing project of the medical auxiliary.

The Cardiac Pacemaker Scandal

A recent U.S. Senate investigation into the sale and implantation of cardiac pacemakers could prove to be just another swipe at the medical profession, or it could uncover the worst abuse of all: the profit motive.

The Gay Patient

With the stigmas attached to homosexuality gradually lessening, medicine has found it easier to provide care to the patient nobody talked about. In this candid report, the fallacies and facts of treating the homosexual patient are discussed and analyzed.

The article on homosexuality appeared as a two-part series in the November and December 1982 issues. The author, Marcel Richard Doublier, M.D., described sexually transmitted diseases, including experiments on antiviral agents at such research centers as the University of California at San Francisco.

In addition to its lively content, *Miami Medicine* also has brightened its graphics, including color cover photographs by physicians. The November 1982 scene of autumn foliage was photographed by Edward Feller, M.D.

Happy Anniversary!

The 50th, 100th or other key anniversary of the founding of a medical or pharmaceutical association or hospital often is the occasion for a historical article in the organization's publication. These articles can be dull chronologies or opportunities for inspired writing and photography.

The February 1980 issue of *San Diego Physician* was a doubly important special issue. First, it welcomed the California Medical Association, which was holding its annual session, the 109th, in San Diego for the first

time. Second, it commemorated the 100th anniversary of the San Diego
County Medical Society.

Dr. George M. Mahan, Jr., then editor of *San Diego Physician*, supervised a splendid special issue which was particularly outstanding in its treatment of the anniversary. "Let's Look Back," a nine-page section, featured
two articles by Clifford L. Graves.

Among the 10 photos were several of the physicians who started the
medical society, with this candid, creative caption.

"The seven doctors who started our medical society were a mixed lot.
Undoubtedly, they had their secondary motivations: Dr. Hoffman was
thinking of a defense against the quacks; Dr. Burr was thinking of help with
his job at the pesthouse; Dr. Fenn was thinking of professional prestige; Dr.
McKinstry was thinking of somebody to leave his practice to when he
retired. Dr. Stockton was thinking of the social advantages. Dr. Allen was
thinking of his appeal to the voters (he later became postmaster). Dr. Gregg
was thinking of what he might learn from the others. However this may
have been, the thrust was better care for the patient. In this respect, the
philosophy has remained unchanged for over a hundred years."

At the medical journalism workshop conducted by Sandoz Pharmaceuticals in Los Angeles on April 26, Paul Jacobi (professor of journalism at
Northwestern University) noted that vivid writing involving interviews with
real people (or fictionalized composites or historical recreations) requires a lot
of work. The staff of *San Diego Physician* obviously knows how to do this.
(Coincidentally, Dr. Mahan was one of the participants at the workshop.)

You don't have to be a San Diego physician or a history buff to appreciate the following article by Clifford L. Graves in *San Diego Physician*.

San Diego Centennial

"Come quick, doctor. An accident."

Dr. Hoffman looked up and saw a boy in the doorway, wide-eyed and
panting.

"Where?"

"Over on Seventh."

"What happened?"

"A horse ran away and the buggy went flying all over."

"Who was in it?"

"They say it's Mr. Horton."

Mr. Horton was the most important citizen in San Diego. Dr. Hoffman
grabbed his bag and ran with the boy to the next block where a buggy lay on
its side, the wheels still spinning. To his consternation, Dr. Hoffman saw it
was indeed Alonzo Horton. His right ankle had been smashed.

"Easy, my friend," said Dr. Hoffman, pulling the leg into alignment.
Horton let out a yell. Blood stained his trousers.

"You pull on this leg while I get a splint," said the doctor to a man standing next to him. "And don't move."

In a few minutes Horton was stretched out on the examining table in Hoffman's office.

"How does it look, doc?"

Dr. Hoffman tried to say something reassuring but it did not come off very well. As soon as he cut away the trousers, he saw that the fracture was compound.

"I will have to do a little cleanup here. Maybe we better get you some ether."

"No ether for me, doc. Just do what you have to do. I can take it."

Dr. Hoffman set to. He scrubbed the wound, dug out the dirt, and put things back together as best he could. When he was done, the patient was in a dead faint.

It was the summer of 1870. San Diego was swinging. Horton could not have picked a worse time to be laid up.

During the long convalescence that followed, doctor and patient became very close. They had known each other from the day Horton landed here, but not well. Now they talked of many things.

Horton was the greatest promoter San Diego ever had. He arrived in the spring of 1867 because he had heard that San Diego was a great place to live. The only thing that was great about it in 1867 was the climate. Old Town was a hotdog hamlet. New Town was a wide open space with three small buildings in ruins. Horton was not discouraged. He engineered a public auction and bought 960 acres of what is now downtown for 265 dollars. The next year he built a wharf at the foot of Fifth Avenue and threw a big party in the old barracks on the corner of what is now Market and Kettner. That did it. People began to buy, by the block and by the lot. In 1869 New Town was going a mile a minute. So impressive was the activity that even the well-established citizens in Old Town began to move to New Town. Dr. Hoffman did, on September 22. His office was on Eighth Avenue near F.

In 1870 Horton built or helped build the first church, the first theater, the first meeting hall, the first telegraph office, the first bank, the first big hotel, the first everything New Town had. His accident came in the middle of all this. It was up to Dr. Hoffman to keep the patient from being completely demoralized. They shared each other's hopes and fears. One thing that Dr. Hoffman was concerned about was the influx of new doctors. Some of them were little more than charlatans. Hoffman stressed the dangers.

"What can you do about it?" asked Horton.

"Maybe we ought to have a medical society. Then we can set up standards."

"Why don't you go ahead then?"
"I will."

The San Diego Seven

At 43, Dr. Hoffman was the leading doctor in San Diego. He had come here in 1853 when Old Town was little more than a Mexican village and looked the part. For years, he was the medical establishment. But now, suddenly, he found himself at the center of a growing body of doctors, some competent, some incompetent. It was up to him to see that the citizens were not cheated. He called a meeting, inviting ten. Seven came. Besides himself, they were Jacob Allen, Edward Burr, Charles Fenn, Robert Gregg, George McKinstry, and Thomas Stockton. The date was July 19.

Of the seven, George McKinstry was the oldest. At 60, he still cut a fine figure. He always wore a large black silk tie over which appeared the points of a standing white collar. Still, he had roughed it for much of his life. Medicine was never more than a part-time occupation with him. He had arrived in California when it was still Mexican territory. One of his first jobs was to help with the rescue of the Donner party. He did this so well that he temporarily gave up medicine to become sheriff of the northern district with headquarters in Sutter's Fort. He then began to travel, dropping in on San Diego as early as 1852. He bought a ranch near Santa Ysabel and for years divided his time between ranching and doctoring. An expert horseman, he thought nothing of riding 100 miles to see a patient. Finally, around 1867, he settled in Old Town. His office was in the Wrightington building. Many doctors kept diaries in those days. His was the only that has survived. Alas —it is a collection of trivia.

Edward Burr was the next oldest. Born in Ireland and married into a fine Spanish family, he came to San Diego in 1868 when he was in his fifties. All we know is that he was "on the Plaza." In the absence of a distinguished record to boast about, he let it be known that he had been appointed physician and surgeon to the county hospital. The county hospital was an almshouse on the way to the cemetery. He did have a lively sense of duty and always sprayed the passengers on the Seeley coach when it drew up at the Franklin House. That was supposed to stamp out smallpox.

If Dr. Burr was a bit short-tempered with his patients, he was kindness personified with the new doctors that began arriving now. Legend has it that he invited both Dr. Gregg and Dr. Stockton to office with him. Early in 1870 Dr. Burr followed the general exodus. He moved to New Town where he installed himself in the New San Diego Hotel on State and F, "a new and first-class hotel where all persons visiting San Diego in search of health, recreation or pleasure will find good accommodations."

Robert Gregg, an uncle of our own Dr. Harold Gregg, was next to arrive. Just graduated from Jefferson College, he was full of steam and book learning. After a brief alliance with Dr. Burr, he moved to New Town on July 4, 1869. Here, he found Dr. Jacob Allen already ensconced. Dr. Gregg was a scholar and a gentleman. Anatomy was his forte. Philosophy was next. Who else in San Diego could quote the classics by the hour? In conversation he sparkled. His patients thought he was a wizard. If they were not too rushed, they got a dose of Plato and Socrates along with their bottle of medicine. Dr. Gregg proved durable. He lived and worked here till 1915.

Jacob Allen was the first doctor in New Town. He opened his office on Fifth near F on December 8, 1868. Later he added a drug store which became a popular rendezvous for the town loafers. In 1870, Dr. Allen was a man in his fifties, swarthy and heavy set, and no nonsense. In his advertisement in the *Union* he went right to the heart of the matter.

J. Allen, M.D.

Physician, Surgeon and Accoucheur

"I have permanently located in the New Town of San Diego where my friends may consult me at any time, day or night; and, as I have been 35 years in the practice of medicine in its various branches, and for the past 15 years have given special attention to the treatment of chronic diseases and the diseases of children and females, I will give special attention to that branch of the profession."

Dr. Allen faded quickly. Apparently, there were not enough chronic diseases in San Diego at that time to keep a doctor in the chips. He moved to Riverside in 1873.

Thomas Stockton was cut of a different cloth. His dashing figure was everywhere although New Town was hardly a place to dash around in with great effect. A relative of the famous Commodore, he arrived here from Canada with impeccable family credentials and a diploma from Bellevue Hospital. Socially, he mingled with the best. When he became engaged to Minnie Slade shortly after his arrival, the news filled the paper for weeks. The Slades were from Buffalo and definitely upper crust. So well impressed were the elder Slades with their new son-in-law that they moved here themselves. Their house was only a little bit smaller than Horton's.

Dr. Stockton was more than a social ornament however. He was capable, conscientious and progressive, and he kept extensive clinical notes on his patients. This reputation plus his social standing got him a call to see the governor of Baja who lay gravely ill in Ensenada. A coach-and-six came especially to San Diego, picked up Dr. Stockton, and headed south, but the journey was so rough that the doctor was in worse condition than the patient when he arrived. Both recovered.

Charles Fenn set up shop shortly after Gregg. A young man, he was not as handsome as Stockton nor as literate as Gregg, but he made up for it with an engaging personality. Stockton and Fenn were great friends. With offices only a block apart, they were in a good position to help each other. In the waning days of the Hoffman reign, Gregg and Remondino were the town pundits while Stockton and Fenn operated on the popular level. When a prominent patient got sick, he usually asked for Gregg or Remondino but he usually got Stockton or Fenn because the other two were probably in seclusion. Pill Hill in those days was Fifth Avenue from E to G. Old Town no longer had any doctors unless you counted McKinstry.

Strife and Dissolution

The main topic of conversation at the meeting on July 19 was eligibility. If the new society was to serve its purpose, it had to have tight rules. After much argument, the seven doctors phrased their thoughts in a simple manifesto. To be admitted as a member, they said, a man had to have (1) a good primary and medical education, attested by a diploma from some known medical school of good repute, and (2) good professional and moral standing in the community. At the same meeting, they nominated the officers: Dr. Hoffman for president, Dr. Allen for secretary-treasurer. The meeting was then adjourned to the 23rd for ratification and installation.

At the meeting on July 23, attended not only by the doctors but also by a number of distinguished guests, the officers were elected and the rules adopted. In his acceptance speech, Dr. Hoffman said that doctors should treat the whole patient and throw the quacks out. That is not much different from what we are saying today. Everybody went home, happy in the knowledge that the doctors were on the job. The event was duly reported on the front page of the *Union* of August 4, sandwiched in between intelligence of the Franco-Prussian war and news of a dreadful heat wave in the East.

San Diego remained cool that summer but only as far as the thermometer showed. Elsewhere, the temperature went up. The new society was being besieged with applicants, but who was to say whether they met the qualifications? What was a medical school of good repute? Without a list of accredited schools such as came 50 years later, it was impossible to tell. Friends fell out, distrust crept in. Pressure built up. Dr. Hoffman caught the full blast. Challenged, accused, badgered, he had a choice of giving in or giving up. He gave up. The new society died.

The Dream Comes True

Years passed. Old doctors died. New ones moved in. In 1887 they numbered 33. They wanted to be in the state society. But first they had to form a local society. A man by the name of McSwegan gathered support. At a meeting on February 15, the minutes of which are forever lost, he sounded the clarion and took command. Apparently he was an egomaniac and perhaps a paranoiac as well. At any rate, he declared himself president of the medical society. A provisional constitution was drawn up, but the date of the annual election was left open. The meeting broke up amid uncertainty and confusion.

We pick up the trail on March 16 when the next meeting was held. McSwegan said that he was being sabotaged. To sabotage the saboteurs, he announced that the next election would be in December. That meant that he could stay in office almost a year. Others said that the election should be right now so that a delegate could be chosen to represent San Diego at the state meeting in April. Dr. Stockton so moved. McSwegan ruled him out of order. Stockton objected. McSwegan called him a saboteur. Stockton called McSwegan an impostor. McSwegan called Stockton a snake in the grass. In the general tumult that followed, Stockton appealed to the meeting. He was upheld. Fighting mad, McSwegan grabbed the papers and stalked out. There is no record what he did with them. He probably used them for toilet paper.

With McSwegan out of the picture, the assembled doctors adopted a constitution, elected officers and signed the roster. This part of the proceedings has been preserved. Dr. W. N. Smart became president, Dr. C. C. Valle vice-president, Dr. R. E. Armstrong secretary, and Dr. D. B. Northrop treasurer. Among the first to sign was Dr. Stockton, who had also been a charter member of the earlier society.

The dispute had an aftermath. Not one to give up, McSwegan put a note in the *Union* of March 18 that the organization under Dr. Smart was *not* the San Diego County Medical Society. Dr. Smart did not dignify McSwegan with an answer. Next, McSwegan put a notice in the paper that he was going to the state meeting to read a paper and represent San Diego. Now Dr. Smart could see trouble ahead. He quickly called his supporters together and had them sign a statement to the effect that McSwegan was an imposter. This statement was hand-carried to the state meeting in San Francisco by Dr. Armstrong. Apparently, he did his job well. The California Medical Association recognized Dr. Smart and rejected Dr. McSwegan. For a while, McSwegan tried to maintain his satellite society but after a few years he quietly stole away.

The next year, 1888, Dr. Hoffman died. He had seen his dream of a medical society come true.

Annual Report

A 1982 annual report that is a beautiful desk calendar for 1983.

Saint Joseph Medical Center of Burbank, California, has succeeded brilliantly in pulling off this trick. What started as a legal necessity evolved into a powerful communications piece that produced hundreds of congratulatory letters and calls. Everything about this extraordinary publication reflects the superb creativity and dedication of the people who worked many hundreds of hours on it.

The format is 13 inches wide and six inches deep, spiral-bound, with a hook for hanging, and the back cover split so that it also can sit atop a desk.

Each sheet consists of a magnificent, tightly cropped four-color photo of a former patient flying in a hot-air balloon, enjoying a family picnic, jogging on the beach, playing the piano and, in general, enjoying life.

Beneath each photo is a calendar for the month, a few dates of hospital and local events of interest to patients (CPR, breast-feeding and other classes) and a quotation by the patient. On the facing page is a dramatic article about the patient.

For example, accompanying the January 1983 photo of Lori Jaffe and a male companion about to ascend in a hot-air balloon is this:

"One day I was going to college, dating, looking forward to my whole life. The next day it was all gone," remembers Lori Jaffe, whose car went careening 500 feet over a cliff.

The text on the adjacent page dramatically indentifies the young man in the photo and touchingly tells their story. It is reproduced in entirety on the next page.

A few of the patients are celebrities, including Hank Grant (a columnist for 27 years at the *Hollywood Reporter*) and singer Frankie Avalon. All of them have a powerful story to tell. They range in age from a 5-year-old boy with a slashed cornea to a 91-year-old woman with a hip fracture and a 92-year-old man who is a concert pianist, and include a physician who had a heart attack, a veterinarian and a hospital volunteer who had logged 36,000 hours.

As for the conventional annual report material, Saint Joseph Medical Center pulled another coup, with all of the data on one easy-to-read page, plus a one-page letter from James E. Sauer Jr., Administrator.

The statistics about the 647-bed Saint Joseph Medical Center (owned and operated by the Sisters of Providence) include a chart, which is a model of language simplification.

Sandoz Pharmaceuticals indeed was pleased to present a special prize to Saint Joseph Medical Center and to commend:

Rhoda Weiss, Public Relations Director, and Andrea Rosenwein, who was the primary writer. Surprisingly, the designer, Corporate Graphics Inc., and the photographer, Charles Harbutt, are located in New York. Ms. Rosenwein, who received a master's degree in communications from Boston University, is from Los Angeles.

The Saint Joseph Medical Center annual report was designed to bring hope to sick and injured individuals. The report is dedicated to the career woman contemplating her first pregnancy late in life, anxious patients, and to those wishing productive lives following tragic incidents. It shows that as hospitals deal with increased Government regulations, recession, decreasing dollars to support health care and changing consumer demand, the people at Saint Joseph Medical Center continue to dedicate themselves to their patients, their most important concern.

Profile of Paul Fisher

Paul Fisher has been an integral part of the medical journalism program since the first workshop, which was held on a 95-degree summer day in 1975 on the University of Missouri campus in Columbia. About 20 workshops have been conducted since then at universities and other sites in California, Florida, Illinois, Kentucky, Louisiana, New York, Ohio, Rhode Island, Texas and Wisconsin—and Paul Fisher has been at every one. Dozens of editors, who now know him, therefore will appreciate an article about him which appeared in the *Missouri Alumnus,* titled "Journalism's Gentle Cynic." Following are a few excerpts from Carol Baskin's delightful tribute.

One of Fisher's file cabinets contains a folder bulging with articles on "this business of professoring," as he calls it. He'd been looking at one of them before heading out. "It says here, 'The decision to tenure a professor can cost a university upwards of a million dollars over a lifetime.' I am struck with the enormity of the crime I have perpetrated on the State of Missouri."

Fisher's assessment surely would be challenged by the students and faculty colleagues who call him a classic scholar and perhaps the journalism school's most intellectual professor. Yet, such barbed comments are typical. Ever the cynic, Fisher directs most of his criticism and contempt toward himself.

Fisher never escapes his New England heritage. He thinks of his native Cape Cod as austere and lean, and so is he, in body and in mind. Fisher demands much of himself and finds joy in living his visceral philosophy that "less is more." He often repeats that phrase in his lectures, themselves masterful examples of succinct eloquence. There is no waste in his talk, be it in the classroom or conversation. Everything seems edited before it is spoken. Fisher is fiercely individual, yet he resents the label of an eccentric. He scoops snow from the courts in winter to satisfy his passion for tennis. He wrestles rocks from Boone County's stubborn soil, then hauls them home to build walkways and walls. Perhaps it is his homage to New England, where "good fences make good neighbors."

His career revolves around graphic design and typography on the one hand, and press freedoms and control of information on the other. The seemingly disparate members of this curious marriage do have a common focus. Fisher's original attachment to the J-School was as a teacher of printing. Historically, printers in the Western world were persecuted for the contents of the books their presses produced, whether or not they originated the thoughts they put to paper. So Fisher values highly his own freedom to pursue the craft of printing. . . .

Drawn by the J-School's reputation, Fisher first came to Missouri in 1937 as a student. Little did he know he would earn a bachelor's, master's and PhD degree from Mizzou and spend his entire career at the University. He says he turned to journalism after discovering "about the only thing I could do was to write a sentence." His dream had been to be a craftsman, a builder of grand objects, but he says a lack of ability in math prevented that. "The greatest thing imaginable would have been to build a bridge," he laments. But from childhood, Fisher had had another fascination: the alphabet. His intrigue with letters led him to a course in typography, and that in turn set the direction of his career. He studied for several months with Frederick Goudy, America's leading type designer, and worked in the design rooms of American Type Founders at Elizabeth, N.J. . . .

If Fisher has cost the State of Missouri a million dollars, likely he's earned it.

Disaster

Almost every community has experienced a train crash, bridge collapse, major fire, hurricane or other disaster. After most of these tragedies, medical and hospital journals publish articles which review the events and describe the heroic measures and other dramatic details. Triage is one of the key words.

San Francisco Medicine, the monthly magazine of the San Francisco Medical Society, often publishes articles about nuclear war, earthquakes and other potential disasters. The March 1984 issue, which featured a photo from the 1906 earthquake, included several articles about disasters.

The prologue, headlined, Letters—in the wake of the quake, was compiled by Henry Gibbons, M.D., from his family archives. A page of dramatic photos of an earthquake in Coalinga, California in March, 1983 was taken at the Coalinga District Hospital by Donald Chev, M.D.

Two short articles about medical aspects of disaster planning were followed by a Medical Emergency Operations Plan by Mervyn Silverman, M.D., Director, and Joseph Mignola, Jr., deputy director for institutions, of the San Francisco Department of Public Health.

The concluding article, by Steve Heilig, a staff member of the San Francisco Medical Society, stated:

> "If we accept the opinion of many seismologists that a major earthquake is extremely likely in this century, then each passing day puts San Francisco at greater risk. The likely consequences of a big quake are frightening, to say the least, but most San Franciscans deal with this threat—as with the prospect of a nuclear war—with a mixture of fatalism and psychological denial. While the possibility of catastrophe must be recognized, it is not something we feel empowered to prevent, and thinking about it is not a pleasant pastime. Besides, most of us are too busy. The result, however, is often an unwillingness or inability to make the best possible preparations for such a disaster as a major earthquake.

In April 1984 the San Francisco Medical Society presented an evening seminar on disaster planning. One of the speakers was photographer Donald Chev, M.D., who is Chair of the California Medical Association Committee on Disaster Medical Care. Dr. Chev stated:

> "Much of the responsibility for earthquake preparedness rests with the local medical community. Local government made a valiant effort with the limited resources available, but much of the initiative for disaster preparedness must be taken in the private sector."

Running and Wrestling

The medical benefits and risks of exercise, particularly running, are subjects of continual fascination among all editors, ranging from newspapers and other consumer media to medical journals.

For example, the *Journal of the Kentucky Medical Association* featured a scientific article, titled "Sudden Death of a Runner," in its January 1984 issue. The author, Jeffrey A. Hilb, M.D., F.A.C.P., combined a personal style with a scientific review, which is typical of many of the articles in this excellent journal. The editorial staff is headed by A.Evan Overstreet, M.D., editor, and Donna Young, managing editor. Each issue starts with a scientific section of several articles, followed by an editorial, association news and departmental features, including letters-to-the-editor, book reviews and other items.

The scientific articles start with a summary or introductory comment by the editor. Following is an excerpt from Dr. Hilb's article.

Despite the promotion of running as a healthful activity, there is evidence that such aerobic activity may be potentially harmful or even fatal. An illustrative case report is presented. The recent medical literature is reviewed to support the contention that caution is in order before giving unrestricted endorsement to running for cardiovascular fitness.

It has been strongly advocated that running and other such aerobic activity are conducive to good health.

In recent years, however, it has become apparent that runners are not immune from heart disease. The following is an illustrative case:

Case Report

A 50-year-old white male collapsed 49 feet from the finish line in the annual 13.1 mile Kentucky Derby Mini-Marathon. He was taken immediately to a local hospital, but emergency medical measures failed to save him.

The runner was in previously good health and on no medication. He was careful with his diet, consumed an occasional beer, and rarely smoked a cigarette. He took supplemental Vitamin C on occasion. The subject was orphaned, with no family history of heart disease in any known relatives. He retired from the Army after 27 years of service. During that time he was active in the infantry and qualified as a paratrooper, continuing to make jumps and maintain good physical fitness. His discharge physical examination revealed only hearing loss in one ear. After separation from the service he worked for four years until his death as a foreman for a cement company. His work was not particularly strenuous, but he continued to maintain himself in good physical condition by running an average of about six miles per day, running almost daily unless the weather was prohibitive. He had been running regularly for the last nine years. According to family members, the runner had no prodromal symptoms such as fatigue or chest discomfort in the days preceding the race and told people that he felt well-prepared for the run.

The runner presented to the emergency room after CPR had been instituted with a flatline EKG. Because of his age and previously good health, he was in desperation taken to the operating room and placed on cardiopulmonary bypass. Acidosis was corrected and the patient received a blind double bypass graft to the left anterior descending and lateral marginal coronary arteries. In spite of these heroic measures the patient died in the operating room of acute coronary insufficiency, metabolic acidosis, and cardiac arrest. Gross examination during surgery revealed that the LAD was moderately sclerotic. There was no aortic calcification or stenosis noted, nor was there any significant cardiac muscle hypertrophy. Subsequent biopsy specimen revealed minimal arteriosclerosis of a section of aorta. An autopsy was not performed. The patient presumably died with existing coronary artery disease; however, an unrelated cardiac arrhythmia, electrolyte imbalance, or other contributory cause cannot be excluded.

There would seem to be more than sufficient data to totally disprove the "Bassler hypothesis" that marathon runners are immune from coronary artery disease. One could speculate about certain pathophysiologic concepts that could enter into the picture. Exercise may precipitate arrhythmia, as ventricular fibrillation and severe exertion are associated in maximum-effort testing. Most certainly a heart attack during exercise in a person with existing coronary artery disease could be a consequence of either increased myocardial oxygen demand outstripping the blood supply and/or disturbances of the cardiac rhythm and conduction induced by exercise. Because of the release of free fatty acids after exercise and the stimulation of excess catecholamines, a coronary event may actually be more common in the period immediately following vigorous exercise. To explain how a myocardial infarction could occur with normal coronary arteries one could incorporate the notions of thrombocytosis, platelet-fibrin emboli that subsequently lyze, abnormal hemoglobin-oxygen dissociation, or coronary artery spasm. One could go as far as arguing that a marathon runner may be at a lower risk of a cardiovascular death when not running, but at a higher risk during or shortly thereafter running. Even with autopsy proof of coronary disease, the possibility of concurrent heat stress or electrolyte imbalance cannot be ruled out in an individual case.

From a common sense standpoint, one could suppose that a young, healthy individual might benefit from the aerobic exercise of running whereas a person with already existing coronary artery disease might only be unduly stressing an already compromised cardiovascular system. The data seem to bear this out as the cardiac deaths in the younger athletes seem to be largely from cardiomyopathy or some congenital abnormality, whereas the vast majority of deaths in those over 40 are from coronary artery disease.

What practical considerations may we derive from all of this? There is no real proof that a thorough physical exam should be advocated for a beginning runner since this has not prevented catastrophic running events from occurring, nor would exercise stress testing be justified. On the other hand, an echocardiogram done on a young athlete with a seemingly benign heart murmur could, perhaps, lead to the early diagnosis of a condition that could be aggravated by strenuous physical activity. Although some, but not all, of the runners experienced some prodromal symptoms prior to a cardiac death, they were often vague and seemingly inconsequential. Further, some of the runners did experience significant symptoms very compatible with coronary artery disease and tried to "run through" them with an ultimately fatal outcome.

I have tried to present arguments disproving that runners are absolutely protected from coronary artery disease, I am not, however, advocating that running and other such aerobic activity are not worthwhile enterprises. In fact, the large body of evidence would seem to demonstrate that physical activity is a positive factor in the prevention of coronary artery disease. Further, the qualitative aspect of a more fulfilled lifestyle should be emphasized along with any quantitative consideration of the very small, but finite, probability of a cardiac death from running.

Incidentally, Dr. Hilb, who is an internist in Louisville, is a runner.

Articles about runners' injuries have appeared in many other medical publications. Robert A. Pruner, M.D., an orthopedic surgeon, wrote an article in the Spring 1984 issue of *On Call*, the quarterly magazine of Roanoke Memorial Hospitals, Roanoke, Virginia. This external magazine is primarily for community leaders, contributors and other lay people, so the article focuses on consumer advice. Illustrations included a color cover photo, a full-page drawing and two large-space black-and-white photos of runners.

After discussing problems related to running, Dr. Pruner provided general comments about training and equipment, and then summarized specific injuries. Here are excerpts.

Skin Injuries

Problems affecting the skin may include such things as corns, callouses and blisters, and are usually caused by abnormal pressure. Preventive measures include good well-fitting shoes, good socks and proper padding in the shoes to relieve pressure. A thin layer of petroleum jelly can be helpful in relieving areas of friction. Commonly there may be some structural deformity that may require surgical correction. Continued areas of skin irritation that do not heal with simple measures should certainly be checked by your physician.

Subungual Haematoma

This is a collection of blood under a nail and is very common in runners. It is caused by repeated trauma and may be related to a shoe with a toe box that is not deep enough. Many times the condition may not be painful, but if so, it may require release of the blood under the nail surgically.

Plantar Fasciitis

This is characterized by dull aching pain under the weight-bearing part of the heel. There may be different causes of this pain, such as a flatfoot, or a foot with an excessively high arch or tight Achilles tendon. Treatment may consist of padding the heel, arch supports and stretching exercises. The use of heat before and ice after a run may help, as well as the use of anti-inflammatory agents such as aspirin and occasionally a steroid injection in selected cases. In very refractory cases surgery may be helpful, but it is not always successful.

Tendinitis

This is an inflammation that occurs in a tendon and most commonly occurs around the foot or ankle. Two of the more common tendons affected are the large Achilles tendon, running behind the ankle and attaching to the heel, and secondly, the posterior tibial tendon in the front and inner aspect of the tibia or shin bone, and continuing around the inner part of the ankle. Prevention of tendinitis can be aided many times by adapting a realistic training program, good shoewear and above all a good stretching exercise program for the afflicted tendon. Once the condition has developed, it may require a period of rest, oral anti-inflammatory agents, such as aspirin, and refraining from running. Injections with cortisone or steroids into the Achilles tendon are usually not indicated since they may cause further weakening and even rupture of the tendon.

Stress Fractures

With repeated cyclic loading the bone may not be able to withstand the forces and a fracture may occur. These fractures may occur anywhere in the lower extremity, but are more common in the lower tibia, or shin bone, and in the small bones of the foot. The most common symptom will be pain at first aggravated by activity and relieved by rest. These fractures usually occur in someone beginning to run or in an experienced runner who is increasing his distance too fast. The diagnosis can be hard to make, as it may take two to three weeks for an x-ray to show the fracture. A special procedure called a bone scan, may show the bone changes much earlier and can be helpful in making the diagnosis. The treatment for a stress fracture may not necessarily lead to a total cessation of training, but may well require decreasing one's activity level to one that is not painful during the activity. Once healing has occurred and the pain has been totally alleviated, training can again be increased gradually over a period of time.

Patellar Pain

Pain around the knee cap can be related to and caused by many different problems. This may include abnormal position and tracking of the knee cap, bow legs, knock knees, abnormal rotation of the leg, muscle weakness or some problem with the foot. Most runners with poor alignment of the patella will usually experience more pain running on hills or descending stairs or inclines. Complete evaluation of the lower extremity may be necessary to determine the cause of the pain. Fortunately, many of these problems around the knee cap can be helped with a proper knee strengthening exercise program and other simple measures. Shoe orthotics may be helpful if the foot is malaligned and changes in the running pattern, such as avoiding hills, may also be necessary until the symptoms subside.

Knee Pain

Another very common cause of pain around the knee is a condition called the iliotibial band syndrome. This is characterized by pain on the outer side of the knee, just above the joint. This is caused by snapping of a strong band of tissue over the bone with the resultant irritation of the bursa near the tissue and between the bone. This condition will usually respond to a period of rest, along with heat, and again, oral anti-inflammatory agents such as aspirin. Occasionally an injection into this area may be necessary if the pain persists over a period of time and there is failure to respond to the above measures.

The preceding injuries are in no way meant to be a complete list. They are some of the more common ones that may affect the runner.

Most problems faced by the runner can be treated with good common sense. An acute injury should be treated with rest, ice, elevation and compression. Pain that should be checked by a physician would include traumatic joint injuries, injuries with severe pain or pain lasting more than a few days and injuries causing apprehension or undue concern.

An injury does not have to signify the complete end to one's activity. As the pain subsides a gradual resumption of activity can be started. Other types of activity can also be substituted to maintain one's fitness for running. Two of the best things are bicycling and swimming. These activities can maintain one's aerobic fitness and be less harmful to an injured lower extremity.

Prevention is always the best treatment. Remember not to overtrain, and do not adapt poor training methods. Have any anatomical problems checked prior to training by a competent professional. Always stretch and maintain good flexibility. The runner should heed the advice of George Sheehan, M.D., and "listen to his body."

Thus, Dr. Hilb concluded the article in the *Journal of the Kentucky Medical Association.*

Wrestling

Sports medicine is a major subject in many medical journals, particularly paraplegia and other severe injuries resulting from football, diving, boxing, motorcycling and other popular leisure activities. Not too many people are wrestlers, but apparently there are enough of them in Iowa to warrant a research project, the Iowa Wrestling Study. Reports on the project appear regularly in *Iowa Medicine*, the journal of the Iowa Medical Society.

The most recent, in September 1984, was written by Charles M. Tipton, Ph.D., and Robert A. Oplinger, M.S., of the Department of Exercise Science and Physical Education and the Department of Physical Education and Dance at the University of Iowa, Iowa City. Though wrestling has relatively little interest, the article has considerable relevance to other sports, particularly with regard to medical issues associated with the "making of weight." Following are excerpts.

Wrestlers in Iowa and elsewhere continue to lose a high percentage of their body in a brief period of time before competition. Few educational and medical authorities realize the youngest wrestlers are the ones who lose the highest percentage of body weight to become certified. It is of interest that when assessments of emotional stability were made during a wrestling season, the greatest declines were noted in the individuals within the 98–119 pound weight classes. These individuals were also the youngest subjects in the study. While the significance or importance of this observation is unknown, it does reaffirm that younger wrestlers need to be monitored closely during a competitive season.

Not unexpectedly, wrestlers make weight by a combination of food restriction, fluid deprivation and thermal hydration. Of these approaches, dehydration is the method used most frequently and intensely by wrestlers.

High school wrestlers seldom consult their parents or their physicians on "how to make weight." Only in 30% of the cases do they seek the advice of the coach, hence, the peer wrestler becomes the most important source of scientific information on this process. The concept that scholastic and collegiate wrestlers can consume a 500 kcl a day diet to reduce should be discarded because wrestlers expend from 7–15 kcl/min when "working out" and our calculations show that the daily minimum number of calories needed by 15–16 year-old wrestlers will range from 1500 kcl to 2100 kcl depending upon the age, height and weight of the wrestler.

It is our experience that the majority of wrestlers easily identify fat as being a component of body weight; but very few understand the meaning of lean body mass, or can explain what is meant by essential lipids, or know the significance of the various fluid compartments in the body. Contrary to general impressions, most wrestlers do not possess a high percentage of body fat several weeks before the season starts. Because of long traditions and continued practices, second-string wrestlers will invariably lose weight to try to become a starter at a different weight class. As most wrestling fans know, very few "nonstarters" will ever move up to a heavier weight class. However, this practice of trying to compete at a lower weight class creates serious problems for the sport, the participants, the state athletic associations and the physicians, because it results in a situation where a large number of wrestlers are certified for a small number of weight classes.

In the last decade biopsies have been secured from muscles of numerous athletes to learn more about their energy requirements and their fiber type involvements. When this approach was employed with wrestlers who lost 8% of their body weight, muscle glycogen levels decreased by 30% during the first day, and by 55% at the end of the third day. Interestingly, muscle glycogen levels were still below initial values 3 hours after the study was terminated. This finding indicates more time is needed after weigh-ins or at tournaments for muscle energy stores to be returned to pre-experimental conditions.

It is well accepted that outstanding wrestlers will make weight 20–30 times each season. Hence, it is likely they will repeat this process 200 times in their careers. One structure that could be affected by the practice is the kidney. The chronic effects of fluid deprivation and dehydration on the anatomy and physiology of the kidney in animals or humans are not well-known. It has been reported that renal blood flow and glomerular filtration rates are decreased by dehydration. Since many wrestlers combine exercise with thermal dehydration while wearing rubber suits, the functioning of their temperature regulating and/or water balance systems are at a considerable risk of being impaired.

In our early studies on the urinary profiles of wrestlers before and after weigh-ins and during the tournament, we found signs of dehydration (high specific gravity, high osmolarity, low pH) before the weigh-in, after the weigh-in, before their first match and during the competition. Because of the increases in urinary potassium and leucine-amino-peptidase levels, we speculated the dehydration process had caused renal ischemia. This speculation has yet to be proven or disproven, but the possibility is of sufficient importance for exercise scientists and clinicians to study kidney functions in current and former wrestlers.

Urinary tests are routine in many laboratories; hence, there has been a movement by certain clinicians to use a specific gravity value to assess the degree of dehydration by wrestlers. One suggestion is under consideration to disqualify wrestlers if they have a urinary specific gravity higher than 1.015 at the time of weigh-in. Recently, we measured the resting urines of wrestlers obtained two–three weeks either before certification or competition and found values that were significantly higher than expected. Consequently, we believe more research is necessary before any group, conference or state organization accepts the 1.015 value as the "cut off" limit. However, statements on the deleterious physiological effects of dehydration are warranted because it has been shown that decreases in cardiac output, stroke volume, and blood volume occur with this practice. To minimize the consequences of dehydration, many coaches, exercise scientists and physicians favor weigh-ins immediately prior to the match. The rationale is that the dehydrated wrestler would suffer an "object lesson" in performance because of insufficient time for rehydration to occur. This approach may emerge as the most effective method to reduce dehydration before competition because to date education has not succeeded.

For more than 15 years we have been developing a scientific method that can be used in schools to predict a minimal wrestling weight before the season commences. Using information from various sources, we have proposed that a minimal wrestling weight be established as one that has five-percent fat.

The article was sprinkled with references, totaling 35. However, *Iowa Medicine* does not list references or bibliographies, and instead concludes its articles with a statement that references are available from the authors or editors. A few journals have this policy. What do you think of this?

Wine and Health

The California vineyards and wineries are mostly in Napa and Sonoma counties, so it's fitting that a symposium on wine and health was held recently in Sonoma county. Daniel S. Tuft, M.D., discussed the symposium in the November 1984 issue of *Sonoma County Physician*, the monthly publication of the Sonoma County Medical Association, Santa Rosa. The article was documented with 27 references, from an array of publications including the *Bulletin of the Society of Medical Friends of Wine, Journal of Food Sciences, Chest, American Review of Respiratory Diseases, Clinical Allergy, Journal of Allergy and Clinical Immunology, Journal of Physiology, Headache, Annals of Allergy* and the *Journal of the American Medical Association.*

Following is an excerpt from the article by Dr. Tuft, who is an allergist in Santa Rosa.

Documented cases of anaphylaxis related to wine were reviewed at the Sonoma County symposium, and it was noted that a number of foods have been implicated in causing anaphylactic sensitivity including nuts, beans buckwheat, fish, shellfish and others. The literature substantiating anaphylactic reactions to wine is, however, very limited and that formed an essential point of this conference. Several reports in the literature in which anaphylaxis was associated with wine were not substantiated by controlled challenges to wine and/or its components.

In one study, 11 asthmatics had a history of severe reactions to wine or other alcoholic beverages. Of these patients, six responded with decreases in pulmonary functions, and three responded to a specific beverage, but not ethanol alone. There was no correlation between skin test reactions and clinical reactions in that study. This has been true in other reported cases as well.

It was also brought out that the most common adverse reaction to wine and, in fact, to all alcoholic beverages is that due to overindulgence. In discussing the hangover syndrome we heard that some of the theories of this syndrome include the possibility of withdrawal since some people report relief of symptoms by returning to drinking, i.e., the hair of the dog.

A cellular basis for hangover has never been adequately proven. In some people, however, the hangover may be partially blunted by high oxygen concentrations suggesting a delayed clearance of metabolic products of ethanol oxidation. Hangover syndrome has also been related to specific kinds of alcoholic beverages and it is believed that those containing large number of congeners such as aldehydes, methanol and fusel alcohols are more likely to produce symptoms of hangover. Wine drinkers commonly tell us that white wines are less likely to produce hangover than red wines.

Following the hangover discussion, the association of classical migraine with beverages containing ethanol and wine in particular, was noted. As far back as 1909 the possibility existed that tyramine, a vasoactive amine found in wine, could trigger vascular headaches. And studies now indicate that foods high in tyramine or similar substances can trigger migrainous attacks in patients so predisposed.

This brought us to the serious problem of sulphur dioxide or metabisulfite in wine. It is found that it is nearly impossible in today's technology to make wine without the use of sulphur, and that sulphur in the wine generally exists in the form of metabisulfite. Studies performed by the Allergy Laboratory at U.C. Davis as well as at Scripps Clinic indicate that certain asthmatics have a unique sensitivity to metabisulfite, which results in violent asthma episodes frequently requiring hospitalization and, in at least some instances, death.

At this symposium, wine makers from Sonoma County expressed their interest in furthering within the wine industry itself the knowledge of possible adverse reactions, particularly the problem of metabisulfite. Some of the technology discussed may eventually lead to eliminating the use of sulphur in winemaking, at least to the extent that it can be reduced or removed from the final product. And, of course, the winemakers are concerned with the marketing aspects of this. Reports of adverse reactions to wine, particularly those related to metabisulfite are in a highly competitive atmosphere, a significant problem from a marketing point of view.

Finally, to sum up briefly, we can say that wine is an extremely complex substance because it is the end result of natural fruit production and fermentation. Many chemicals end up in the wine, some of which may produce various kinds of adverse reactions such as anaphylaxis or anaphylactoid type reactions, vasomotor type reactions such as vascular headaches, and others due to toxic effects. It is important to prove the existence of the reaction particularly if the food or wine is important to the individual.

The article included a photo of Dr. Tuft. As with many of the author's photos in *Sonoma County Physician*, it was not the usual formal "head shot" but instead the smiling Dr. Tuft was shown in a sport shirt. The article was delightfully titled, "Vintage Wheezing: Adverse Reactions to Wine."

Following the wine report was another well written article, which also was brightly titled and illustrated with a crisp photo of the smiling author. Titled "Rheumatism, Recognition of an Old Syndrome," the article by Elizabeth S. Smith, M.D., started with this "grabber:"

Semantics can be a pursuit in trivia, but in medicine, exact terminology is essential. Using the wrong word, even though it may be a popular misnomer, leads to confusion and improper treatment.

One pet peeve is the use of the word *arthritis* for any and all musculo-skeletal aches and pains. *Arthritis* literally means inflammation in the joint(s), and nothing more. Unfortunately, lay and professional people alike use *arthritis* loosely as a general term. Thus "your arthritis" may actually be tendinitis, bursitis, muscle spasm, and/or arthralgias. These latter diagnoses are treated differently than most forms of arthritis. I spend a lot of time informing patients that they don't have arthritis.

Even more confusing is the fact that lay people often consider the word *arthritis* to mean a single disease. Arthritis is no more a diagnosis than abdominal pain is. We all know that there are more than a hundred diseases that can be associated with arthritis and rheumatism. So let's attempt to be more specific when discussing these problems with our patients.

Dr. Smith candidly discussed the medical details of rheumatism, fibro-myalgia and other related diseases. Dr. Smith, who is a rheumatologist in Santa Rosa, could become a successful writer of popular magazine articles because of her skill in mixing complex materials with personal observations, humor and other delightful comments. She concluded with two quips about the word *arthritis*:

If I hear it pronounced "arthur-itis" one too many times in a day, or if I find I can't spell it, I know it is time to take a vacation.

Other issues of *Sonoma County Physician* also are a pleasure to read. For example, here's the contents page of the December 1984 issue.

Cover: Winter in Yosemite National Park, Calif. Photo by George McClary, MD.

Cedric Johnson, M.D., is editor of *Sonoma County Physician* and Pamela Roncini is editorial coordinator.

Special Issues

Centennials and other anniversaries, openings of new buildings and other major events generally call for special issues of publications. Editors rise to the occasion with design effects, extra pages, use of freelancers and other contributors and, in general, a contribution of additional time, money and creativity.

A superb example was the Tenth Anniversary Issue of *QRB (Quality Review Bulletin)*, the monthly journal of the Joint Commission on Accreditation of Hospitals, Chicago. The 238-page (8½ × 11 inches) perfect-bound magazine, labeled Collector's Edition, was published in December 1984. Undoubtedly, the approximately 8000 subscribers (who pay $70 a year) appreciated and saved this "book" about quality assurance (QA).

Close to 100 physicians, nurses and other authors contributed 39 articles grouped into six sections:

Issues in Physician Performance
QA Management and Organization
Methodology
Cost and Quality
Discharge Planning
Risk Management/Malpractice

Each section was introduced by a two-page commentary (on colored paper), analytically written by a member of the editorial advisory board. The issue opened with a three-page introduction by Maryanne Shanahan, director of the department of publications of the Joint Commission on Accreditation of Hospitals, and Karen Gardner, executive editor of *QRB*. Following this was a two-page review by Robert H. Moser, M.D., executive vice president of the American College of Physicians and member of the *QRB* editorial advisory board. Dr. Moser's article was so well written that we are pleased to reprint it in entirety.

Copies of the December, 1984 issue are available for $40 from Dawn Carlsen at the Joint Commission on Accreditation of Hospitals, 875 N. Michigan Avenue, Chicago, IL 60611. Incidentally, the magazine does not accept advertising, so the tenth anniversary issue indeed is a book. Congratulations to Maryanne Shanahan!

QRB: Messenger of Quality

Quality is an elusive virtue. Everyone can recognize its texture: the shape, color, surface design, finish of a fine urn; the bouquet, taste, color, body of a celebrated vintage wine; the performance of an elegant prima ballerina. And we all recognize "high quality" physicians and other health care professionals. But when it comes to pinning down the definition of quality, to quantifying and measuring quality—that is when the going gets tough.

"Decline in quality" and "lack of pride in workmanship" have become great popular lamentations and preoccupations of modern society. The contemporary climate of mass production and consumption engenders a sentiment that quality is a virtue whose time has passed. Grace, durability, and performance seem less important than do immediate availability and a plethora of styles, colors, and models, be it in automobiles, breakfast cereals, clothing, or medical services.

But what about health care, health care professionals, and the *QRB*? When I first encountered this slender journal, I had ambivalent reactions. On the one hand, I pondered the presumptuousness of the title; but if the Joint Commission on Accreditation of Hospitals (JCAH) is not a champion of health care quality, who is? Even conceding this point, I wondered upon reflection if the journal's undertaking was not naively quixotic.

Professionals in health care, as everywhere else, can recognize quality, but it still defies description. We all know the best physicians and the best hospitals, for example, but how can such things be measured? Undaunted, the *QRB* has tackled this problem with gusto. Its editorial content has ranged widely, with quality always as its benchmark. It has looked into the performance of staff (eg, physicians, nurses, pharmacists, administrators); it has scrutinized the performance of departments (eg, pharmacy, nursing service, food service, management); it has examined the issue of costs. The *QRB* has probed every manner of "process" that affects health care quality.

Has the *QRB* made a difference? That is not a fair question, for there are no data, just as there are no data to indicate the impact of a specific continuing medical education event on physician competence or the impact of *Time* magazine on the political persuasions of its readers. In health care facilities, quality *should* have an impact on patient outcomes. Yet I know of no study relating patient outcomes in a specific disease or group of diseases to the quality of care provided by physicians, much less to the quality of the total hospital experience. In health care, we face a major difficulty when we try to relate any antecedent event to patient outcomes: There are simply too many variables involved.

If the *QRB* has made a difference, it is because of the very nature of its existence as a journal dedicated to excellence in health care. The *QRB* is a positive indication that, at the highest levels of the professions, concern and desire exist to seek optimal patient care. It serves as a steadfast reminder that JCAH and its parent organizations are concerned that quality not be trammeled and shunted aside in the hectic, pell-mell pursuit of cost control. The *QRB* says, in essence, that the raison d'etre for all of us in health care is our dedication to the welfare of patients: to make them well when possible; to keep them functioning with a minimum of pain and disability when cure is not possible; to let them know that we care under all circumstances. And the best way to achieve this noble purpose is to seek excellence in all aspects of our ministrations.

The danger in deliberating about aspects of quality in any area, especially in health care, is that we face the risk of becoming mired in "process" and losing sight of the ultimate purpose: patient welfare. At times, in pursuit of operational efficiency, the rounds of physicians and nurses and the work of the pharmacy or the food service or the janitorial service become so autonomous that we forget the patient, the hapless recipient of the independent "efficiencies" of the various departments.

This point was dramatized for me last month, while my wife was recuperating from serious surgery in one of the world's most distinguished hospitals. On the first day back in her room, after 72 hours in the recovery area, she was visited by 38 different people in 12 hours—I counted them! They included representatives of medical staff (operating room surgeon and team, consulting cardiologist, ward officer); nursing service (chief nurse, ward nurse, medications nurse); hospital administration (special representative of the operating surgeon, public relations, insurance people); food service (supervisor, nutritionist, tray deliverers, tray retrievers); the chaplain's office (chaplain and civilian volunteers); building maintenance (air conditioning repair, light bulb checker, cleaning people); a "do you want the TV" person; record room people; multiple delivery persons from florists; mail deliverers; and other assorted people with and without clipboards. All were cheerful and pleasant, and each had a job to do. Each represented a well-run department, but there was no evident coordination among them. Each individual was operating efficiently and autonomously. But to understand their cumulative disruptive effect, one need only count the total hours of uninterrupted rest possible (or impossible) for the patient during daylight hours.

This episode occurred in a splendid, well-run hospital, and similar ones occur in every well-run hospital that I know of. It is a primary demonstration of "process" becoming more important than health care's ultimate goal: the welfare of the patient.

Quality assurance is the conscience of the health care industry; *QRB* is its messenger. As I have indicated, no one can measure this journal's impact, but I submit that it must be salutary. The editors and writers who created the *QRB* have done an admirable job of keeping the quality banner aloft and ensuring that it does not become lost on the battlefield of cost containment.

As I indicated earlier, the definition of quality is beset with critical yet immeasurable intangibles; but these intangibles are so real that, in the case of a physician, a patient is willing to bet his or her life on them. In evaluating a physician, how does one place on any scale such diverse items as sensitivity to patient needs; recent knowledge about fibrinolytic agents or nuclear magnetic resonance spectroscopy or second-generation calcium channel blockers; speed of response to telephone calls, some of which are answered by an answering service; time spent at the bedside; time spent explaining exactly "what happened to me"?

When evaluating a health care facility, how does one grade the rapidity of response to the nurse call button pushed in the middle of the night; the smile or frown of the food service tray deliverer; the coordination of efforts to ensure a few hours' nap in the afternoon; a nurse who is unfamiliar with a patient's medications and brings the same pill received an hour earlier, when it is due every eight hours and the patient knows the nurse is in error, or when eight hours have passed and the medication is not delivered; and so on? These and many other factors are what I have called the critical but immeasurable intangibles that are essential to the evaluation of health care quality.

In health care's current climate of economic travail, one is tempted to believe that sound health care and cost-effectiveness are mutually exclusive. This is not the case. In every health care facility in the country, means are being sought to become more cost-effective, to eliminate frills, to avoid redundancies, to correct inefficiencies, and to coordinate operations. These efforts are made not merely in the interest of cost-effectiveness but in the pursuit of quality. Just as with a well-turned vase, there are elegance and simplicity in a lean, uncluttered diagnostic workup, the swift, efficient management of a patient, and the operation of a need-sensitive, coordinated, well-organized health care facility. All are works of beauty.

Thus the *QRB* must continue its vigil—to help us keep the goal of quality paramount in our considerations—as we negotiate the potential obstacles that lie ahead. Congratulations on your anniversary, *QRB*—long may your quality banner wave.

HAPPY ANNIVERSARY *QRB*

Robert H. Moser, MD, FACP
Executive Vice President
American College of Physicians
Philadelphia, Pennsylvania
Member of the *QRB* Editorial Advisory Board, 1979–Present

Joys of Scribbling

Word processors now are in millions of offices, including medical facilities. But the physician still considers a pen as essential as any medical instrument. Jokes are made about the illegible handwriting of many doctors, but, of course, it's a serious matter! Here's a commentary by J. Mostyn Davis, M.D., of Shamokin, PA, which appeared in the November 1984 issue of *Pennsylvania Medicine*. We asked Dr. Davis, who is chairman of the publication committee of *Pennsylvania Medicine*, to send us a sample of his handwriting. It appears at the end of the article.

It seems unreasonable to me that an intelligent, caring physician who takes a good history and does a thorough physical examination, would then sit down and literally scribble an undecipherable prescription, thereby defeating the entire purpose of the whole visit. How can a doctor who expresses himself with verbal precision suddenly degenerate to the level of a second grade student when he takes his prescription pad in hand? All of the efforts of a highly trained professional are often sabotaged by the illegible scrawl on the prescription. Imagine your reaction if your banker filled out your loan request form with undecipherable numbers. Our abysmal record with regard to prescription writing legibility has potentially far more serious implications. We deal daily with the lives of our patients.

By the nature of the beast, physicians fail consistently in the test for humility, and pharmacists are not rated high on the assertive scale. The May 1983 issue of *American Druggist* details the results of a survey of pharmacists with regard to this problem. One might reasonably expect the doctors whose prescriptions are not legible enough that the pharmacist can fill them without question might be grateful for help in avoiding a possible malpractice action by way of a call from the pharmacist. This is not, however, the case. The study reported that 50.5% of doctors who were called about illegible prescriptions were indifferent, 22.4% were defensive, and 14.9% were downright nasty, when notified by the pharmacists that they could not safely decipher the doctor's handwriting. Only 12.2% of physicians were said to be receptive.

Nearly one-fourth of pharmacists reported that a phone call was necessary at least once daily, on average, for a poorly written prescription. Another 14% reported they do this more than once daily. If these incidents were local in nature, the problem would be far less serious, but they seem to be nearly universal. Pharmacists nationwide answered the survey and no area of the country appears to be exempt. Why such an important matter is treated so lightly by doctors is a mystery. The government appears to be antagonistic toward us, we are not the most favorite group in the eyes of trial lawyers, and even the American public appears to be losing confidence in us—must we intentionally alienate another large segment of those with whom we always have had close ties? What is especially disturbing is that some doctors treat the whole problem as if it were a joke. These are physicians who have not yet had a malpractice action brought against them as a result of their handwriting.

The practice of slovenly penmanship is generally carried over to all written communications by physicians. Malpractice problems may develop because the patient's chart is undecipherable. These remarks, however, are limited to the problem of doctors' handwriting on prescriptions. Nearly all of the pharmacists in the survey acknowledged making prescription errors because of physicians' scribblings. On average, the respondents reported that they spent approximately 4¾ hours each month trying to unlock the secrets of the poor handwriting of physicians. Claiming that "bad handwriting wastes everybody's time," the pharmacists noted that the prescriber's signature was singled out as the most common problem with a prescription. Next came the patient's name, then the name of the medication, and finally the dosage directions. Some examples: Hydroxazine 25 for Hydrazoline 25 mg., Amanase for Orinase, Periactin for Percodan, Cascara for Casec, Medrol for Moderil, and on and on. How unfortunate for the patient, who after paying the physician to diagnose and prescribe, pays another fee to the pharmacist for the medication but is given the wrong drug!

The prescriptions contain many errors because of abbreviations. It is wonderful to be able to make all those Latin inscriptions—few professionals anymore write in that dead language, but I know some people who say they are sure it was the doctors who killed Latin! Writing plainly, clearly, and in English (keep the RX = take thou—if you wish) would cut down on the pharmacist's eye strain, speed the filling of the prescription, decrease the time you or your staff spend trying to decipher information from the chart, and most important, assure that your patient will get the medication you order at the times you specify.

There is no doubt that the prescription, as a document, is a very important element in the physician/patient/pharmacist interaction, but this concept does not appear to be recognized up to this point. Some of us learn by watching and doing, others must be punished before they make an effort to change their behavior. The prescription continues to be a weak link in the health care chain.

HUMOR

Poking Fun At Oneself

Humor rarely is found in the pages of medical journals. We don't recommend it as a regular feature, if for no other reason than that it requires considerable talent to produce funny written material that has medical relevance. A few editors use cartoons—originals or reprints—to lighten and brighten their pages. One publication that uses humor regularly and effectively is the *Bulletin of the Orange County Medical Association* and it is a delight to read. One subject was advertising by physicians, in which Dr. Alex Dworsky took a satirical approach, as was obvious from the title, "Let's run this up the flagpole, guys."

Here are a few of the rapid fire proposals of A.H., an advertising executive.

We have this guy take out kids' tonsils—two for the price of one."

We use the magazine coupon tear-out gimmick . . . bring in the coupon and get a reduced fee or an extra visit!"

We operate on a Dine-Out basis . . . the patient buys the book that lists the participating doctors . . . then he can bring his wife along for a free visit.

We use the "Special this week" idea . . . stuff like complete blood count for only $3 this week only.

We offer the patients short of cash—operate now, pay later.

We give 'em something—say the surgeon does a gallstone operation and he offers to make up for the patient a beautiful necklace made up of her own gallstones at no extra charge.

We have this bird who does geriatrics. He guarantees to keep you alive or else he picks up the funeral expenses.

The article also included sample TV commercials, such as Joe Namath endorsing his orthopedist and Zaza Gabor speaking up for her plastic surgeon. The *Bulletin* featured a newspaper ad on the cover for a Dr. William Strikland (fictional, we hope!) listing this week's specials, including sutures for $2.95 each and bone fractures at $19.95 for arms and $29.95 for legs. Plus S&H stamps, of course, and a chance to win a free ski trip.

Lest you think that medicine in Orange County, California is all fun and games, the same issue also included a daily calendar of local meetings, editorials and articles about malpractice, legislative news, a debate by two physicians on AMA membership and a 16-page section of reports from 19 hospitals.

Humorous Cartoons

Kevin P. Glynn, M.D., an internist and pulmonary medicine specialist, may have been the country's only regular creator of medical cartoons. He operated a unique service from his home in La Jolla, CA producing a monthly "cartoon strip" which he sold to medical journals at very low rates. Subscribers included county medical societies in California, Connecticut, Indiana, Kentucky, Minnesota, Missouri and Virginia. His cartoons have also appeared in *Modern Medicine* and *Medical Tribune*. Dr. Glynn had no art training and thought of himself as a humorist or social critic. He said, "I have felt for a long time that our contemporary medical scene is so full of inconsistencies and contradictions that gags which are timely and slanted for practicing physicians should have a message. The pictorial route is not only succinct but attracts attention."

Humor in Medical Writing

Is it possible to brighten your pages with colorful writing, perhaps including humor, and still maintain the dignity of a scientific journal? The answer, of course, is yes—though it's not easy. Following is a discussion of this subject from the book by Dr. John H. Dirckx, *Dx and Rx: A Physician's Guide to Medical Writing.*

The last sentence (this was a reference to an article which concluded with a personal comment) brings us closer to the writer, tells us more about him, sells him and his ideas to us more persuasively than all the rest of his paper together. The personal touch must not, of course, be overdone, or permitted to degenerate into a patronizing or insolently familiar manner.

"Why," asked Horace, "should we not spice up the lesson with a dash of humor?" In two thousand years no one has even tried to find an answer. When we consider the importance to the physician of a cheerful and genial temperament, which can ease patients' sufferings, lighten the burden of work and smooth relationships with colleagues, it seems surprising and regrettable that a little gentle humor does not more often find its way into medical literature.

Admittedly, medical writing does not offer a wide scope for humor. Ribaldry and sarcasm are always out of place. A paper on multiple sclerosis or teenage suicide would be marred, not enhanced, by any attempt at wit. But a hint of quiet drollery may sometimes enliven material which instead of being lugubrious is merely dull. Nothing makes technical exposition so boring and unpalatable as an undue gravity of tone.

"Don't pull on the umbilical cord," said one of my teachers, and immediately hammered home his point with an Irish bull: "You may pull it off, and then you won't have anything to pull out the placenta with." As every good teacher knows, humor can be of immense value in emphasizing an idea. A writer who wanted to underscore the importance of the rectal examination made good use of a pun when he concluded his paper with the advice that the physician "*digitalize* every patient." A vivid simile may also reinforce a message while keeping the tone light and interesting.

It is said that pityriasis rosea will fade completely after systemic administration of adrenal steroid, but this seems rather like going after ants with dynamite.

Humor and figurative language must be administered in small doses. A flippant or bantering tone undermines the whole effect of technical writing. The intelligent reader recoils in disgust from fustian drivel like the following.

Abandoning these superficial haunts, the vessel plunges boldly into the depths of the last-named fossa, courses inferiorly in familiar association with its faithful venae comites, and at length emerges triumphant . . .

and from mere silliness like this:

During the first 48 hours the patient may experience chills, fever and a slight cough, with a pinch of nausea thrown in for good measure.

A well-chosen metaphor can energize technical prose and wake up the reader.

The suprascapular and transverse cervical arteries clamp the phrenic nerve to the scalenus muscle.

It may sometimes be possible to snake a smaller catheter inside the larger, past the obstruction.

Notice how *clamp* and *snake* lend color and vividness to these sentences, shedding a glow of life over their neighbors like diamonds set among humbler stones. We cannot, after all, replace technical terms with anything more brisk or pungent without straying into inaccuracy and obscurity. But the judicious insertion of a single colorful metaphor among these mundane, workaday words gives sparkle and freshness to the whole passage.

The best and most engaging writing has a sort of warmth or geniality, a quality which assures the reader that there is another human being across the void of time and space. Good writing is not a monolog but a conversation between writer and reader. Never lose your awareness of your audience, its capacities, its temperament, its expectations. A novelist or a musician who did so would soon have no audience. You must commune with your reader, not just jabber at him. Do not commit the blunder of playing to the grandstand, couching your ideas in the arcane mumbo-jumbo of a super-specialty to impress a handful of readers while alienating all the rest.

Warmth in writing comes across in many subtle ways: in the respect which the writer shows for the reader, in his evident enthusiasm for his subject, in the little glimpses he gives of his own personality, individuality and good nature.

> The reflex hammer should be gripped firmly and swung smartly and decisively through a substantial arc, say 60°, of which the examiner's wrist joint forms the center of rotation. A satisfactory hammer needs a certain weight, of which the usual medical supply house article falls short. The "hammer" that I have used for the past eleven years is an eight-inch length of solid brass curtain-rod covered with rubber tubing.

If there is anyone capable of writing a whole paper or book along these lines, would you be surprised to learn that he pours champagne and ketchup over his corn flakes every morning?

No matter how picturesque his language or how piquant his wit, the technical writer must never forget what he is doing and allow his presentation to degenerate into pure entertainment. Neither should he surround his subject with a spurious aura of tension and melodrama. The popular novelist may find it expedient to manufacture atmosphere in this earnest, hamming way, but the manner and tone of technical writing must always be suited to and subservient to the matter.

It is possible to write vigorous, appealing, even amusing prose and still preserve a due formality and decorum. It is not possible to write slang like *heading up the lab team* or *now for the bad news* without descending to sloppy informality. A correctly formed taste complements vividness and humor while keeping them in check; it ensures that the writer will not sew purple patches on burlap and call it finery, or try to juice up his paragraphs with forced and mirthless jocularity.

Not only does good taste protect the writer from conspicuous eccentricity, but it also adds a final polish to his style. Tasteful prose is nearly always pleasant to read. Indeed, the very foundation of good taste in writing is an intimate familiarity with good literature. One who does not himself derive pleasure from reading can hardly be expected to give pleasure to others through his writing.

EDITING

Blake Kellogg's Workbook

The following detailed advice on the various aspects of editing appeared in a workbook prepared by Blake Kellogg, associate professor of journalism at the University of Wisconsin, Madison, for use during a session on editing at one of the Sandoz Medical Journalism Workshops.

Editing

The purpose of editing is to make copy more readable. Usually the following steps will help:
1. Eliminate unnecessary words.
2. Substitute short words for long words.
3. Substitute single words for phrases.
4. Convert verbs from the passive to the active voice.

Short sentences are to be preferred over long sentences because they are more readily comprehended by the reader. Short sentences allow the reader to catch a breath of air. Short sentences help the reader take information a step at a time.

Not all sentences can, or should, be short. As a rule, however, short sentences are easier for the reader to handle than the long ones.

Read the following 37-word sentence and see if you can make it easier to read by changing it into several short sentences.

"The use of quantitative biochemical methods to investigate dystrophic muscle in tissue culture permits the most objective determination of pathological changes and the possible effectiveness of therapeutic agents, but also requires relatively large amounts of experimental material."

Messages are always clarified when excess words are eliminated. Even writing in plain English can be improved by the elimination of unnecessary words.

Perhaps the Red Queen in Alice in Wonderland said it best when asked how to tell a story. She said, "Begin at the beginning, go through to the end, and then stop."

The Lead

The purpose of the lead is to carry the reader into the story. In order to accomplish this, the writer must use the most interesting material in the lead. A dull lead will simply cause the reader to abandon the writing and move to something else.

Many writers, especially those who are inexperienced, try to incorporate the five W's of journalism into the lead—who, what, where, when, and why. Frequently emphasis seems to fall on the when and the where, and almost without exception, the when and the where are the most boring parts of the story. In journalism, this is known as leading with the "time element." It's a common mistake. The time element should be used in the lead only if it's the most interesting or important part of the story. For example: "President Kennedy died at 2:03 p.m., Dallas time."

The Paragraph

The paragraph serves both a graphic and a writing function. It relieves masses of gray type, either by indentation or extra spacing; and, it indicates to the reader a change in thought or pace. The paragraph is a "breather" for your reader.

An old printer put it this way, "I set type as long as I can hold my breath, and then I put in a coma. When I yawn I put in a semi-colon. And when I want a chew of tobacco, I make a paragraph."

Most writers look at the paragraph as a unified statement on a single point.

A common mistake, especially when writing about meetings, is to lead with uninteresting information, usually the time, date, and location. The reader will be so turned off by the triteness of the lead that he or she will simply skip the story.

Several steps can be taken to "grab" and "keep" the reader. First, write an interesting headline. Second, lead with the most interesting or exciting information.

The most interesting things to take place at any meeting are the statements of the participants. If you are at the meeting, write down some direct quotes. If you have a correspondent covering the meeting, have that person write down some direct quotes. Then, use a quote as the lead.

Another way to handle meetings is to print the routine information, in tabulated form, which the reader can catch at a glance or ignore. Then you can concentrate on what happened and what was said without having to worry about jamming the five W's into the first paragraph.

For example (and set the material in boldface):

What?   The Executive Committee Meeting of the Polk County Medical Association.
When?   Wednesday evening, September 6, 1978.
Where? The Watson Clinic Library.

Who?   President Stanley Lipinski presiding, etc. (after listing the
participants, you then begin your story).

Speeches

With limited exception, speeches don't look as good in print as they sound
to the audience. This is especially true of extemporaneous speeches.

As a journal editor, you will be faced with the prospect of publishing
speeches from time to time. The best way to handle speeches is to write a
brief editorial note before the lead explaining that the following is an
abstract of a speech by so-and-so. Then you can cut out all of the unnecessary material. Doing this will be a service both to the speaker and the reader.

There are other approaches. You can handle a speech as a straight news
story. Unnecessary words and long transitional phrases can be omitted. You
can also use indirect quotes as a technique to save words and space.

Still another way is to write a brief introduction, giving the time, location, and name of the speaker, and then use selected quotes divided by subject matter. The subjects of the quotes can be designated by boldface
subheads.

Whatever technique you choose almost anything is an improvement
over using a verbatim text of the speech.

Subheads

Long stories should be broken up with subheads. Subheads serve a typographic
function and aid comprehension. They break up the monotonous mass of
gray body type, and they separate the principal elements of the story—making understanding easier for the reader.

Shorter stories are more likely to be read than long ones—especially
when the audience consists of busy doctors or pharmacists.

The editor should avoid long stories about meetings, especially annual
meetings. It is better to report on a long meeting with several short stories
than with one long one. However, if a long story is used, it should be
broken up by subheads. This assists the reader, who may be interested in
only one part of a meeting story.

Subheads underline the themes, call the reader's attention to themes,
help the reader understand progression of thought, rekindle his/her interest
in the continuing story. The subhead should:

1. tell precisely what the following paragraphs are about, or
2. present some colorful or surprising aspect of the material contained in the following paragraphs, or
3. quote or refer to provocative or striking words in the following
   paragraphs.

There are other functions, depending on the content of the story. The editor decides what kind of subhead will keep the reader's interest and present the information clearly.

Should every page have subheads? A page with five or six short compact pieces might not need subheads, might even have a chopped-up look if subheads are used.

You might think it desirable for the overall appearance of a page to have a balanced design of subheads, but the meaning and logic of the subheads are the first consideration. The subhead must truly relate to the copy.

Subheads break up the page, make it look lighter, suggest a smorgasbord of reading, allow the reader to jump from one column to another and find the way back to the starting place. If possible, subhead placement should have symmetry or balance, but not at the expense of meaning.

A subhead's influence may extend over three, four, or five paragraphs, or only one paragraph. Sometimes its influence will run out after two or three paragraphs, yet the new theme will not clearly begin in the very next paragraph. Do you put the new subhead in at that point? Or wait until the next theme is actually at hand? It is not always possible to keep the reader clearly under the precise dominance of one subhead. The reader may occasionally have to float between subheaded areas.

Headlines

The purpose of headlines is to index stories for readers' convenience and to attract readers' attention to stories.

A single typeface should be used for headlines. One size is sufficient, but two may be used for variety. Three or more sizes usually cause clutter.

A common mistake in headlines is setting them in type that's too large. Newspapers used to use bombastic headlines because they were hawked on the street. The newspaper no longer needs such headlines and newsletters and magazines have never needed them.

If your body type is 9 or 10 point, or pica typewriter type, then a suitable headline size is 14 point or 18 point. Your magazine isn't sold on the street. Instead, it's read in the quiet of home or office. Headlines should be friendly, helpful guides to stories, rather than billboards shouting at your readers.

Don't write headlines that repeat the story lead. A headline doesn't have to be, nor should it be, the lead. A headline should indicate the flavor of a story.

Headlines should not be longer than three lines; one or two lines are usually better.

Current style is flush left, caps and lower case. Other styles are (1) centered and (2) stairstep. Flush left is to be preferred because it is more convenient for the reader. Only one style should be used throughout the newsletter or magazine.

Questions That Editors Should Ask Themselves

The editor of any publication has many responsibilities. Among them are to make the copy as readable as possible, to create leads that captivate the reader's interest long enough to get into the story, to know how to break up long articles so that they become palatable to the reader, to write headlines that both index articles and attract the reader's attention, and ultimately to combine all information and graphics into a finished, integrated, informative, and attractive publication. A big job, indeed!

Vincent F. Downing, then medical editor of Lederle Laboratories, suggested in an article in *Medical Journalism* that editors should ask themselves the following questions, among others, if they wished to assess their contribution to their publication:

Original Articles

Has a letter been sent to each member of the County Medical Society soliciting articles? Have the rules and regulations for the submission of articles been kept to a minimum? Have articles been solicited from others in the health care field, such as nurses, hospital administrators, pharmacists (hospital and local) and registered technicians? Have these articles, when edited, or even rewritten, satisfied author as well as editor? . . .

Composition

Is the typography readable? Is the layout appealing? Are articles kept together? There is nothing more frustrating than searching between and around advertisements for the last few paragraphs of an interesting article. Are ads of competitors placed on separate pages?

Printing

Does the printer keep his due date? Is the printing clean, crisp, and uniform? Is the binding strong? If color has been used, is it uniform? Are photos and line drawings reproduced clearly?

Mailing

Have the alternative postal rates been thoroughly examined? Could redesign of the journal (paper-weight, cover address vs. envelope enclosure, etc.) result in a lower rate? Could a switch to another post office which eliminates slow passage through a "central" office expedite delivery?

Editing Test

An Introduction to Medical Editing is a little book (43 pages, plus a bibliography) written and published by Cathleen E. Swee, who was medical editor at Letterman Army Medical Center.

The five chapters are organized by learning objectives:

Organizing Format
Detecting Contradictions
Eliminating Redundancies
Removing Verbiage
Ensuring Clarity

The most useful feature consists of practice sections. For example, a case report is presented in its original and edited forms, with marginal notes which explain the editing.

Here's an excerpt from the practice section on detecting contradictions:

1. *The disease improves with age.*
   What is the contradiction here? What is your suggested revision?
2. *The pain in these cases is not as uncomfortable, nor does it exhibit as much visual loss.*
   What contradiction(s) do you find? What is your suggested revision?
3. *The patient's arterial blood should be checked for oxygen content.*
   What one word makes this sentence contradictory? Why? What is your suggested revision?

In case you can't wait for your copy of the book to arrive, here are Miss Swee's comments. Incidentally, the book can be purchased for $5.77 from Cathleen Swee, 3246 Anza St., San Francisco, CA 94121.

Example 1. *The disease improves with age.* The contradiction here is that it is the patient who has the disease and it is the patient who grows older. The disease, on the other hand, gets better or worse. For example, as a child gets older, certain diseases are not as life-threatening. The disease begins to subside. My suggested revision of this sentence is:

As the patient gets older, the disease subsides.

Example 2. *The pain in these cases is not as uncomfortable nor does it exhibit as much visual loss.* I see two problems in this sentence. First pain is always uncomfortable, although it may be either severe or mild. Second, pain cannot exhibit visual loss. It can be a factor causing visual loss by debilitating the patient. My suggested revision is:

The pain in these cases is not as severe, nor does the patient exhibit as much visual loss.

Example 3. *The patient's arterial blood should be checked for oxygen content.* The one word in this sentence that is imprecise is *content.* Checking for oxygen in arterial blood is like checking for air in an inflated tire. In a living person, arterial blood carries oxygen to the tissues. The intent here is not if there is oxygen in the blood, but how much. I would substitute the word, *level,* for the word, *content.*

Working With Freelancers

How do you recruit, motivate, manage and compensate freelancers? Here are some answers from Robert Leon Baker, which appeared in *impact*, a monthly newsletter he publishes in Chicago. Except that he hyphenates *freelancer*, we heartily endorse Mr. Baker's comments.

As deadline-pressured editors with far too many peaks and far too many valleys in our editorial workload, it's nice to know that out there somewhere, preferably in commuting distance, is a small but competent contingent of free-lance writers, photographers, and artists ready, willing, and generally available (for a price) to lend us a helping and creative hand.

Reassuring as this sounds, there are still problems in tapping the resources of this talent pool.

The first is budget. If you lack funds or the authority to dictate the use of funds, better forget the free-lancer. The good performers are expensive; the poor you probably don't want.

The second is putting a finger on the proper talent, since the gems—the real pros—are hidden in the sands of a million amateurs. The real pro, unfortunately, is a rarity in the free-lance field. The hack is not.

This army of amateurs makes selection a vital step in the employment of any free-lancer. How does one separate the amateur from the pro? Check samples of past work (and make sure they *are* the past work of the person in question). Also contact the editors of publications that have employed the free-lancer to get an idea of temperament, reliability, working procedures, and pay scale.

Actually, a good free-lancer has a lot to offer any hard-pressed editor who may be forced to dig up material without adequate staff or the personal time to do extensive research or extensive travel.

The unfettered free-lancer, in comparison, has time for the long project and the involved story. He or she is a welcome temporary staff addition for special issues, organizational histories, and other extraordinary editorial projects.

The free-lancer brings in an outside view, resources possibly unknown to the editor, and a fresh style. A periodical produced by a limited staff, often one person, frequently suffers from monotony in both content and style. The free-lancer can provide the creative input for the new approach or the new idea in covering even the old but necessary subjects. And, possibly best of all, the free-lancer has the ability to lop off mountains of creative work and relieve editorial pressures.

This is why the subtle, calculated, targeted motivation and management of contract talent in writing, photography, and layout art is one editorial knack worth cultivating.

To explore the critical elements of this cherished skill, let's start with the free-lance writer and then follow with the free-lance photographer and contract artist, the three specialists we are most likely to deal with as editors and publishers.

The Free-Lance Writer

First, of course, you have to *find* the free-lance writer who is *right* for your publication. Some suggestions:

• Build a file (city by city in your territory of interest) of "specialist" free-lancers active in your field. Check general listings and directories. Trade associations; e.g., The International Association of Business Communicators, the Associated Business Writers of America, the Society of Magazine Writers. Also check your personal friends and directories in advertising, public relations, publicity.

• Note bylines on well-done articles in other publications.

• Once you locate a prospective free-lancer, arrange an interview. Ask for samples. Verify and evaluate the work. Talk to editors who have used the free-lancer.

• Written contracts are generally unnecessary unless the scope of the effort (a history of your organization, for example) is of sufficient commercial importance to merit such legal protection.

If you plan frequent use of free-lancers, prepare a "briefing sheet." Include brief profiles of your organization, publication, reader mix, key people, the kind of articles you publish, editorial style, editorial and organizational taboos, working procedures, other pertinent data a free-lancer needs to know.

In a briefing, preferably in person, cover length of story, the reason you want it, the elements to emphasize, the persons to be interviewed, the deadline for all copy. Provide background material on the subject if you can. Suggest a few key questions to ask, research approaches, printed sources to investigate.

Come to an agreement on the fee, the payment policy on revisions, cutline writing, the "kill" fee in case a story in progress must be scrubbed, travel and out-of-pocket expenses. You can pay by the word, by the column inch, by the page, by a flat fee for a single article assignment (the best way in our book), or by the hour (not recommended). Evaluate the assignment— the time and travel involved; the difficulty of the subject in both research and writing. Establish a minimum fee in your own mind and negotiate from there.

For our publications, we suggest you use $50 a printed page as an average rule of thumb. In brief, $300 for an article which would run six pages in your publication. Forget word counts.

Revisions, at least a reasonable number not related to your editorial whims, should be included in the flat fee. Cutline writing, if it involves extra work on the writer's part, and if the writer is not being paid for photography, calls for extra compensation.

Generally, the editor should agree to pay all out-of-pocket expenses (at cost). If a writer is "double dipping," that is, covering more than one story on a trip for more than one employer, expenses should be pro-rated.

To maintain adequate supervision while a story is in progress, be accessible to the free-lancer at office or home.

Know how you can pick up the phone and reach your free-lancer just in case you have some bright new ideas about the assignment or if there is a sudden switch in your editorial plans.

Set a definite deadline and permit no unjustified deviation without penalty. For an extensive effort, require periodic progress reports, even if they are nothing more than a phone call.

Request clean, double-spaced, amply margined copy ready for typesetting. If you have special, scaled copy paper, this can be provided to the free-lance writer. Rely on the writer for all revisions of copy. If after two revisions the copy is still unsatisfactory, there may be doubts that it will ever be acceptable, and you might be ahead of the game writing off the free-lancer. Certainly, by this time you may have been better off if you had done the article yourself.

Pay promptly *upon acceptance* once the free-lancer has fulfilled the assignment to your satisfaction. Buy all "rights." Satisfaction should imply impeccable accuracy, thorough research, good writing with no need on your part for excessive re-checking or re-writing, or any struggle to salvage a weak presentation.

The Free-Lance Photographer

If you lack a talent file and are forced to start your search cold for a technically competent, creative, cooperative, open-minded, and reasonably priced photographer, there are several sources: the yellow pages of your telephone directory, professional trade associations, picture agencies, wire services and press associations, daily newspapers in your area, other editors, other publications (look for credit lines).

Before committing yourself, ask to see a portfolio. Concentrate on picture stories similar to the ones you do or plan to do. Don't be snowed by a few one-shot assignments, even if they are award winners. Evaluate the photographer's creativity and temperament. Will he or she be cooperative?

Settle on the fee in advance, along with such matters as expenses, photo rights, control of negatives, deadline for submission of contracts, payment for blow-ups. Remember that the editor usually dictates price; not the photographer. Prices are flexible. They now average about $350 a day plus expenses and processing costs.

Photographers will work for less on a regular "bread and butter" account. The good photographers know what you can afford to pay for the job.

In briefing a photographer make certain he or she is perfectly clear on: (a) where the shots are to be made and the person to contact; (b) the date and the time (better the paid photographer waits than your subjects, so schedule the photographer early); (c) the shooting site or sites (the photographer may need special equipment); and (d) some idea of subjects and story line.

Regarding the latter, discuss your shooting script shot by shot. Give your photographer some leeway, but specify your ''must'' shots, the ones vital to the story that cannot be omitted. If you hope to get a cover shot out of the shooting make this clear to the photographer. He or she may balk at some of your suggestions for photos, but don't hesitate about asking the impossible. You may get it!

If you can accompany a photographer on assignment so much the better. It will help you get cutline information, look for new angles, assist with difficult multiflash situations. Don't be backward about pointing out interesting angles or picture possibilities. Never, however, interfere in the technical aspects of taking a picture and always leave the photographer freedom to operate.

You can't depend on photographers for cutline data; reporting is really not their responsibility on most jobs. So it's the writer's duty to get the complete facts for each picture taken. This includes full name indentification of the subjects pictured, and a generous accumulation of such small, pertinent, and colorful details as eye color, gestures, startling statistics, etc.

Ask the photographer for contact sheets, not finished prints. Some will mark up their contacts to help the editor with the selection. It's generally advisable to heed their advice, but don't be bound by it.

When you order, order full negatives. Photographers pre-crop occasionally if they think their photographs will look better if they do so. Unfortunately, such unsolicited cropping could conceivably eliminate a very vital part of a photograph. The moral: always do your own cropping and always from the full negative.

Retain absolute right of approval for all future use of the negatives of your job in the photographer's possession. You don't want pictures suddenly appearing in other media without your knowledge or approval. There is always the chance that they could become embarrassing to you and your organization.

DESIGN AND PRODUCTION

Appraising Your Publication

Editor's Newsletter (no longer published) compiled a 100-point evaluation form to help editors assess their publication. Here are some sample questions that were asked regarding design and production. (The answers to all of them should be "yes.")

Do you stick to one or two type families throughout?
Are facing pages (spreads) laid out as a unit?
Do you use white space effectively, not as "holes?"
Do you offer readers a change of pace (special issues, a new look)?
Is there one dominant photo per page and/or spread?

The newsletter then went on to say that "Simplicity is the key to effective layout, and keeping it simple is simple". The following steps were recommended to insure attractive, readable typography.

1. Square off the type masses in harmonious rectangles where possible. The square-off should be on a straight line. Body type should not meander across the page in zigzags.
2. Put punch in the 4 corners of the page, or in as many as are open. The corners are the hot spots and they need strong elements.
3. Use plenty of white space. It frames each package and provides contrast.
4. Throw away the ornaments. They detract from readability because they drag the eye where you don't want it to go instead of guiding it where you do want it to go.

These principles have one purpose—to provide a product that's easy to read—to make it easier for the reader.

You see, the average person has about 10,000 eye fixations a day. Students, office workers, and the like have up to 15,000. Such things as signs, signals, words, door knobs—anything on which the eye focuses.

About the only comparison that comes to mind is that the average person breathes about that same number of times in 16 wakeful hours.

No wonder the old eyes get tired.

Therefore, it is up to the editor to put before readers the easiest-to-read publication possible; otherwise, they're going to flick on the television and have some more eye fixations without any mental effort.

We cannot stress too much the importance of white space. White space properly used is not wasted space.

There are lots of ways to inject white space. We can frame our photos and stories in white space the same way we frame a painting.

The chief criticism to be made of many publications is their excessive use of ornamental rules and borders.

They're used on almost every page, for boxes, for hooded heads, for cutoffs.

These publications would be more effective if all that gingerbread were removed and beautiful, clean, airy white space were substituted.

Ideas About Graphics

According to Paul Fisher, professor of journalism at the University of Missouri, a prime function of graphics is to make differences sharply visible. News stories ought not to be confused with articles, and no element of an advertisement ought to be echoed in the editorial.

Simple and effective separation of news stories is achieved by not duplicating the typeface used in article titles. Assuming a *serif* face has been used over articles, then a *sans serif* would function well over news and other short, stray inclusions. A few journals set off news and related matters by printing on tinted sheets—an expensive, though effective, practice. Where the layout of articles emphasizes depth in the top margin, effective contrast —separation—of other materials is achieved by adopting a narrower top margin. Again, this assumes the articles are presented in a non-interrupted section, for the appearance would not be pleasing if the margin wavered with every turn of the page.

Different text faces do not afford effective contrast. Varying type size to, for example, make news pages smaller, may be a valid economic practice, but it is not a graphic one. Variation in design carries neither economic nor graphic value. It is not sufficient to invite the reader's attention, only sufficient to impart an impression of disjointedness, of disorder. Certainly, some publications do vary text face, but they have things working for them that professional journals do not.

Every so often the old editor, and every new editor when first he sits down at his desk, needs to look at his publication and ask himself, "Do I have the right bag here for what I am about to drop in it?" And sometimes the answer is, or ought to be, "No," for, frequently, limited-page and limited-circulation publications carry nothing but short-item materials and are no more than newsletters disguised as journals. Some would, in fact, be happier if they reduced their graphic style of living from the periodical magazine to the newsletter.

Improving Magazine Layouts

The following advice by Raymond Dorn was taken from his book titled *How to Design and Improve Magazine Layouts*, published by Brookwood Publications. Mr. Dorn was then manager of art and layout for the publications of the American Medical Association.

Proportion is the principle of design that involves a pleasing relationship among all parts of the page design and the page's relationship to what precedes or follows it. Remember that no one story is an entity by itself. It relates to the preceding page as well as the following pages.

Editorial pages almost always consist of a basic vertical design in their general format. This is because pages that consist of copy are in either a two-column or three-column format. Straight copy, therefore, creates two or three grey tone vertical shapes, separated by a thin strip of white space, called an "alley." Pictures placed within this vertical design should complement it. Here are several points to remember.

Page Design

1. A vertical *plus* a vertical is usually monotonous.
2. A "change of direction" will make a page more interesting. A strong horizontal picture, for instance, will cause a visual "change of direction."
3. A "change of form" will also make the page more interesting. An outline halftone picture will add interest. An L-shaped grouping will provide a change of direction as well as a change in form.
4. White space, used as a design element, complements the verticals. White space, used as a deep sink, is actually a horizontal movement, which will complement the grey verticals.
5. A change of form *within* the picture will also create its own center of interest. An example would be a picture, or even a chart, with a strong sawtooth design. This gives movement within a controlled area.
6. Color used as "spot designs" can draw interest away from the vertical pattern. An example of this would be a chart, already vertical in design (as the columns might be). When a chart carries the same de-

sign as the columns it creates a feeling of repetition. Adding color, even a change of tone values of grey, can effect a diversion from the verticals. These added "spots" are just enough to provide a seasoning of interest from the design.

7. Optical illusions which create interrelationships within the page are easy to achieve by placing the pictures so they pull the reader's eye away from the verticals. This is particularly effective when using bleeds. Do not "nail down the corners" in any case. This phrase means placing a picture in all of the four corners. While this may distract from the vertical pattern it creates another pattern equally monotonous.

8. Space division, or how one utilizes white space *within* pictures can also create sufficient interest to detract from strong verticals. An example of this would be a halftone placed within a ruled border or box. A frame, such as this, if equal on all four sides, will keep the picture placid. If the top and right are equal, and the left and bottom are unequal, the picture will optically move in one direction.

9. Variety can be defined by John Dewey's remark that "There is no excellent beauty that hath not some strangeness in the proportion." Variety, as far as the layout artist is concerned, is the interjection of just enough strangeness to create interest. An example would be three pictures—two of them square, and the third round, oval, or outlined.

Factors Relating to Good Design

An example using fabric patterns will illustrate this point. Utilizing texture or the "feel" of a picture within a page can highlight both pictures; particularly if the difference is far enough apart. Silk and tweed are good examples. One can emphasize the "feeling" of each by placing one next to the other. In pictures the layout artist looks for patterns and designs that can be utilized to play against each other. This helps divert the reader from the page-column verticals.

Many trade magazines have few halftone pictures but are replete with line drawings. This includes charts, graphs, and schematics. These should always be examined for classification. Most fall within groups defined as "strong horizontally," "strong vertically," "light and airy," and "dark, with massed detail." There are problems and answers with each.

Every design needs some note of interest that catches the eye and arrests the attention. These can be divided into the following groups.

Emphasis

When emphasizing an area, do so by drawing the reader's eye to it. An example of this would be the use of a contrast in colors or hues, values or intensities. This can be done on a chart or graph by the use of a color and variations of the same color. It can also be done by the use of unusual detail or grouping.

Center of Interest

This can be defined by the question, "What draws the eye to any particular spot or area on the page?" Center of interest can be planned and can, in effect, direct the reader's eye almost anywhere the layout artist chooses to move it. Probably "optical center" is the easiest. This is in the middle and two-fifths down from the top of a page. One does well to remember that every page has a point of interest, even if it's only the upper lefthand corner, where the reader's normal eye pattern takes him. Creating a center of interest may be a little more difficult when all the layout artist has to work with is straight copy. Title areas *can* be utilized to advantage. Standup, indented, or decorative initials are another.

Rhythm

This is a change from one line to another, from one dimension to another, from one value to another, or from one color (or tone) to another. In application this would mean establishing a pattern to the layout and then utilizing that pattern to create interest.

A design is not necessarily good just because it sets out to *deliberately* achieve balance or pleasing proportion, or to locate a center of interest. Often such a positive approach results in a flat monotone or sterotyped format. The design just lies there in its functional form. Something left to the imagination is always more interesting. More tips:

1. Horizontal lines suggest repose or calmness, as well as width.
2. Vertical lines suggest activity as well as height.
3. Zigzag lines suggest activity or motion.
4. Squares, rectangles, and triangles suggest stability.
5. Circles, ovals, spheres, and ellipses suggest movement.
6. Round corners, diagonal corners, and mortises change the "feel" of a square, rectangle, or triangle.

White Space

Editors of low-budget publications often try to cram as much material as possible onto their pages. The unwieldy result is a particular problem among small-size publications, such as many county medical journals.

The Sandoz award judges recently commended the prize winners for their effective use of white space. At our workshops, neophyte editors often are perplexed about white space. A common question is, "Doesn't white space, particularly at the end of an article or between news items, make it look like an unplanned hole which the editor was unable to fill?"

The answer is simply that the effective use of white space requires as much planning and careful thought as type and art. Editors should not be embarrassed about white space, but rather should use it as part of their design. The following discussion of white space by Lawrence Ragan appeared recently in *The Ragan Report*, the weekly newsletter for communication executives (407 S. Dearborn St., Chicago 60605).

You've heard the rule: don't trap it. Don't scatter it throughout the page. Use it to enclose material.

In a workshop we attended, Jan White demonstrated how splotches of white space dissipate the effect of the spread. Then he redesigned the same page, accumulating all the white space near the top. Great, we said to ourselves. But wait! He has inserted the headline at the very top. Doesn't that mean that there is trapped white space—i.e. between the headline at the top of the spread and the copy beginning beneath the halfway mark of the pages?

He answers the question: "No, I want to give the spread a design edge." He wants, he says, to put the headline at the top, to show that the designer is in control, that the designer wants the headline at that point to give a dramatic emphasis to the spread.

Somebody asks, "Why not put the headline down the page, next to the copy itself? Then the white space won't be trapped?"

Replies White: "That would be a good solution, but I don't want the white space to fritter off the pages as if it were merely there because we had too much space. So I would have put a rule at the top of the page to define its edge.

Our good friend, Phil Douglis, with whom we have conducted many workshops and have broken bread since he was hardly out of his teens, would refer to that as the hole in the doughnut, that the eye would go to the white space, not to the copy.

Who is right? Well, as I grow older and more sympathetic to opposing points of view, I would like to see both of them argue it out, but I think perhaps they are both right, depending upon how the particular spread would relate to the page and how it would fulfill the objectives of the designer and editor.

Magazine Design Checklist

The University of Missouri School of Journalism has developed a magazine Design Checklist which can be useful to journal editors. The primary value of the list is to encourage you to think about the *many* design components of your publication. Paul Fisher, professor of journalism at the University of Missouri, notes:

"No set of criteria, however broadly drawn, can be applied without reservation to any given publication. Treat this list with reservations. Only one-on-one criticism fairly faces up to the problem of diversity of editorial/graphic purposes of publications."

Cover

Is logo distinctive, not out of the printer's case, a fitting trademark? Do illustration and major cover line sharply relate to inside contents?

Contents Page

How functional are the graphic effects? Overblown? Does the page accurately prefigure the publication's style? Is it a cleanly presented slate?

Display Typography

Is there a standard (recurrent) face in use, and does the publication achieve pace thru range of graphic effects within limits of that face? Does display interrelate with other elements for maximum impact? (If display typography is varied, is there an editorial rationale?) Do departmental items separate sharply from articles in titling? Do they echo logotype design?

Text

Do the size and weight make it appear easy to read? How well—with what range, what restraint—has the text been accented? Does layout enforce unity of text, no blocks isolated, no runover snippets?

Captions

Are they in a face that distinguishes them from the text but that never dominates the page? In the exceptional case—usually photo essay/story—do caption lines signal exceptional quality through bolder, more innovative typography?

Photo Layout

Does it best serve the interests of the photography? Has it contributed to or heightened photo meaning? Does layout make the photos integral to the page rather than presenting them as ornaments and/or page fillers? (Obviously, the criteria are hollow if the photography is without substance.) Quality of reproduction?

Second Color

Is it used with discretion, with purpose, i.e., as an accent, illustrative of meanings (charts, etc.). (Process color: would the images have been meaningless without its use?)

Makeup

Are parts so arranged as to achieve the impression that the publication is foremost an editorial product to which advertising, if not incidental, is at least not an overpowering presence? How extensive is the main editorial well? Is there order in back of the book editorial matter quietly distinguishing it from advertising?

Style

Does the publication have a look—a predictable appearance—quite unlike any other publication? Does that look seem to be in keeping—in accord with the nature of—the editorial content and the perceived audience?

The Grid

Blake Kellogg, who has lectured at many Sandoz Medical Journalism workshops, is associate professor of journalism at the University of Wisconsin. Following was his advice about using the grid system to design a publication.

A grid is an arbitrary division of the page, into rectangles, usually of equal size. The rule of the grid is that everything that goes onto the page (heads, text, photos, and art) should either fit into a single unit of the grid or a combination of units. The remaining space should be left blank. The benefits of the grid are that a magazine laid out on it imparts a sense of unity, continuity, harmony, and order. Further, the grid gives flexibility in layout, and an opportunity to always handle white space attractively and correctly. As a rule, grid lines are printed on layout pages, but do not appear in the final printed version of your magazine. One exception is the occasional use of column rules.

A full measure grid gives you a page with margins, and horizontal guide lines, but not a grid in the same sense of the word that you can have with a two-column or three-column format. With a full measure page, it's a good idea to begin all (or at least most) elements on the same horizontal line. For example, if you drop the headline of one article to the second horizontal line, it's probably a good idea to drop the headlines of the other articles to the same line. This gives a nice sense of continuity throughout the issue.

A two-column grid gives a much greater opportunity for flexibility. Any number of format possibilities are available with a two-column grid. The greater the number of elements you have to put on your pages, the more detailed your grid should be. That is to say, the greater the number of rectangles it should have.

A three-column grid gives even greater opportunity for variation because it provides more grid units as a result of the third column. One of the major advantages of the three-column grid is that it allows a maximum accommodation for ads.

The grid approach to layout is becoming increasingly more popular with many editors. While it is definitely not a panacea for all your layout woes, it offers a systematic approach to design that may work out better for some of you than the method you are presently using.

More on Grids

The following comments on the use of grids were reprinted from *Editors Workshop*, a bimonthly publication edited by Ralph Reynolds and published by Cara Publishing, Box 5256, Fort Wayne, IN 46895.

The grid system is a mechanical (or mathematical) way to divide space into proportional sections or blocks. The blocks in any given grid may be all the same size, or they may vary. For example, an 8½ × 11 page may be broken into 12 blocks 14 picas square and have some of these blocks divided even further into halves, thirds, quarters, etc.

These blocks assist in selecting starting and stopping points for the elements of the layout. For instance, a photograph or illustration would be cropped and sized to fill one or more blocks. Similarly, headlines, copy and white space are arranged to fit into a block, or combination of blocks, giving unity to a layout.

Since there is no standard grid, you can make your own personalized grid layout sheets by using your standard columns and dividing them into blocks that will best serve your layout needs. Going back to our 8½ × 11 page with 12, 14-pica blocks having a pica space between each block, for instance, you might want to run a one-column picture either 14 or 29 picas deep. Two-column photographs may be run 29 × 14 picas, 29 × 29 or even 29 × 44. Dividing the page into smaller blocks gives an even greater variety of possibilities. You do not have to make the blocks square, You can devise any grid system that works well for your needs.

You can't expect the sections to do the designing for you, but they will guide you by showing where to start and stop elements of the layout. Then you can flow freely with a design by integrating the horizontal and vertical areas, or you can create patterns by repeating shapes and, perhaps even rhythms, with periodic spacing within the patterns.

After making a rough sketch of your layout, go back and edit a bit of copy or enlarge or reduce some items so the elements fit neatly into the blocks.

As your eye follows a horizontal line, it need not stop at the first vertical line. Emphasize and exaggerate by using white space. Remember, not every block must be filled.

The grid is mechanical only from the point of view that the basic blocks can be arranged and overlapped in a calculated number of ways. But the elements placed in the blocks and the combinations of blocks used are infinite.

Many Publications Adopt The New Look

It is gratifying to see the "new look" of many medical, pharmaceutical and hospital publications. Generally, the redesign of a journal includes a new logo, cover and page format.

Major improvements have been made by quite a few editors, particularly the increased and more effective use of photography and art. If color is added, it's often limited to the cover, particularly among the pharmaceutical journals.

The quality of text composition still needs attention. For several years after the introduction of various systems of photocomposition, the editors of medical and other small-circulation publications were fortunate in the continued availability of hot-metal composition, such as Linotype and Intertype. This equipment is almost vestigial, for now some of the cheapest systems of composition are generally in use. Their economic advantage is not to be disputed, and, aesthetically, the poverty of design may not be an issue. But, if readability is a function of type, then some of the systems must be questioned on the feebleness of stroke, poor fit of letters, poor spacing and lack of hyphenation capability. In short, medical and pharmaceutical editors should consider the need to upgrade their text composition.

A Design Critique

As part of the annual Sandoz Medical Journalism competition, critiques are sent to all publications that enter the contests. Here is the design critique sent to one of the state pharmaceutical journals:

The new look that is increasingly being used in medical, pharmaceutical, hospital and other health-related publications derives from a new editorial approach. Shorter professional articles and an increase in brief news items combine to allow a more vigorous typography.

A single typeface, Korinna, for text and display replaces the melange of faces formerly used. This specification is important to the restyling which is further defined, very happily, through a minimum of means.

Means include unjustified text columns, tighter margins, and 1-point vertical rules separating columns and establishing margins. Departments are identified by a single title appearance reversed in an 18-point rule composition.

Single unfortunate change: bold horizontal rules top and bottom of every page, including cover, that unduly detract from the impact of the page. Following are a few specific comments about how the new specifications work out.

Cover. Impact of poster presentation replaces the diffusion of the typographic cover. Not mourned is the loss of excessively spaced capital lines. However, the background color remains too heavy.

Contents page. More efficient use of space in such editorial changes as title dropouts and addition of calendar. However, there still are too many sizes in display, and the title is too large.

Title page. Korinna, a face of some individuality and yet without idiosyncrasy, replaces the bold and bland sans serif. Downrule and unjustified columns enhance the change.

Text page. As with contents, a more efficient use of space. Use of rule, unjustified text and increase in boldface subheadings combine for a livelier page.

Departmental pages. Reduction in typographic impact of departmental identification allows sharper, quicker focus on story headlines, where it belongs. Departmental title treatment is consistent throughout the magazine.

Special Sections
And Regular Departments

If you have an editorial page, it should be in about, or exactly, the same location for every issue. It should be typographically distinctive. This is most easily accomplished by setting it in wider measure and/or setting it in larger type. Some magazines (particularly those serving professional associations) carry late-close sections. These usually contain the latest, up-to-the-minute legislative or administrative actions. Frequently they resemble a newsletter. Late-close sections often: (1) use different paper from the rest of the magazine, (2) use a different typeface (such as typewriter type), (3) carry a late date, (4) byline an editor or special correspondent, (5) carry short items, (6) carry no photos, (7) carry a special dateline.

If you carry a special section, it should bear the magazine's nameplate.

There should be a strong family resemblance among the various departments of your magazine. They should look like brothers and sisters. This is best accomplished by identical typography and use of the same grid.

By having the departments resemble one another typographically, a strong sense of continuity is provided to the reader. All of the parts belong to the same whole. Uniformity and consistency help the editorial departments of your magazine override the overwhelming and dramatic visual impact of the ads.

Jan White advises that you repeat your patterns rhythmically, in an exact, precise, absolute repetition. He says that only this kind of repetition, which is so precise that it is simple, cannot be missed.

Try to use a format that is distinctive and peculiar to you. This is best accomplished with type and with a grid. Occasionally, a format can be enhanced by the use of graphic devices, such as borders and column rules.

Each article might require a slightly different sequence of emphasis regarding the various elements, which will be nameplate, headline, subhead or summary, byline, art, author's picture/biographical sketch and text.

No one hierarchy is better than another, but you should clearly articulate what the hierarchy is for each story. In terms of reader ease and appeal, your choices regarding amount of space and location would probably be:

(1) double spread with the illustration on the left-hand page and the head and article on the right-hand page, (2) right-hand page, with an ad on the left-hand page and (3) left-hand page, with an ad on the right-hand page.

A pitfall with the opening article and with those that follow is the urge by every editor to make every article "look" interesting. This usually leads to a variety of graphic tricks which end up making the magazine look cluttered. Ultimately it is a good idea for you to view your periodical as the reader does—as a complete product.

Since the days when you were a child in grade school art class, you have received the advice, "Use white space." However, more than likely, the advice did not extend beyond that. There was no explanation as to "how" to use white space. Here's how.

Bunch your white space. Keep it together on the page so that it stands in contrast to the gray space (type and art). To put it negatively, don't split your white space. Usually white space works best when it is contiguous to the margins and can thereby be unified with even more white space. Don't leave bits and dabs of white space scattered around a page. Jan White says this "blows the page apart." Avoid splitting white space. One of the major advantages of the grid is that it lets you use white space in a bold, creative, and planned way.

Common Mistakes To Avoid

1. Running type at an angle.
2. Running type on the vertical.
3. The use of too many typefaces.
4. The use of too many type sizes.
5. Inconsistent up/down type style.
6. Splitting white space.
7. Overuse of reverses.
8. Overuse of boxes and column rules.
9. Too few or too many elements on the cover.
10. Contents page shifted from issue to issue and thereby difficult to locate.
11. No grid, resulting in the haphazard placing of elements on the page.
12. Overuse of spot color, such as the printing of headlines, subheads, column rules and the like in color, just because there is a color run on the press.
13. Printing pictures too small.

Preparing Copy and Art Work
For Print Production

Preparing copy and artwork for print production requires knowledge, experience and attention to detail. The last of these factors—attention to detail —offers many opportunities to improve quality and control costs.

Properly prepared copy can keep the cost of typesetting 10 (or more) percent under the cost of setting carelessly prepared copy. Savings accrue whether your copy is set with hot-type or cold-type composing equipment.

The following advice was prepared by Tibor Taraba, advertising and sales-promotion manager of The Reuben H. Donnelley Corporation, and appeared in *Promotion Power*, a sales-promotion newsletter published by Donnelley.

Anyone who prepares a promotion piece, booklet or medical journal must know about preparing copy for efficient and economical reproduction. You therefore may want to obtain free copies of *Promotion Power*, by writing to The Reuben H. Donnelley Corporation at 825 Third Avenue, New York 10022. Here's the advice:

Copy for typesetting should be double-spaced with consistent margins, on white 8½-by-11-inch paper typed on one side only. Occasional erasures or x-ing out of words is acceptable. All changes, however, should be neat, clear, and in ink. It's a good idea to avoid splitting and hyphenating a word at the end of a line in the copy. The compositor's measure will rarely coincide with the length of a typed line, and split words in the copy will not usually be split in the type. So a typed hyphen at the end of a line of copy just distracts and slows down the compositor. It's an extra effort to simultaneously keyboard and edit out hyphens introduced solely to split words. Errors, as a result, creep in and add to costs.

Some additional rules for copy preparation: Avoid using proofreader's symbols except for paragraph signs, carets, standard underlinings for capitals, italics, and boldface, strokes through letters altered to lowercase, and explanatory abbreviations in the margins(*lc. Caps. bf. uc. ulc.* and the like). The need for such explanatory marks explains why margins should be generous on *both* sides of the copy and at top and bottom. You can use margins for insertions, too; but it is safer to indicate all changes as close as possible to the place where they belong in a line, preferably right over the line. The reason for this is that when copy is *first* being set, the compositor works best and fastest by scanning each line and paragraph in sequence.

Once your copy is in type, proofreader's marks have their function because now only changes are being made in an existing setting.

An especially important rule is to make deletions with a single neat horizontal stroke through unwanted words. The deleted words should be legible enough so that you can restore them if you change your decision about removing them. You should cancel unwanted or altered punctuation marks with a short stroke (possibly curved to fit between lines) ending in a small loop. Also useful are curves to show where letters should be closed up, and vertical strokes between words that should be separated.

Numbering pages meticulously can save expensive mistakes. If you must omit a page in a previously numbered set of pages, the preceding page should bear a notation: "Pg _____ follows."

If you must make insertions on a single page, but you cannot fit the insertions above the existing lines, the best practice is to retype, using inserted pages if necessary. You can also cancel part of a page and insert new matter on additional pages: "2A," "2B," etc. If the next page is page 3, page 2B should be marked "Page 3 follows." Any other procedure will slow the typesetting and cause errors. For example, it's asking for trouble to type out an insertion on a slip of paper and tape it to an existing page. Writing insertions in the margin also wastes typesetting time.

When galley proofs come back from a compositor, your handling of the proofs can greatly affect the cost and quality of the finished job. The same rules of good practice apply to Xerox copies of photoset type as to galleys pulled from hot type. Generally you should have at least two sets of reading proofs, plus a set of reproduction proofs for assembly on mechanicals. Photoset repro proofs often are retained at the compositor's shop for safekeeping until all type changes have been made. You should use one set of reading proofs as a master set, on which you enter all changes plus a final OK with dated initials of the job supervisor. With this master set you should keep the copy used for the typesetting, but you should enter *no* changes on the typewritten copy after it has been used for typesetting. You should keep master proofs *intact*, not cut up or separated.

These procedures insure that you have a clear picture of how the typesetting is progressing and how your intentions match the latest state of the type. You should date each set at the top to prevent mistaken use of obsolete proofs. Ultimately, someone should read the repro proofs against the master set bearing all corrections and changes. It's often wise to retain the master set in house and send changes to the compositor on a separate set.

If you find it necessary to mark instructions on reproduction proofs, write them with *light* pressure in nonreproducible blue. Pencils and ballpoint pens are available for marking matter to be used for reproduction. Remember that reproduction proofs are delicate. If you mark a repro proof lying on top of another one, you may wind up with an embossed or smudged proof that will have to be replaced. Similarly, beware of paper clips and any handling that will crease or fold repro proofs. The best places for repro proofs when they are not being used is inside a loose envelope, without clips or rubber bands, on a secure shelf or in an uncluttered drawer. Nothing should be placed on top of repro proofs, except a flap or overlay taped to a mechanical.

Page Size

Big or Small Page?

Many county medical journals publish in digest-sizes, such as 5 × 7 or 6 × 9. Most of the state journals have a larger page size, generally 8 × 11. Is a large page better than a small page?

In his discussion of page size at a Sandoz workshop, Paul Fisher suggested that county journal editors consider the advantages of a large page size. The recommendation prompted the following letter from Dr. Warren W. Smith, editor of the *Bulletin of the Academy of Medicine of Columbus and Franklin County* in Columbus, Ohio.

Dear Professor Fisher:

Thank you very much for the splendid presentation on design, format, and make-up that you gave to us at the recent Sandoz workshop. Your presentation, alone, would have been worth the trip.

I am editor of a journal of small page size and was very much interested by your suggestion that publications of this size undergo enlargement. As you noted, a major factor in the inertia impeding such a move is the fact that there are decades' worth of bound volumes. Another deterrent to enlargement is the attitude among some readers that the small page size allows a more portable publication, and one that invites casual reading during brief opportunities. I remember very clearly comments of this sort that I had heard among my colleagues when *Medical Economics* enlarged from its *Reader's Digest* size to its present large page size.

Here is the reply of Prof. Paul Fisher of the University of Missouri School of Journalism.

Dear Dr. Smith:

To continue the small vs. large format argument . . .

Tradition has its reasons, all good. Librarians who maintain bound volumes of periodicals will not appreciate an explosion in size.

Tradition aside, I find these justifications for the larger format (8½ × 11, or very slightly smaller):

I question whether portability is operative. Do professional people stuff publications in their pockets? No, no. I see them constantly in my travels, briefcases on laps from which they pick. It's as easy to pick up the larger as the smaller format. (Was it *Reader's Digest* that popularized the idea of portability, back some 50 years ago—stick it in your back pocket, read an article a day at lunch or whenever, and be a whiz at conversation!)

Do you know the publication *Yankee*? It's hugely successful as a regional magazine and only a bit larger than your *Bulletin*. It would love to go to the large format but does not dare disturb its success.

Why larger? You get a chance at size across the board, particularly text size increase. Most small publications want to escape the bookish appearance of a single crossline and so they employ the two column grid. This means an approximately 14–15 pica line at most, which mandates a point size rarely beyond 9, and often 8. That's a "mean" reading size. (Take a specimen of the *Journal of the Iowa Medical Association's* text column. Place it by your own and compare.)

Though photos are minor elements in most medical journals, their upward sizing would greatly improve the graphic impact of the publication through the change-of-pace that sizing would give. (A group shot in a width of not much more than two inches is just about meaningless.)

Finally, the larger format would allow some increase in title sizes, which presently are often no larger than the text size in the smaller publications.

So I end the arguments and close with these wonders. Do you lose some advertising because of your size? I suspect that a considerable amount of advertising is being prepared for the 8½ × 11 format. Possibly photographic reduction takes care of this difficulty.

Is the smaller format as economical as the larger in production costs? That's a question only your printer can answer.

Stock

Our desk dictionary (*Webster's New World*) provides 17 definitions of stock as a noun and six of stock as a verb.

Let's take stock of stock. To lots of physicians, the most common use of stock is with regard to their investments, but to editors it means paper.

Medical and pharmaceutical journals generally are printed on glossy paper of the type used in offset magazines. Special sections or late news pages sometimes are printed on non-glossy book paper. Hospital publications often use heavier paper to obtain better reproduction of color photos. *The Bulletin of the Camden County (N.J.) Medical Society* is unique. The page size is 5⅜ wide and 8½ high, which is a bit more vertical than the typical 5 × 7 or 6 × 9 digest-size. The covers are 8 pt. coated-on-one-side stock, which is thicker than most small-size publications, some of which are self-covers (same cover stock as the contents). Incidentally, paper is described by weight except for a few special types of cover papers that bear point (.001 inch) designations.

It's the inside of the *Camden Bulletin* that is unusual. The pages (generally 36) are printed on embossed coated paper with a stipple finish. This texture, which rarely is used in magazines, adds a depth to photographs and gives the magazine a distinctive "feel."

Improvements In Design

From the September 1983 issue of the *Medical Journalism* newsletter, a comment on the publications that had entered that year's Medical Journalism contest:

In general, the largest number of improvements, particularly in design, have been among the city/county journals. A few of these small-circulation publications have capitalized on the graphic possibilities offered by their concern with news and issues, beyond anything being done by many of the state journals. Some of the spreads, heavily dependent on photography/art could have come from consumer magazines. Clearly, professional designers have been called in, with worthwhile results.

No category shows a wider variety of formats, but the 8½ × 11 size is winning the day. The advantages are numerous. Bedeviled as the city/county publications are by numerous, relatively small and odd-shaped advertisements, they find the larger sheet size provides opportunities to minimize the disparate graphic quality of the advertisements.

Several Design Issues

The trend continues to sans serif composition. A major winner in last year's Sandoz competition embraced this style. The look is fashionable, the texture is undeniably smooth, and every typesetting system is equipped to turn out Univers, Helvetica or derivatives. Yet, a very serious concern remains: Are these faces as readable as serifed, thick-and-thin romans? Our answer is that the serifed typeface generally is better than the serifless (sans serif) for easier identification of the letters—for readability.

It is disruptive to the texture and unity of the publication to vary text sizes and line lengths. In the hands of professional designers, such variations can be accomplished, but they are generally too difficult for most medical and pharmaceutical journals.

Entries in the Sandoz competition continue to improve with regard to "display type," with less dependence on the centered and 18- and 24-pt. Futura headlines (and similar faces) that not so long ago made so many of the journals virtual carbon copies of each other. A current weakness in display lies in the refusal of some editors to distinguish typographically the various editorial departments and repeated features from the one-time, unique inclusions, such as the professional articles.

Helvetica is not the only display face. It and its clones appear often in advertisements and this blurs the sharp separation desirable between editorial and advertising matter, particularly if on the same page. Serif typefaces generally are more readable as text than sans serif. Aim for 10-point text typefaces, or at the minimum, 8 or 9 point. Typewritten tables save money but often conflict with typography. With all the word processors now available, surely better tables can be composed.

Layout and Production Criteria

The following are the criteria used to evaluate the graphics for the Sandoz medical journalism competition:

1. Publication achieves order at no sacrifice of interest, is simple but never dull, interesting but never precious, placing ease of the reader over gratification of the designer (e.g., limited reverses, overprints). Publication has a graphic identity achieved through practice of echoing graphic effects spread to spread within the issue, and issue to issue; that is, there is a recognizable graphic character.

2. Publication is sequenced in the interests of the reader. Professional articles (the "editorial well") are clustered in non-interrupted layout. Ideally, articles are self-containing (no "continueds") though they may flow through advertising matter. Departments and general news flow through the front and back of the publication as advertising dictates.

3. Major parts—articles, departments, news and advertising—are

given sharp graphic separation (usually through choice of type face and/or size). The reader knows instantly what page he has turned to.

4. Publication avails itself of the possibilities of the spread in horizontal sweeps (breaks across gutter of titles, photos) and vertical accents.

5. Unrelated pages on the spread are graphically defined by opposing horizontal versus vertical layouts, rule, color, double-burns, etc. against absence of same on facing pages.

6. Back-of-the-book pages and/or others forced to carry many disparate items show reductions in parts wherever possible for simplicity (i.e., in head styles, sizes, composition styles).

7. Wide expanses of text are relieved by such devices as subheads, boldface leadins, capitals, interior blurbs.

8. Cover is effective (basic criteria as in No. 1; e.g., order without sacrifice of interest). Title design distinctive, identifying.

9. Contents page is easy to find, easy to scan, achieving separations through uses of space (e.g., indentions) rather than in wide range of type sizes or, worse, faces. Deletes or subdues distracting elements (e.g., symbols of associations, awards).

10. Color uses are functional; e.g., used to accent not ornament.

11. Quality of advertising is commensurate with (or superior to) editorial layout. Advertising is so positioned as not to intrude on editorial layouts unnecessarily.

12. Basic column width is appropriate to the format, is in the interest of readability and cohesion.

13. Inking is consistent, solidly black. Contrast with the sheet is firm.

14. Paper is sufficiently opaque as to avoid strike-through of backup pages.

15. Imposition does not waver; e.g., margins do not waver.

A Magazine Design Bibliography

In this comprehensive guide, Paul Fisher lists and describes a multitude of books on various aspects of magazine design. An asterisk indicates an especially valuable book.

Layout

Dorn, Raymond. *How to Design and Improve Magazine Layouts.* Oakbrook, Illinois: Brookwood Publications. 1976. 164 pp.

A comprehensive gathering of the author's lectures on magazine layout and design. The first part of the book covers the basics of layout such as how to choose a typeface. The last part of the book discusses applications of the basics and includes sections on Dorn's "Mid-West Style" and "Clock Grid System" methods of layout.

Glaser, Milton. *Graphic Design.* Woodstock, New York: The Overlook Press, 1973. 239 pp.

Prefaced by an interview with Glaser, the book contains more than 300 illustrations, posters, record covers and magazine designs. Of special interest to the magazine art director would be Glaser's comments on the design of *New York, Paris Match* and *Audience.*

Hawkens, Arthur. *The Art Director at Work.* New York: Hastings House Publishers, 1959. 72 pp.

Includes a chapter on the editorial art director at work in which four art directors relate how they went about designing a certain spread. This section begins with a brief introduction by Allen Hurlburt, who was art director at *Look* at the time.

*Hurlburt, Allen. *Publication Design.* New York: Van Nostrand Reinhold, 1971. 138 pp.

Distillate of the wisdom of an important and influential magazine designer in unpretentious language bearing out the unpretentious subtitle: "A guide to page layout, typography, format and style." (See also by Hurlburt, *Layout: The Design of the Printed Page*, Watson-Guptill, 1977).

Hurlburt, Allen. *The Design Concept.* New York: Watson-Guptill, 1981. 151 pp.

This book is organized into chapters on the creative process, the design process, the word and image, editorial concepts. Illustrations for these chapters come from advertising and editorial designs by Helmut Krone, Alexey Brodovitch, George Lois, Milton Glaser and Herb Lubalin. For the designer who is not already familiar with these designers' works, this book is a good starting point.

*Nelson, Roy Paul. *Publication Design.* (Third Edition.) Dubuque, Iowa: William C. Brown Publishers, 1983. 320 pp.

An excellent beginner's book. Discursive and chatty as Hulburt is not, Nelson has written the book on magazine design that should be purchased first.

Silver, Gerald A. *Graphic Layout and Design.* New York: Van Nostrand Reinhold Co., 1981. 312 pp.

This workbook is for the beginning student of layout and typography, covering principles of layout, considerations in letter and word spacing, mechanical aspects of design and the appropriate use of color. Each section contains a brief chapter with specific lesson. The section on letter and word spacing is particularly noteworthy.

Smith, Cortland Gray. *Magazine Layout.* Plandome, N.Y.: Cortland Gray Smith, 1973. 208 pp.

Available from author at 248 Circle Drive, Plandome, New York, 11030. Short on continuity and organization, the book is long on random observations and layout ideas. A logical (and expensive—more than $20) choice for those who want more than Nelson has to give.

White, Jan V. *Designing for Magazines.* New York: R.R. Bowker Company, 1976. 176 pp.

> A sequel to *Editing by Design.* Illustrated by the author's work for trade publications, the book presents recommendations for the design of covers, contents, openers, editorials, departments, and—uniquely—for late closing forms and that peculiarity of trade publications, the new products page. Greatest value is in larger, profuse before-&-after illustrations of various page designs.

*White, Jan V. *Editing by Design.* (Second Edition.) New York: R.R. Bowker Company, 1982. 248 pp.

> The chief value of White's book is his discussion of layout in terms of the article and the publication. The author also stresses the importance of the working relationship between the art director and editor in achieving effective communication.

Typography

Biggs, John R. *Basic Typography.* New York: Watson-Guptill, 1968.

> The title says it all. There is limited discussion of use of type in magazines.

*Craig, James. *Designing with Type: A basic course in typography.* (Revised Edition.) New York: Watson-Guptill Publications, 1980. 176 pp.

> An excellent introductory manual on the subject of typography. Examples are limited primarily to five typefaces which are shown in variety of sizes with various leadings.

Dair, Carl. *Design with Type.* Toronto: University of Toronto Press, 1967. 162 pp.

> This basic introduction to typography should be required reading for anyone interested in typography. Dair provides a thorough and concise examination of type relationships and contrasts.

Frutiger, Adrian. *Type Sign Symbol.* Zurich: ABC Verlag, 1980. 151 pp.

> An extensive discussion of typefaces: why new ones are designed, how technology affects their development, and how various typefaces differ in legibility. The author includes specific and well-executed examples to accompany each facet of the discussion.

Harvey, Michael. *Lettering Design.* New York: Crown Publishers, 1975. 160 pp.

> Has the basics on letter forms: their proportions, various weights and thicknesses, and negative and positive shapes. Most valuable are the author's examples of lettering techniques and tools, and how they have shaped typefaces throughout history. Included are large-scale illustrations.

Lewis, John. *Typography: Design and Practice.* New York: Taplinger Publishing, 1978. 144 pp.

> This begins with the development of typographic design and continues through to modern trends. Sections on production have some practical guides for choosing size of typeface, for using justified or unjustified columns, and for using one layout over another. It also covers the grid, leading, copyfitting and specifying type. This book is recommended for one with some exposure to typography, because it is written in a more technical language.

*Spencer, Herbert. *The Visible Word.* New York: Hastings House Publishers, 1969. 81 pp.

Spencer presents a progression of studies on the legibility of type and summarizes the findings in one page (page 55). His chief criticism is that although studies have shown legibility can be improved by a knowledgeable use of typography, so far there has been little collaboration between researcher and printer.

*Swann, Cal. *Techniques of Typography.* New York: Watson-Guptill Publications, 1969. 96 pp.

A succinct, liberally illustrated primer that concentrates on the methods and criteria of composition. Grid system sections is particularly valuable.

Specimen Books

A Book of Ornamental Alphabets, Initials, Monograms and Other Designs. New York: Universe Books, 1976.

The designs can be copied freely and are printed on paper suitable for reproduction.

Alphabet Thesaurus. (Vol. 2) New York: Reinhold Publishing Corporation, 1965. 930 pp.

The second volume of a proposed three-volume series. This one updates the previous volume and contains examples of more than 4,000 alphabets.

Berthold Fototypes. Berlin, Germany: H. Berthold AG, 1974. 506 pp.

Approximately 1,200 photographic typefaces in complete alphabets.

Biegeleisen, J.I. *Handbook of Typefaces and Lettering.* (Fourth Edition.) New York: Arco Publishing Co., Inc., 1982. 245 pp.

This revised edition of *Art Director's Workbook of Typefaces*, features 75 typefaces in "jumbo size" and in full font. The author includes such large sizes, "In order to reveal readily the fine nuances which make each typeface unique." Each typeface is accompanied by a brief description of its characteristics and practical applications. Also includes a section covering the basics of typography.

Gates, David. *Type.* New York: Watson-Guptill Publications, 1973. 207 pp.

Part one of the book contains one-line showings of all typefaces commonly available in America. In part two, complete alphabets of the major typefaces are shown.

Hutchins, R.S. *Decorated Typefaces.* New York: Hastings House Publishers, 1965. 96 pp.

The introduction of the book includes a historical record of the various categories of type presented in the book. Each alphabet is accompanied by a brief commentary.

The ITC Typeface Collection. Farmington, Conn.: International Typeface Corporation, 1980. 572 pp.

A "general specimen book of types designed for current technologies." The preface also informs the reader: "The volume covers typefaces and ornaments produced since the founding of ITC in 1970." Each of the 26 families of typefaces show six to 72 point alphabet samples, with body text samples for the smaller point sizes. More recent type designs show expanded fonts which include foreign accents, small caps and old-style figures.

Kennedy, Paul E. *Modern Display Alphabets.* New York: Dover Publications, Inc., 1974.

> Contains 100 decorative display alphabets. Copyrighted.

*King, Jean Callan and Esposito, Tony. *The Designer's Guide to Text Type.* New York: Van Nostrand Reinhold Co., 1980. 319 pp.

> Extensive showing of specimen text blocks of 51 popular typefaces, many of them classics. Sizes range from six to 14 point, set solid and leaded one, two and three points on a 20 pica measure. Invaluable.

Merganthaler VIP Typeface Catalog, (Vol. 1, 2.) New York: Volk and Huxley, Inc., 1980.

> Each volume has over 50 typefaces from six to 36 point each. All typefaces are set in the same paragraph of text, so types can be compared easily and quickly. Typefaces have complete fonts. Also, a 12 point sample of text is set with three different leadings.

Lieberman, J. Ben. *Types of Typefaces.* New York: Sterling, 1967.

> Forty-eight familiar typefaces variously set with comments on legibility, tone, and suggestions for best use.

Photo Typositor Typeface Catalog. Miami: Visual Graphics Corporation, 1972.

> Contains more than 800 complete alphabets. One of the more complete specimen books.

Rowe, William. *Exotic Alphabets and Ornaments.* New York: Dover Publications, Inc., 1974. 72 pp.

> The first part of this copyrighted book contains 18 complete alphabets designed around natural forms such as butterflies and palm trees. The remainder of this book includes natural images surrounded by Art Deco borders.

Rydertypes. (Vols. I, II, with Supplements A, B and C.) Chicago: Frederic Ryder Company.

> An extensive collection of metal and film display and text faces available from this company. Complete alphabets are shown for most of the display faces.

The Type Specimen Book. New York: Van Nostrand Reinhold Company, 1974. 622 pp.

> What film typesetting has wrought no specimen book can encompass. But here's a good effort—544 typefaces in capital and lower case—alphabets, in sizes commonly ranging to 48 point and, not too uncommonly, beyond. (A commercial reprint of the book of V & M Typographical, Inc., 1652 McDonald Ave., Brooklyn, N.Y. 11230.)

Production

Arnold, Edmund C. *Ink on Paper 2.* New York: Harper and Row Publishers, 1972. 364 pp.

> A book for the non-printer about printing. Arnold takes the reader through the printing process from type specifications to binding.

Bahr, Leonard F. *ATA Advertising Production Handbook.* Advertising Typographers Association of America, 1963.

A terse, excellent, well illustrated introduction to the basics of printing production—sources of type, type printing processes, etc.

Craig, James. *Production for the Graphic Designer.* New York: Watson-Guptill Publications, 1974. 207 pp.

The focus is on creative possibilities available to the designer within the mechanical restrictions of the printing medium.

Dennis, Erwin A. and Jenkins, John D. *Comprehensive Graphic Arts.* Indianapolis: Howard W. Sams and Co., Inc., 1974. 530 pp.

A basic but extensive introduction to the many facets of the graphics arts industry. Profusely illustrated, the book covers layout, design, composition and the major printing processes.

Field, Janet N., ed. *Graphic Arts Manual.* New York: Arno Press, 1980. 650 pp.

"The purpose of this book is to provide a comprehensive guide to creating, producing and purchasing printed materials." Given the rapid change in graphic production, the challenge will be to keep this, as the preface promises, "an up-to-date reference book for the graphic arts industry."

Graham, Walter B. *Complete Guide to Paste-up.* Philadelphia: North American Publishing Company, 1976. 244 pp.

An instructive guide of ideas and techniques for camera-ready preparation, this book describes the paste-up process from the mark-up of the manuscript to the final camera-ready page.

Hanson, Glenn. *How to Take the Fits out of Copyfitting.* Ft. Morgan, Colorado: The Mul-T-Rule Co., 1967.

It ought to do it.

*Lem, Dean. *Graphics Master.* (Second Edition.) Los Angeles: Dean Lem Associates, (P.O. Box 46086, L.A. 90046), 1977. 36 pp.

Loose-leaf binder "designed for use by people who create, plan, estimate, produce and buy or sell printing . . ." A mini-encyclopedia at a major price. Selection of information is judicious in this useful, non-cumbersome piece.

Romano, Frank. *Automated Typesetting: The Basic Course.* Salem, New Hampshire: GAMA Communications, 1974. 120 pp.

A quick-reference glossary to the automated typesetting field.

*Sanders, Norman. *Graphic Designer's Production Handbook.* New York: Hastings House, 1982. 195 pp.

This well-thought-out reference book is for those who must prepare mechanicals or finished art for printers. Each illustrated spread has an explanation of a technique or concept in one of three categories: pre-printing preparation, halftone reproduction and finishing operations. A sampling of entries includes "Dropping Type from an Image," "Bleeding" and "Photographs Across the Spine." The guide is most useful because it helps the designer understand production procedures from the printer's perspective, which will, in turn, help keep printing costs down.

*Skillin, Marjorie E., Robert M. Gay, et al. (Third Edition.) *Words into Type.* Englewood Cliffs, N.J.: Prentice-Hall, Inc., 1974. 583 pp.

A complete style manual. It details under seven major headings the steps taken to transform the written into the printed word—from preparation of manuscript through copy editing and page markup to the processes of typographic composition.

Photography and Illustration Sources

Bettman, Otto L. *Bettman Portable Archive*. New York: Picture House Press, 1966.

> The compiler of this archive presents in minuscule form several thousand illustrations, indexed by subject, available upon request—and for a fee.

Gill and Lewis. *Illustration: Aspects and Directions*. New York: Reinhold Publishing Co., 1964.

> A basic introduction to the subject and variety of illustrations.

Hornung, Clarence. *Handbook of Early Advertising Art*. (2 Vols.) New York: Dover Publications, 1956.

> This is the third edition of the book that pioneered the idea of presenting for reuse art and illustrations on which property had expired. Since Hornung, there have been many such books, among them: Reissue of Tuer's *1,000 Quaint Cuts*. (Detroit: Swinging Tree Press, 1968); Cirker's *1,000 Woodcuts by Bewick*. (New York: Dover, 1962). For the best review of such publications—all within public-domain-art—write Dover Publications, 180 Varick St., New York, N.Y. 10014.

McDarrah, Fred W. *Stock Photo and Assignment Source Book*. New York: R.R. Bowker Company, 1977. 481 pp.

> Lists over 4,000 picture sources in the United States and Europe. Entries include free and pay sources who have stock photo files and/or willing to shoot and deliver assignments.

Sutphen, Dick. *The Wildest Old Engravings and Illustrations*. Minneapolis: The Dick Sutphen Studio, Inc., 1966. 190 pp.

> A copyright-free handbook of illustrations printed between 1850 and 1925. Other books in this series by Sutphen include *Uncensored Situations* and the more recent *The Early Illustrators*, published by Art Direction Book Company.

A Little Inspiration

Art Directors Annuals. Annuals of Advertising, Editorial, and Television Art and Design, by the Art Directors Club, Inc. New York: A.D.C. Publications, 1981.

> An excellent collection of each year's award-winning designs in the communications industry. Sections of note are: Magazine Editorial, Art and Illustration, and Photography. An inspiring source for jarring loose ideas.

Berryman, Gregg. *Notes on Graphic Design and Visual Communication*. Los Altos, Calif.: William Kaufmann, Inc., 1979. 45 pp.

> A hand-printed primer on the design process with brief discussions on the placement of text on a page, on thumbnail sketches, and on the advantages of grids. Of note is a section on "typographic hints" for using various type point sizes and weights and for choosing serif or sans serif faces. The author also lists other design sources as well as names of designers he considers to be "giants of typography."

Booth-Clibborn, Edward and Baroni, Daniele. *The Language of Graphics.*
New York: Harry N. Abrams, Inc., 1980. 320 pp.

> The foreword sets the mood for the rest of the book: "The successful communication of any message requires a visualization that is based not only on the application of graphic techniques but also on the expression of meaningful values . . ." In-depth discussion on social and psychological forces in relation to the graphic message. This work is recommended for its thoughtful analysis as well as the wealth of historical graphic art examples.

Carter, David E. *Ideas for Editors.* Ashland, Kentucky: Decathon Corp., 1978. 244 pp.

> Contains 366 ideas to help improve the appearance and editorial content of company publications. Sections include covers and graphics as well as articles and features. The ideas shown are reproduced from leading company publications in the U.S. and Canada.

McLean, Ruari. *Magazine Design.* London: Oxford University Press, 1969.

> But for a few paragraphs of observations on magazine design, this is a collection of outstanding magazine covers and spreads, many of them European.

Thompson, Philip and Davenport, Peter. *The Dictionary of Graphic Images.*
New York: St. Martin's Press, 1980. 263 pp.

> A survey of current and historical uses of imagery, containing, says the cover, "more than 1,700 fully-captioned examples" by "leading graphic designers, photographers, illustrators and artists of the last four decades . . ." As a quick reference for visual interpretations of universal symbols, this guide is unique.

Typography 1/Typography 2. The Annuals of the Type Directors' Club.
New York: Watson-Guptill Publications, 1980–1981. 216 pp. each.

> A survey of designs judged to be the best by a panel of distinguished designers. The books are divided into four categories: Promotional, Advertising, Editorial and Informational. With each design, there is a notation of the principal type used.

Periodicals

Communciations Arts Magazine. Coyne and Blanchard Inc., P.O. Box 10300, 410 Sherman Ave., Palo Alto, California 94303. Richard S. Coyne, Editor and Publisher. Bi-monthly.

> The best-known source for those who would keep abreast of the latest graphic trends in all media.

Folio. Folio Magazine Publishing Corp., 125 Elm St., New Canaan, Connecticut 06840. Charles I. Tannen, Publisher & Editor.

> "The magazine for magazine management" publishes a substantial number of articles concerned with aspects of magazine layout and production, e.g., "What Price Color," "Bringing Your Typesetting In-House," etc. Since the demise of *Better Editing,* there is perhaps more here for those concerned with magazine appearance than in any other periodical.

Journal of Organizational Communication. IABC (International Association of Business Communicators), 870 Market St., Suite 928, San Francisco, California 94102. John N. Bailey, Editor. Quarterly.

The *Journal* weighs heavily to editorial problems of industrial or company publication editors, but publishes an occasional article concerning periodical graphics.

Ligature. World Typeface Center, Inc., 145 East 32nd St., New York, New York 10016. Tom Carnase, Editor. Three times a year.

Much like *U&lc*, this publication is a showcase for WTC typefaces. Departments in the periodical's March 1983 issue include: Typecasting, a column concerning jobs, portfolios and trends in the marketplace; Type Tech, on calligraphic letter design using computers; and Showcase, highlights of the Type Director's Club annual competition.

Print. RC Publications, 355 Lexington Ave., New York, New York 10017. Martin Fox. Editor. Bi-monthly.

Art directors will note differences in editorial objectives between *Print* and *Communications Art.* These will be lost on one solely interested in magazine design who must count either publication as a luxury.

U&lc. 261 E. 45th St., New York, New York 10017. Edward Gottschall, Editor.Quarterly. Controlled circulation.

Introduced in 1974, *U&lc* is pre-eminently a magazine (tabloid format) for the designer. Trend setters speak and show their work here. The owners, International Typeface Corporation, make *U&lc* a specimen book for their types and a wailing wall for lack of copyright protection afforded typeface design.

TYPOGRAPHY

A New Vocabulary
for the Medical Journalist

Physicians and health professionals who also are medical journalists often have to learn an entirely new vocabulary. This may include initials and various terms used in the editing of copy, providing typesetting instructions to the printer, makeup, layout and other symbols involved in artwork and publication production.

A glossary of typographic terms can be extremely helpful as a learning and reference tool. The following one is excerpted from the glossary of the International Composition Association, 2233 Wisconsin Avenue, N.W., Washington, DC

As you will note, all of these terms also have a medical connotation or an anatomical or physiological orientation; but here we provide only the journalistic usage.

Absorption In paper, the property which causes it to take up liquids or vapors in contact with it.

Alignment An imaginary line at top or bottom of letters and characters.

Alteration A change from the manuscript copy introduced in proof, distinguished from a correction made to eliminate a printer's error. Alterations made by the author (author's alterations—colloquially, "AAs"), or some part of them, are customarily chargeable as a separate item.

Backbone The back of a bound book connecting the two covers; also called spine.

Balance A symmetrical plan for page makeup.

Beard Beveled space below the printing surface of a type letter.

Bad Breaks An incorrect word division; an improper hyphenation, i.e., not between syllables. Also, the setting of a hyphenated word as the beginning of the first line of a page.

Bleed An illustration that continues off the page when the edge of the paper has been trimmed away in binding is said to "bleed."

Blow Up To enlarge photographically. A heading, photograph, chart, figure, etc., subjected to such treatment is termed a "blowup."

Body The part of a piece of metal type that serves as a base for the raised printing surface. "Body size" (measured in points) is the dimension corresponding to the height of the printed letter and is the same for all characters in the font.

Break   The place for ending or dividing a line of type.

Caps   An abbreviation for "capital letters;" upper case letters.

Cast   To force molten metal into a mold, such as is done in a linecasting machine.

Cut   A term originally referring to a "woodcut" but now generally used to denote a zinc etching, halftone engraving, or other illustrative matter.

Cut-in Head   A head placed in a box of white space cut into the side of the type page. It is usually set in type different from that of the text and placed under the first two lines of the paragraph; also, a head cutting across the body of a table.

Dermatitis   In lithography, a skin disease, characterized by an itching gash or swelling; caused by photographic developers, chromium compounds and solvents.

Doctor Blade   In gravure, a knife-edge blade pressed against the engraved printing cylinder which wipes away the excess ink from the non-printing areas.

Dummy   An unprinted or partially printed or sketched sample of a projected book, pamphlet, book cover, or other material to suggest the final appearance and size of the completed work.

Extract   Printer's term for "block quotation," a long quotation marked off from the text by being set in smaller type or on narrower measure than the body copy.

Face   The printing surface of a piece of type. The type commonly used in books and all classes of ordinary reading matter is known as roman. Although all roman types are essentially the same in form, there are two fairly well-defined divisions or styles.

Feet   The bottom of the type body.

Figure   An illustration printed with the text (hence also called a "text figure") in distinction from a Plate, which is printed separately.

Flush   The term "flush" designates the absence of indention. Flush left lines of type begin at the left margin. The term "flush right" indicates that type aligns at the right.

Hairline   Used to describe any very fine or delicate line in type, brass rule or engraving; commonly applied to any character which is very light throughout.

Head Margin   The white space above first line on page.

Hickeys   In offset-lithography, spots or imperfections in the printing due to such things as dirt on the press, dried ink skin, paper particles, etc.

Hypo   An abbreviation for sodium thiosulfate, or sodium hyposulfite, a chemical used to fix the image on a photographic film after it has been developed.

Ligature   Two or more connected or tied letters cast on one body.

Live Matter   Type composition or pages that have not yet been printed. After there is no further need of it, it is dead matter, ready for breakup and distribution.

Mask   In color separation photography, an intermediate photographic negative or positive used in color correction. In offset lithography, opaque material used to protect open or selected areas of a printing plate during exposure.

Negative   Photographic film or paper on which tonal values are reversed, so that what appears black on the original is white, or transparent, and vice versa.

Run-Around   In composition, the term describing a type area set in measures that are adjusted to fit around a picture or another element of the design.

Running Head   A title repeated at the top of each page of a book.

Shadow   The darkest parts in a photograph represented in a halftone by the largest dots.

Shoulder   The blank space on the top or bottom of metal type not covered by the letter; specifically, the space above and below the letter.

Silhouette   Photo or illustration of subject only, without any background.

Stripping   In offset lithography, the positioning of negatives (or positives) prior to platemaking.

Tissue Overlay   A thin, translucent paper placed over artwork for protection; used to indicate color break and corrections.

Tooth   A characteristic of paper, a slightly rough finish, which permits it to take ink readily.

Widow   A single word or part of a word in a line by itself at the top of a page. Also, a word or part of word standing alone in one line of a heading; an extremely short last line in a caption.

Rules on Typography

The following advice on typography, taken from a newsletter edited by Lyle L. Erb, appeared in the first issue of *Medical Journalism* in 1975. One or two of the suggested rules are somewhat controversial, but most are still useful. The newsletter, *in black and white*, no longer is published.

If a typographic element isn't necessary, don't use it. Don't gussy up your masthead with gingerbread art. Don't use standing heads with fancy type and art.

Don't use reverses, block tints, and overlays. They're illegible.

Don't use boxes, Ben Day or heavy rules, fancy rules and squiggly lines. If you're using column rules, consider using white space instead.

Use plenty of white space; 12 points of white space isn't too much between elements. Use it between headlines and the story or picture above and the story below.

Use flush-left, ragged right headlines. Except for one-line heads, don't center headlines. It gives a zig-zag effect, dizzying to the eye.

Don't use all-caps heads. For that matter, don't set body text all caps. It impairs readability.

If you're setting your heads in caps and lower case, consider going to the all-down style, capitalizing only the first letter and proper nouns. That's the way we learned to read, and that's the way it's easiest to read.

Don't mix head letters. In particular, don't use Old English, script and fancy serif types. Pick one family in a good, strong headletter and stick with it. Clashing headfaces undermine the consistent tone and character a publication should reflect and give it a split personality.

Don't use subheads in text. Typebreakers? Sure, but why subheads as typebreakers? Usually they turn out to be idiotic labels, saying nothing, or repeat the first words of the paragraph beneath.

All you need do is mark about half the line for bold face. Caps and lower case is better than all caps. Then, mark the copy for a slug of white space above the black line. It's easy and fast and helps to air out the page.

Another thing: Many paragraphs are too deep. This makes for unattractive gray areas in the page. You can forget about paragraph unity in writing news stories. There's something about short paragraphs that is inherently appealing to the eye, because they squirt white space into the page.

The ragged-right style of setting body copy appears to be used increasingly in school publications. It is attractive and lends an air of informality to a page. Besides, it squirts in some more white space.

Sometimes, though, some lines are set too short. That's because some printers think there's a rule against hyphenating in ragged-right copy. There's no such rule. Tell your printer to run the line out as far as the width permits, hyphenate at an appropriate place, and don't bother to justify.

Criteria Used For First Sandoz Journal Competition

The criteria used to judge the typography of the medical journals participating in the first Medical Journalism contest sponsored by Sandoz Pharmaceuticals were relatively few and simple. They were designed to standardize the judging and yet permit the judges to take into account a variety of factors. Following were the criteria:

Display

1. Title typefaces are in character with the publication as established by the editorial content and the identity sought for the journal. Whether the choice of typefaces is varied or restricted, approach to usage remains constant issue after issue to achieve identification value for the publication.
2. Where contrasts of typefaces are attempted (title to title, title to blurb), they are decisive in choice of face and/or size.
3. Weight and interest qualities of the display faces used carry, yet do not dominate, the spread; they gain attention—but not through obvious striving.
4. Where varied sizes must appear on a given spread, as on news pages, they are used with restraint. Three is considered a practical maximum.
5. Faces are contemporary in spirit or classic—timeless. They are not dated, and are not related to a fashion no longer popular.
6. Photographic enlargements have not disfigured fitting of the letters.

Text

1. A typesetting system of reasonable quality has been used, as evidenced by letter fit, alignment, hyphenation range, airspacing when required.
2. Size is large enough for easy reading: 10-point would appear to be the minimum for most fonts.
3. Width of the face is in harmony with basic column width employed— i.e., relatively narrow to relatively wide.

4. The face maintains tonal harmony (gray to black) with the tonal intensity of the photography.
5. Face is contemporary or classic, but not so antiquated or stylized as to invite attention to the design.
6. Leading seems to be in the best interest of the reader and the "color" of the face chosen.

These criteria, and others, are listed in the award chapter on pages 199–202.

Fisher On Typography

The following comments on typography are excerpted from an article by Paul Fisher that appeared originally in an American Bar Association publication. The remarks are totally applicable to medical, pharmaceutical, and hospital journals.

Consider the column. Two columns make a more variable page than does the bookish, very static, full-page measure. True, shorter lines may indicate specification of smaller type size, but this resort ought not be necessary if some of the wasted space in margins is put to use.

The top margin should be one of emphasis. The drop-off in white space here ought to be all that the publication can afford. Whatever elements occasionally may be introduced into it, the broad band of space at the top serves to alleviate the weight of the text on the next page, while imparting flow or continuity to the issue.

Display type offers the only consistently open avenue to visual interest and change of pace.

What changes might be made? Variation in type size—the best and safest of all dimensions of contrast—must be ruled out at the outset because the extraordinary length of journal titles often does not allow for size flexibility. (Need they be so endless?) Too, the outsider may harbor the suspicion that equal respect to authors requires monotony of size in titles.

But there are other possibilities. An occasional title stacked vertically might replace the usual appearance of one-or-two-line centered headlines across the page. Tight spacing between lines—together with irregular indentation, left and right—makes for a strong but simple contrast.

Occasional use of a non-standard typeface will supply change. The contrast value will be enhanced if the face chosen is totally unlike the standard—e.g. serif to work against an otherwise sans serif schedule. However, in publications limited in size and number of pages, the practice of varying title faces over articles should be used most sparingly.

Bolder journals can achieve simple and strong change of pace in titles through use of such background effects as ruled boxes, screened backgrounds with titles over-printed, and (within limits) titles reversed on black backgrounds. Where the title face is large, it may be varied by screening it back to give a gray, rather than a black, value.

The blurb clearly merits more attention than it presently enjoys in the journals. They either brief the article or play up the major statements in it. Graphic definition from text and title alike is essential.

An introductory blurb occurs on the title spread. Running ones appear on the continuing spreads—usually either in the top margin (which then must become proportionately deeper) or internally, through columns of type from which blurbs are cut by rules above and below.

Taylor's Suggestions

Howard B. Taylor, an expert on layout and design, declares that simple typography is easier to live with than ostentatious typography.

"Heads, for example," he says. "It's a cinch your printers have contemporary faces—Univers or Helvetica or Americana. Avoid the gothics, the scripts, the texts and the Egyptians." Following are other suggestions from Mr. Taylor.

Instead of mixing all-caps with caps and lower case, modern typography uses the all-down style in heads. This capitalizes only the first word and the proper nouns.

Choose a family of body type and stick with it, instead of mixing head faces. Mixed type families tend to give a *split personality* to a publication. Use one family and use it in its variants—roman and italic, bold, medium, and light.

Given the chance, a printer will use every display face in his catalog to show his versatility. Don't let him do it.

A sans-serif body type, unless large and well-leaded, tends to become monotonous and to lack personality. Although it certainly is unadorned, it becomes stark and difficult to read. It comes out faint-hearted.

A popular text face is Bodoni Book. Bodoni is one of the oldest typefaces. It's beautiful. It's graceful. And that's the trouble. Because of its somewhat exaggerated serifs and its varied thicks and thins, it is difficult to read in narrower measures. It's more adaptable to the book page, as its name would imply.

You might consider Century or Cheltenham, or Corona, as offhand examples. Again, your composing rooms surely have other similar and suitable body faces.

Many publications are going to ragged-right body set. Technically, this is called unjustified. We happen to like it and use it in black and white. Laboratory tests show that ragged-right is easier to read than justified type but for some reason, editors and typographers *and* readers object to it. Perhaps it's because we're accustomed to justified type. Sometimes the excuse that "We've always done it this way" may be the best reason for doing it a new way.

But a word of warning, if you consider the ragged-right style. Many printers think that you cannot hyphenate words in unjustified lines. So you end up with some excessively short lines and get a zig-zag effect that is dazzling to the eye. There's no such rule. Don't let them kid you. Just tell your printer to run the line as long as possible and hyphenate at an appropriate place, if necessary.

Arnold's Ancient Axioms

Here is a sampler from *Arnold's Ancient Axioms*, a collection of hints about typography and layout compiled and written by Dr. Edmund C. Arnold and published by Lawrence Ragan Communications, Chicago. Dr. Arnold is a graphic arts teacher and consultant, and a regular contributor to the *Ragan Report*, one of the most authoritative and influential publications in the field.

Avoid italic body type in masses. The lighter tone of the italic form seems to scare away prospective readers, who feel it is going to be difficult to read—although actually it isn't. "Editor's notes" are often set in italic. Not only should this be avoided, the notes themselves ought to be eliminated . . . An editor's note merely delays the reader from jumping into a story. Material in such notes can usually be included in the story itself, or in a bio note (a short graf about the author and his qualifications to pass judgment on the subject of the piece), which runs at the foot of the page.

Avoid boldface read-ins. The practice of starting a paragraph or caption with a few words set in bold caps, then reverting to lightface lowercase, is a "read in". This is not only non-functional, it's definitely malfunctional.

Avoid reverses of body type. A "reverse plate" gives the effect of white type on a black (or colored) background. Reversed type is difficult to read.

If type must be reversed, it should be no smaller than 10 point and, preferably sans serif. When roman is reversed, there's a tendency for the thin strokes and serifs to plug up with ink. Reverses should be on black or full color. White letters on gray or a tint are difficult to see.

Use tint blocks warily.

Use the dollar gauge. When a dollar bill is placed horizontally on a page, it should always touch at least one display element—head, art or a box. If it doesn't there is too great a concentration of gray, unappetizing body type.

Use a breaker head to break a mass of type. This has the content of the old "subhead." But while that subhead was set in bold caps of body type, the breaker is in 12-, 14- or even 18-point headletter, flush left. The breaker looks like a headline and its first effect is to break up a long story into several apparently short ones, as the reader is always more ready to jump into a short piece.

Blake Kellogg's Questions

Blake Kellogg, associate professor of journalism at the University of Wisconsin, offers editors the following ideas concerning typography.

Ask yourself: What are my magazine's characteristics and what is its personality? Do the typefaces appropriately reflect its editorial personality? Just as your personal dress helps define your personality, attitudes, and social role, so too should your typography define your magazine's personality, attitudes, and social role.

For example, sans serif type generally is colder and more mechanical than serif type. Serif tends to be more humanistic and more traditional. Heavy type is bolder and more assertive than thin type. The roman version of type usually makes a stronger statement than the italic. Italic is softer, more of a whisper.

As a general rule, you should stay with no more than two or three typefaces for your magazine. Actually, one typeface for everything is probably best. The more you stay with one or two faces, the closer you come to achieving typographic continuity and unity.

Your nameplate can be in any typeface that reflects your magazine's editorial personality. Usually it is a good idea to have the department heads in the same typeface as the nameplate. This gives a nice sense of continuity, especially where there is a lot of competing type from ads.

A number of editors prefer their headlines and text in the same typeface; some use different typefaces. If you are ever in doubt, your best bet is to stay with one typeface for both.

If you choose to use one typeface for heads and a second for text, then it is a good idea to have the two typefaces contrast with one another. For example, Helvetica (sans serif) and Times-Roman (serif) would contrast with one another; whereas Helvetica and Futura are too similar, as are Bookman and Baskerville. These latter combinations would impart a confused and cluttered look.

Select the same typeface for the nameplate and department heads. Select either that face or another for the heads and text. Then, if and when you introduce still another typeface onto your magazine's pages, be sure you have a definite reason. Just as you would give careful thought about introducing a new department or section, so should you give careful consideration to the introduction of a new typeface. Fewer is better!

Some editors choose one typeface for headlines, summaries, and bylines, and another for text. Some editors use still another for photo captions. I do not recommend a different typeface for photo captions. I recommend the boldface version of the text.

Type is set in one of four ways: justified (flush left and right), centered, flush left only (ragged, or rag, on right) and flush right (rag on left).

As a general rule, justified and centered type are more formal. Flush left, rag right is more casual. Flush right, rag left is appropriate only for short heads or when using a type as a design element.

Be consistent with type throughout your magazine. As a general rule, typographic harmony can be achieved by limiting yourself not only to one or two typefaces, but also to no more than three or four type sizes.

An excessive number of type sizes conveys a sense of clutter and disorganization. This is especially true where there are ads, which add to the typeface and type size clutter. The same is true of type density (bold vs. light).

Three or four variations are ok, but too many different densities impart a sense of clutter.

Ask yourself how many variations in type size and density you are using for cover nameplate, cover heads, other cover info, contents, nameplate, masthead, dept. heads, headlines, subheads, summaries, bylines, text, photo/art captions and other components.

Most types come in both roman and italic. Most offer a choice of widths —condensed (narrow), medium and extended. Most come in a variety of densities—light, medium, demi-bold and bold. Your best choice for text is always medium width and medium density. Usually your best choice for heads is either demi-bold or bold. Subheads and summaries are usually best set in boldface. The thing to remember is that boldface is very strong and should not be overused. An entire story, for example, should never be set entirely in boldface. Photo and art captions are usually set in bold-roman or medium-italic. I usually recommend bold-roman for photos. Italic medium is suitable for fine art captions and poetry. Great amounts of italic are more tedious to read than roman.

Type ranges in size from 6 point to 72 point (in most fonts), for most typefaces. Limit your typefaces. Fewer is best.

For coverlines, type can be set in one of four ways: all upper case (caps), each word begins in upper and then the rest in lower (caps and lowercase), the first word and proper nouns in upper and the rest in lower (as in text), all lower case. Ask yourself: Am I consistent throughout my issue with my use of type? Is it set the same way on the cover, on the contents page, and over the article?

As to the contents page, ask yourself these questions:

Do I begin the contents page with an identical (but reduced) version of the cover nameplate? Are my contents made more interesting and easier for the reader to perceive by my use of a combination of boldface and medium face? Do I use headlines which are carryovers from the coverlines? Do I carry a masthead? Do I consistently run my contents on pages 1, 3, or 5 for maximum convenience to my readers?

Common mistakes to avoid:

Running type at an angle
Running type on the vertical
Use of too many typefaces
Use of too many type sizes.

Stet

One of the most common terms used by printers and proofreaders is *stet*, and physician-editors are big users of this quick way to indicate a cancellation of a change of a letter, word or entire section of a manuscript or type proof. Though a few journalists may think that stet is an acronym, physicians and other Latin students, know the intransitive verb, stare, to stand, is conjugated stari, steti and statum. Somewhere over the years, the i was dropped from the second person singular, steti.

Stet is an easy word to write. "Let it stand" is the easy way out of many decisions and problems. Change is much more difficult.

In recent years, several medical journals have made radical changes in design, format and content. Undoubtedly, editors had to argue fiercely with board members and others who believe that stet is preferable to change.

To substitute something flashy or contemporary for something old certainly is not progress. To replace a mediocre concept with something equally inferior is a poor substitution. Change for the sake of change is unnecessary. However, all publications, institutions and individuals should be receptive to new ideas. Stet that.

Further Hints

The Editorial Eye is the unusual name of an excellent newsletter published by Editorial Experts, Inc., 4600 Duke Street, Alexandria, VA 22304. Editor Peggy Smith fills each issue with a variety of useful tips which make the $54 annual subscription a good investment. Here's her article on typography, which appeared in July 1984.

Copy that is typeset flush left and ragged right, with uniform four-to-the-em wordspacing and full hyphenation, has everything to recommend it. The format is especially good for setting type from computer (or word processor disks or interfaces) because electronic "compositors" do not always adjust lines well in justified copy.

Peter Smith of Peter Smith Associates is an editor and graphic designer who has shown many people how to work with words—how to write and edit them and how to present them in type effectively.

At the May meeting of the Washington chapter of the Society for Technical Communication, Smith reminded the audience of some of the rules for readable, attractive typography:

• Don't exceed the maximum easy-to-read line length of 65 characters (2½ alphabets). Longer lines cause a reader to "double"—read the same line twice.

• In body copy, don't use less than the minimum easy-to-read line length of 35 characters. Shorter lines cause sentences to be broken into so many lines that thoughts are difficult to grasp.

• Use italics only for a few words on a page and only when essential. Long stretches of italic type are hard to read.

• Reserve boldface mostly for heads and subheads; in body copy, use it for only a few words. Lines of boldface in body copy "flimmer"—the letters fill in and vibrate.

• Avoid using all caps; they slow reading speed and take 30% more space than lowercase. For display, use caps and lowercase or italics and boldface. For emphasis in body copy, use italics or boldface—but use them sparingly or they become ineffective.

The same rules apply to typewritten copy, with this added injunction:

Never justify it. The unequal space between words that results is hard on the reader and makes an ugly page full of holes, rivers, and lakes of white space.

Few designers would argue with any of these rules, but Smith also has some ideas of his own about increasing economy and readability that are worth considering. For example, he prefers a head with just initial caps and the rest of the words in lowercase (as used in the title of this article). He also prefers flush left heads to centered heads. And he may be one of the few designers who have considered the practical uses and the aesthetics of bullets in all their variety.

Shooting at bullets

"Sometimes typographic bullets can be used to good advantage," says Smith. "Bullets are usually better than abc's or 123's if the letters or numbers have no special significance (such as for reference)."

But Smith believes bullets are often used badly.

"Never, never, never, *never* use bullets for a group of items that consists entirely of one-liners," he says.

He also dislikes the popular format in which bulleted items hang and bullets extend to the left of the items. Smith prefers inconspicuous bullets like those used in the first section of this article, where the bullets are part of the block of text—flush left, with the carryover lines also flush left.

As for line spaces between bulleted items, Smith recommends them only for long items (five or six lines or more).

For two- or three-liners he recommends indenting the bullets, which is more economical than adding line space between items. "A group like this could go on and on," he says, "but even so, it's best to drop in a subhead here and there."

Here are four ways bullet lists can be well used:

• xxxxxxxx	• xxxxxxx	• xxxxxxxxx	• xxxxxxxxxx
xxxxxxxxxxx	xxxxxxxxxxx	xxxxx • xxx	xxxxxxxxxx
• xxxxxxxxx	• xxxxxxx	xxxxxxxxxxx	xxxxxxxxxx
xxxxxxxxxxx	xxxxxxxxxxx	xxx • xxxxx	xxxxxxxxxx
Flush	Indented	Run-on	Hanging

PHOTOGRAPHY

Criteria for Judging Photographs

Reports of conventions, meetings, parties and other events appear in almost every issue of state and county medical journals. The photos that accompany these articles are often dull and sometimes embarrassing in their resemblance to high school yearbooks. "Good photography is too expensive" is the excuse offered by many editors who use poor photos. Other editors explain the crammed groupings with "our members want pictures of as many people as possible."

A really good picture is an art form within the scope of any medical journal editor, regardless of time and money limitations. Phil Douglis, a frequent contributor to the *Ragan Report*, suggests, "If you're planning to photograph a meeting, exhibit, party, or other event, go over your goals with the photographer. Instead of asking the photographer to roam around and shoot a lot of pictures, explain what you hope to achieve in terms of mood and impact, not just content."

The following criteria were used by Paul Fisher, Howard Hudson and Richard Weiner to evaluate the photographs of publications entered in the first Sandoz Medical Journalism Awards contest:

• Photographs add to or at least sharpen understanding of text; they do not appear to be thrown in simply to embellish or fill space.

• Photography is properly laid out, not simply strung through the text; e.g. it is positioned in manners that continue or sharply interrupt lines of movement or force.

• Photographs do not appear posed, stiff; they stress activity; they minimize head shots, pictures of buildings, etc.

• Photographs are properly cropped to avoid waste areas; no series of heads in dissimilar sizes.

• Tone and style of photography is consistent through publication (no snapshot to studio range).

• Choice of screen seems in interests of the photography.

Questions About Photography

Here are some questions about photography that were asked by *Editors Newsletter* in an article designed to assist editors in evaluating their publications. (A "yes" to all the questions will mean that you are on the way to making the best possible use of photos in your journal.)

- Do you correctly identify people in all photos?
- Do you avoid groups and mug shots as a rule?
- Do you crop photos for maximum impact and to delete distractions?
- Are photos contrasty and not washed out?
- Do you run photos large, avoiding "postage stamp" albums?
- Do you have the best photo on your cover or front page?
- Is there one dominant photo per page and/or spread?
- Do you photograph more with available light and less with flash or strobe?

Flash Photography

Kill that flash forever. That's the advice of Philip N. Douglis, the photographic expert who writes for the *Ragan Report*. Flash photography is used by amateur and semiprofessional photographers, who may save you money but whose results are often poor. One reason may be their reliance on flash attachments. Mr. Douglas also made these comments in an article in *Medical Journalism.*

If you are among the minority of photographers still using electronic flash to light your "people pictures," stop doing it. You are hurting your pictures with this archaic technique far more than you can help them. Flash is still used because of ignorance, fear and the fact that it is "there." Ignorance is cured with knowledge of three simple facts about light photography:

1) All cameras equipped with a lens opening of f/1.4, f/1.8, f/2, f/2.5, or f/2.8 can easily record things as they are, without the intrusion of artificial light.

2) Kodak Tri-X film, when used in conjunction with special development, can be increased in sensitivity without significant loss of image quality through pushing development so that you get an extra one or two more openings if you need them. Simply set your ASA

dial at ASA 800 or 1600, shoot your pictures and tell your processor what ASA reading was used. And be sure to shoot the entire roll at the same ASA reading.

3) A slower shutter speed can also give you extra lens openings to shoot at 1/15th of a second or 1/30th of a second. Simply keep your elbows tucked into your body, grasp the camera firmly, plant one foot in front of the other, and squeeze—never jab or push or strike —the shutter release button. Or use convenience supports such as tables, chairs, walls and floors to steady the camera.

With these facts in mind, the only thing keeping you from using available light for your photography is fear. Fear can be cured by experience. People often cling to light as a crutch. They are afraid of not getting a "clear, sharp, properly exposed" image. But what good is a sharp well-exposed image if the subject is chalk white, or pasty, with harsh ugly shadows. Flash destroys not only the exquisite natural balance of light and shadow but it calls attention to the process at the expense of the result. It is like waving a flag in the face of the subject. Every time you fire off a light, it is like screaming "I just took another picture!"

Use of Freelance Or Semiprofessional Photographers

According to Gary Wagner, founder of Wagner International Photos in New York, the use of freelance or semiprofessional photographers is often false economy. "Illness, lateness, difficulty in getting prints and other problems are more likely to occur with a one-person photography operation, making the event a potential disaster for the client," says Mr. Wagner.

Here are some tips from Gary Wagner that are likely to result in better-quality photography.

When we refer to an inferior photograph for publication, it does not necessarily mean that the picture is photographically bad. Errors in lighting or focus should not be a factor.

An inferior photo can have many things wrong with it and still be a pretty picture to hang on the wall. The editor, whose job it is to come up with a graphically perfect page, as well as one that makes good news sense, does not judge a photo on quality alone. It simply must make sense and justify its publication.

To illustrate, let us start with a photo of an officer of the medical society or other appointment or promotion.

Most portraits are deadly. They are low-key lighted and soft focus. A formal portrait for publication should be dead-sharp focus all the way through and strongly lighted. Your best bet is a candid close-up, if possible shot under available light in the subject's office. But even this must be sharp, have good clear detail and be well-exposed. It should be printed on single-weight glossy paper only. Matte or textured paper is magnificent for display, but not for reproduction. Above all, do not use a Polaroid photo or a copy of one.

The next type of photograph most frequently published is the award or presentation shot, and it too is abused in most journals.

This photograph should be kept as newsy as possible. This means tightness, that is, limit the picture only to the people actually involved in the award or event. In many of these photographs, a simple presentation ceremony has evolved into a graduation group. Never pose more than three persons in the shot, always keep the grouping tight with shoulders touching if possible ("think two columns") and always keep the grouping away from walls, as far as possible, to eliminate black blob shadows forming behind the subjects.

If your photographer shoots such a group with flash-on-camera, don't ever use him again. He may be working for pay, but he is not a true professional.

The committee photo or society grouping also can be deadly. Avoid photos of large groups or even small groups staring at the camera. Cut down to 3 or 4 people in a working group.

In shooting speakers, use a 35mm camera and a long lens which reduces the angle between the camera and the speaker, eliminating the flash which either distracts the speaker and causes him to lose his lines or leaves moons and stars dancing in front of his eyes. This also affords the chance to get background such as the society emblem behind the speaker.

When the photographer plants himself in front of the dais and pops flashes, he annoys the speaker and winds up with the hackneyed up-the-nostril shot of a hard-to-recognize subject behind a podium.

Improving The Quality
Of Your Photographs

Walter G. Anderson, an experienced editor of hospital publications, noted that most photos in medical and related publications are routine, dull and can be grouped into these categories—people at work, identification "mug" shots, group photos, pictures of facilities or equipment, product still-lifes and what might be termed "symbolic" pictures—photos that represent a general subject or concept. Only a handful of pictures contain striking qualities that would stop a reader (one function of a picture) or which truly represent the nature of the organization or its members (another important purpose of a photo)

Here are 15 tips from an article in *Editors Newsletter* that was written by Mr. Anderson to help you improve the quality and impact of your publication's photographs.

1. Decide what you want to illustrate BEFORE you take the picture.
2. Take lots of pictures, but select and use only the best (less is more).
3. Take both horizontal and vertical for greater flexibility in layout. Also take pictures from three distances: closeup, middle and long distance.
4. Include something in the foreground, middle ground and background. A picture of a secretary at work might show her in the middle, her typewriter in the foreground, and the office where she works in the background.
5. Add interest by changing the angle. Shoot from below and above eye levels as well as at eye level. Some people look better from different angles and the unusual angle will add interest to the picture.
6. Strive for unposed pictures by getting the subject to do something extra . . . working at a job, talking to someone, expressing emotion.
7. Strive for human interest. Most stories can be told through people so features about computers or manufacturing or office work should include people who are or will be involved in some way.
8. Try to interpret for the reader traits or elements in the subject that you know or which represent that person. For example, if a person is a comical individual, get him to do something comical in the picture. If you are reporting the boredom of retirement, capture this. Don't do "the golden years" which is what most company editors seem to do.
9. Avoid lining people up for group photos, especially against a busy background; e.g., a patterned drapery. Get the people to do something, even if only looking at one person or making the sign of victory.
10. Crop photos ruthlessly for maximum impact and eliminate unnecessary distraction and clutter. Zoom in on the most important part of the photo and delete anything that doesn't communicate the message you want to deliver.
11. Select the most effective and interesting photograph and blow it up large. Place it on the front page or cover of your publication, or at least run it as the lead photograph on an inside page or spread.
12. Strive for contrast: big vs. small, dark vs. light, horizontal vs. vertical, people vs. things, individuals vs. groups, etc.

13. Treat pictures in an unusual way, e.g. odd shape (not all horizontal or vertical), bleed, vignette, silhouette, poster-size, frame with white or black edge; use duotones, bendays or tint blocks; place a small picture in a field of color or white space.
14. Group several photographs together for a cluster effect. The impact of several smaller pictures can be greater than the sum of the parts.
15. Repeat pictures for greater impact (e.g., interviews with executives, pictures of jogger in different positions, etc.).

More Advice From Blake Kellogg

The following pointers on photography were taken from a book by Professor Blake Kellogg of the University of Wisconsin and his associate, Rosella Howe:

Photos are most easily used in a newsletter or magazine with a 2-column or 3-column format. The photos should conform to the grid which is used for the periodical.

Headlines are unnecessary for photos (a reader's eye goes directly to the photo). However, every photo should have a caption. Captions should be set in bold face type immediately below the photo. Credit lines should be set in small light-face type, flush right, separate from the caption, and close to the bottom edge.

A photo with a good caption may draw the reader into the story. In fact, it may be the only part of your story the reader looks at. Therefore, captions should be clear and informative and can even contain a part of the story beyond the picture itself.

When a photo is used with a story, the best sequence is: photo, caption, headline, story.

Photos should almost always be printed larger than you think necessary. Big pictures are bold, dramatic, interesting. This is particularly important with pictures that include detail, such as group pictures. Crop photos so that you use only the interesting part. Get new ideas for using photos from other newsletters, newspapers, magazines. Keep a clip file of photo ideas.

Don't make the mistake of running a page of pictures without individual captions. Tell who the people are and what they are doing. Never run the captions together in a single block of type—this makes the reader's job more difficult.

If you have a series of related photos, keep them together and present them in an orderly sequence.

As a rule, one photo should dominate a picture page by being both larger and more interesting. An obvious exception to this rule is if you are showing a series or sequence of pictures of equal merit.

The most interesting photo should be at the top of the page and preferably at the left, since that's the point where the reader enters the page.

Related pictures should be contiguous to one another for the convenience of the reader.

Photography And Crying

Photographs that are relevant, attractive and of high quality are being increasingly used in state and county medical publications.

However, the quality of photos in most of these small-circulation publications is still poor. Cost is one reason but this sometimes is a weak excuse. Another reason given by the editors is political; they say they are "forced" to publish photos of key people in the organization regardless of the snapshot quality. The *primary reason* is actually that many editors know relatively little about photography, photo layout and reproduction.

"Good photography is too expensive," is an excuse offered by many editors who use poor photos. Other editors explain the cramped groupings with "our members want pictures of as many people as possible."

Some of these excuses are valid. Still, a really good picture is an art form within the scope of any medical journal editor regardless of time and money limitations.

"The difference between a good photographer and a great photographer," said William Bernbach of the famed Doyle Dane Bernbach advertising agency, "is, the first one can take a picture of a little boy crying. The second can take a picture that makes you cry."

ART

The Value Of Illustrations

Medical Journalism published the following excerpt from an article by Paul Fisher, Professor of Journalism at the University of Missouri.

Illustration ought to mean something over, above, and far beyond the collection of single and group shots of men from the belly up.

Sadly, inevitably, the nature of the content of professional articles rarely supports photography. Abstract art usually can be employed with marvelous results, but the assumption must be that the services of the artist are not at the beck and call of the editor. Nor does the discovery of clip art end the search, for such art looks to be what it is—characterless line stylizations to fit all situations loosely.

So where to turn? The conscientious editor builds up his knowledge of sources that may, with luck, produce usable art for him on happy occasions where art and article are brought into harmony. Some editors have found the *Diderot Encyclopedia* to be a mother-lode of non-copyrighted art in woodcut appearance. The woodcuts by Thomas Bewick and the pages of 19th and 20th century specimen books also must be rated high among likely sources.

A few journals limit their contents to articles—and benefit graphically from this discipline. But most surround articles with a wide array of forms —advertisements, short and long news stories, departments, convention programs, minutes of meetings, etc. In the more degenerate publications, the contents appear to be whatever the mail brought, appearing in the journal page by page roughly in the order of postal arrival. (The outsider suspects the reader would be better served if much of this material went back by return mail.)

Since such journals must serve a diversity of purposes, it remains for the editor to seek an impression of order, of predictability, issue to issue, by simplification of the forms and, where desirable, their separation.

There can be no talk of simplification without reference to covers. The average journal cover is a spotty soup of various sizes and line lengths, assorted emblems, rules, ornaments, screens, photos and whatever else may be at hand. Three simple questions precede simplification:

- What can be deleted?
- What elements can be combined or standardized in specifications?
- What element is to receive major emphasis?

Inside the publication, group like materials for order. The old practice of collecting all ads together had much to recommend it, and yet a journal probably benefits from the change of pace given by the full-page ad inserted within a sequence of editorial pages. It is an awful practice, however, to allow small ads to justify columns of type. It may kill two birds with one stone by getting rid of the ad while justifying the column, but it also certainly kills the appearance of the page. Journals willing to sell ads in any size bequeath to the editor an insurmountable problem, and he can but group them and hide the groupings as best he can.

To the extent practical, editorial content should also be grouped by kind and consistently positioned, issue to issue. The typography of editorial content other than articles must be suppressed. Where a substantial body of material relates to a very narrow subject—reviews of recent literature, say—then a department complete with departmental logotype (in the spirit of cover design, let's hope) would make a sensible form.

A few journals go the whole route and group all editorial matter other than articles in departments, the sole display being in the departmental heading.

This is all very neat and ordered, but some editors will rightly question placement of stories in departments to which their relationship is tenuous or nonexistent.

Making Effective Use Of Cover Art

The *Bulletin of the Orange County Medical Association* (Orange, California) has many excellent features, including its covers. One of its best covers was a reproduction of a popular newspaper comic strip.

The "Beetle Bailey" comic strip by Mort Walker is distributed by King Features to several hundred newspapers. Perhaps you saw the sequence in which Private Bailey and the old Sarge both sighed and thought about quitting the Army.

Dr. Louis E. Potvin, president-elect of the Orange County Medical Association, saw the comic strip and used it as the lead-in to his editorial about membership in medical associations.

In the column, Dr. Potvin stated:

" 'Maybe I'll quit' has probably been the position of many of the leaders of organized medicine over the past two to 10 years. It has again become a popular trend among the physicians to disassociate themselves from the AMA with the classic quip that 'They do not represent me. . . .' "

Dr. Potvin then listed many California Medical Association and AMA accomplishments and concluded:

"This is not the time for us to consider quitting our organizations, nor for the organizations to quit on us. I would like to take this occasion to invite each and every physician in Orange County to join us, to join the California Medical Association, and to join the AMA for a cause that should supersede all others—that is, the maintaining of the private practice of medicine as we know it and as we would like to see it with the improvements that are necessary. Let us not wait for the government to make the improvements that they think are necessary at a cost which neither us nor our country can afford. Come on in—the water's hot, but the fight is great."

The use of color photos and drawings on covers is one of the major trends noted among professional journals.

Some editors, particularly at small-circulation publications, complain that they can't afford to retain photographers, artists, and art directors. One solution is to purchase stock materials from photo archives and art services. Many libraries, state historical societies, university news bureaus and other organizations offer free or low-cost photographs that often are top quality.

Pat Powers, managing editor of *Florida Pharmacy Journal*, working with Ann Erwin, production manager of Rapido Graphics, operated for a time the Pharmacy Art Service Portfolio. Called PAS Portfolio, the service provided prepared art, photos and other materials which are especially suitable for pharmacy publications. Art categories included drawings for department titles, cover ideas and materials about poison prevention and dozens of other topics.

Lists of "clip art" and other stock photo and art services appear in various directories, including Professional's Guide to Public Relations Services, published by Public Relations Publishing Co., 888 Seventh Ave., NY 10106.

Cartoons range from editorial cartoons (serious or humorous) to multipanel continuity strips, single illustrations for articles, and caricatures. Techniques and ideas are endless, and new styles and approaches in black and white line art, full-color renderings, line and color overlays are constantly being created.

The deciding point on whether one or several panels are needed is governed by the idea itself and the message. Can it be conveyed in a single picture or does it need more panels to "come across"?

Types Of Art

Raymond Dorn, a leading graphics expert, was formerly manager of art and layout for eleven American Medical Association publications. He presents here questions and answers about four types of art used in journals and magazines.

Four Types of Art

1. Strong vertically.
Problem: How to utilize, when the page is predominantly vertical.
Possible answers: Spots of color in the chart content; a two-point color border, changing optical direction; the addition of a textured area other than simple tint values; placement next to a horizontal or "light and airy" shape.

2. Strong horizontally.
Problem: How to keep this from dominating the page.
Possible answers: Reduce to a proportion that will balance the rest of the page; place next to an equally strong vertical; have the platemaker use a percentage of black, rather than 100%; change the straight lines into tints of a light color, put it at the top of a page so the "sink" will help subdue it.

3. Light and airy.
Problem: How to keep the art from flying apart.
Possible answers: Enclose with a border; enclose the art with text on both sides; place rules in color, or tint values of grey, at both top and bottom.

4. Dark, with massed detail.
Problem: How to keep this from dominating the page.
Possible answers: Allow extra white space around it; put it at the top of a page so the "sink" will help minimize it; change the dark black areas to tints of grey (if possible); relieve some of the dark areas by using patterns instead of solids; relate with a light picture or table.

Halftones and Line Art

More editors of medical, pharmaceutical and hospital publications are using a greater quantity and better quality of photography and line art than ever before. It is no longer necessary to convince editors of the value of illustrations. What is needed is continuing education about ways to handle art economically and efficiently.

The following excerpts are from *Impact*, the newsletter published by Robert Leon Baker in Chicago.

Halftones & Line Art

Pick a few; crop them close; play them big. A layout with one dominant photograph is generally more exciting than one in which all pictures are the same size. For impact, crop 'til it hurts to "shape" a picture, trim clutter, "intensify" key elements.

Photomontages require large areas, exciting pictures, interesting contrast, expert air brushing.

Cutlines (in our terminology, a cutline is the copy under a cut, a caption, the copy—usually head size—above the picture) should *serve* the reader.

They should be *adjacent to pictures they describe.* No need for such confusing complications as *below left, extreme left, far right, top left*, etc.

Cutline type should be distinguishable from body type. (Probably a size smaller, in either a lighter or bolder face.) Cutlines should not exceed width of photo.

Half-col cuts or thumbnails offer an excellent way to handle a number of head shots (except for the problem posed by runarounds).

Avoid the use of strange mood and geometric shapes—oblongs, triangles, ovals, etc.

Handle the bleeding of photographs with restraint. Err on the side of fewer bleeds, not more.

Don't butt photographs. Provide at least hairline separation.

Seldom surprint type over halftones. The copy often can't be read without some strain, and usually the illustration itself suffers.

Execute and employ line art with imagination. For example, it can be reversed in color panels, printed over color panels, or given tone shadings within some of the lines.

Sometimes photos or artwork can carry the entire message. *Minutes*, the magazine once published by Nationwide Insurance, ran two pages of pictures of manhole covers. There was no copy, Roy Paul Nelson noted in his book *Publication Design.* There were no cutlines. The variety of patterns stamped on the covers was story enough.

Other suggestions that could help you add even greater impact to your photographs and artwork:

Effective use of the centerfold. It could be a massive gutter-hopping, pull-out photograph or work of art; a photo essay; an organization chart; a process flow diagram; or any other subject requiring large, integrated space, and removability for "keepsake" or "pinup" possibilities.

For emotional appeal, *try a "big dot"* pattern in a halftone. (Up close it will look like pop art!)

Try a full-bleed photograph covering an entire spread. (It helps, however, if the halftone provides some open space for a headline and possibly a few lines of text.)

Convert a halftone to line. (The platemaker simply skips the screen and handles the photo as if it were a line drawing.)

Use an occasional wrap-around bleed—the picture that bleeds off the right-hand page and continues on the left of the following page.

Make your big pictures look even bigger by playing them with much smaller halftones.

Experiment with the different methods of displaying your photos on the page—duotones, vignettes, silhouettes, collages, montages, flopping, mirror images, fogging, partial drop-outs, mezzotint screens, segmenting (you literally pull or explode the picture apart into segments), posterization, split images (two identical negs, cut in half, and stripped together for a new result), the combination line and halftone, mortices. But remember that *nothing* beats the rectangle or square as the proper shape for a photograph.

Innovate in cropping—long verticals, horizontal slices, extreme close-ups of a key element (imagine the impact and visual excitement possible with the combination of cropping for an extreme close-up with play as a full bleed on a spread).

Charts, Graphs, Tables, Maps

You can work up a *flow chart* to show how a product is made; an *organization chart* to show the chain of management; a *line graph* or *bar chart* to show in percentages where the money went; *pictographs* to humanize and heighten the visual impact of a statistical presentation.

The little men, coins, animals, tools, buildings and other objects that make up pictographic presentation offer a colorful way to display statistical relationships. However, you must always be careful of distorting the pictograph and the truth. Show changes in numbers by more or fewer symbols, not by alternating shape or size of each individual figure. Remember that a figure twice as high could cover 4 to 8 times as much area and about 8 times the cubic volume! Some other pointers on the use of pictographs:

Symbols should be self explanatory. They should be unique, interesting, simply designed, instantly distinguishable for what they represent.

They should give only the big picture to dramatize comparisons. Remove unessentials and avoid too much detail.

They should reproduce well in any size, large or small.

The Free-Lance Artist

An article on freelancers included this material from *Impact*, the monthly newsletter published by Robert Leon Baker at 203 N. Wabash Ave., Chicago 60601.

If you can, select an artist whose interpretation is basically the same as yours. If you prefer contemporary art, select an artist whose renderings are contemporary. If you prefer abstract art, select an artist whose work is abstract.

Putting it bluntly, in any initial screening of an artist an editor has to put a quick finger on three factors—fee, talent, and temperament. Of the three, the latter is by no means the least important.

Choose an artist who is aggressive enough to promote personal ideas, and willing to consider and adapt the best of your suggestions.

And, finally, select an artist you can afford. Put a strain on the budget and you put a strain on the relationship.

Artists' fees vary, but the price must be right for you and your publication or the entire relationship is jeopardized. A free-lance artist with minimum overhead may charge as little as $25 an hour or as much as $75 an hour. This will also vary depending on the work to be done. The artist may charge as little as $25 a page for rough layout or as much as $250 per page for a comprehensive layout. He or she may charge as little as $25 for a line sketch or as much as $1,000 for a detailed rendering. Some may charge a set rate per page or prefer to invoice for the entire publication, allowing a limited and reasonable number of alterations.

Once you have made your selection of an artist and agreed upon fees, you will want to acquaint the artist with your organization—its identity or projected image, its management philosophies, its products or services, and its key personnel.

You will also want to familiarize the artist with your publication. Go over back issues. Show him your "futures file" and reveal some of your thinking and plans for the future. Cover such aspects as:

- Format and typography.
- Publication objectives.
- Readership analysis—who are the readers?
- Handling of text, art, and photos. Cover preferred ratio, standing heads, regular columns, other aspects of publication established by traditions, management preference, etc.
- Publication timetable. This will determine work schedule and deadlines.

• Budget. Unusual and satisfying results may be obtained through the artist's ingenuity even though your budget is limited. For example, the artist can achieve artistic results through the use of duotones, shading, other simple yet handsome design and layout approaches. In a generous budget, the artist should still use materials and processes which would achieve the most satisfactory results for every dollar expended.

• Production. The artist needs to know the capabilities and the limitations of a printer's equipment for both black and white and multicolor printing.

Other suggestions to sharpen your control and direction of free-lance artists:

• Make it clear that you want your artist to retain creative freedom.

• Give the artist direction but without excessive limitation. Between the two is the tender thread which separates the successful from the unsuccessful blending of ideas.

• Do not harbor preconceived ideas and insist the artist use them. Neither should you be apathetic, for one state is just as frustrating to the artist as the other.

• Be receptive to your artist's ideas and suggestions concerning typefaces and paper stock. The latter is as important to him as fabric is to a designer.

If the artist has a completely new idea for your publication format, listen with an open mind. If the layout has remained static because you were afraid to change it or because you hadn't thought of it, try the artist's suggestion. It might provide the very vitality your publication needs.

COVERS

The Essential Element

The cover is the most important part of your magazine, because it is what the reader sees first. The cover is what sets the tone and conveys the promise of things to come. The nameplate of your magazine should be perceived immediately.

Probably one, two or three is the right number of coverlines. More than three headlines would seem to introduce clutter to the cover. Further, by emphasizing everything, nothing is emphasized.

Type can be set in one of four ways: (1) all upper case (caps,) (2) each word begins in upper and then the rest in lower (caps and lowercase), (3) the first word and proper nouns in upper and the rest in lower (as in text), (4) all lower case.

Ask yourself: Am I consistent throughout my issue with my use of type? Is it set the same way on the cover, on the contents page, and throughout the article?

The decision as to whether or not you should use an illustration depends upon: (1) if you consistently have good art or good photos available for the cover, and (2) if you usually use photos or art in the articles, as opposed to all print.

Covers should create, as Jan White says, "poster impact." Successful posters usually contain three elements—a dominant illustration, a headline, and some smaller (typographic) information.

If your magazine has a spine which is wide enough to accept printing, you should emphasize the name of your periodical. The date and volume number should be in lighter, smaller type.

It is a good idea to standardize the format for your magazine's cover because: (1) it (the magazine) will be instantly recognizable, (2) it will be familiar (like a friend), (3) it will simplify production for you, and (4) it will give you greater flexibility in that you won't have to reinvent the wheel every issue.

Covering Covers

State and county medical journals, state pharmaceutical magazines and hospital publications, continue to show considerable imagination in creating their covers.

In most cases, the cover art has nothing to do with the publications' contents, but in others there is a definite connection, with the photograph, sketch or montage illustrating an article or the issue's theme.

The *Journal of Kansas Pharmacy* ran a schematic drawing of an oversized pencil to dramatize the fact that the issue contained the annual report of the Kansas Pharmacists Association.

Pennsylvania Medicine created great reader interest in its feature article on "Who Says Doctors Can't Write?" by showing on its cover a broken pencil, several crumpled pieces of paper and an overturned mug surrounding several pages of a typed manuscript.

The Pacemaker, published by Harper-Grace Hospitals, Detroit, Michigan, featured a cover showing two people parachuting to earth. The dramatic caption "An 80-foot fall—he not only lives, but jogs."

Miami Medicine continued its fine nature and sports covers with a front page containing an award-winning photo showing goldfish in a feeding frenzy.

The Ohio Medical Journal uses excellent color photographs to draw the reader's attention to a particular article or series of articles. The publication ran a cover showing a physician checking a worker's blood pressure. The copy with the photo stated, "Health care for the unemployed: Ohio's physicians reduce the pressure." The same issue ran a comprehensive piece on the question of providing health care to unemployed workers who have exhausted their medical and hospital benefits. Another cover contained two photos. One showed a surgical team in an operating room, while the other depicted an ambulance on the go. The copy, "In case of an emergency," connected the illustrations to a series of articles on emergency medical care.

The Journal of the Iowa Medical Society featured a cartoon on its cover, with several people shown thinking, in the traditional cartoon style of "balloons" concerning money. The legend on the cover: "What Iowans Are Thinking About Health Care . . ." Inside was a special eight-page section giving the results of a survey of Iowan public opinion on health care problems.

The quality of photography in most of the medical and pharmaceutical journals has improved tremendously in recent years. Editors of small-circulation, low-budget publications often are ingenious in their methods of obtaining historical and contemporary photos, drawings, paintings, posters and other art at little or no cost. State and local hospitals and health organizations and other sources can provide a dazzling array of photos and other materials.

A typical example of resourcefulness is the Fairfield County Medical Association, which publishes *News Capsule*, a little (6 × 9 inch) monthly magazine for its members in Connecticut. In 1983, all of the covers featured photos of early medical instruments used by Connecticut physicians. In 1984, all of the covers featured photos of new technologies.

For example, the January 1984 cover photo showed a patient in a CT scanner at St. Vincent's Medical Center. The February issue showed a smiling patient in a hyperbaric bed at Norwalk Hospital communicating via an intercom system with a respiratory therapist. The year concluded with an infant in a KDC Warmer at the neonatal intensive care unit of Stamford Hospital. Congratulations to Leonard R. Tomat, executive director of the Association, who also is editor of the magazine.

Publication Scorecard
(PREPARED BY HERBERT AUER OF MICHIGAN MEDICINE)

Ask yourself these questions about your journal cover

Yes No ?

1. Is cover space divided in pleasing way?
2. Does layout move eye from upper area to lower right?
3. Is color used wisely?
4. Is name of publication in distinctive type face?
5. Is copy set in C/lc for easier reading?

How does your contents page score?

Yes No ?

1. Is the name of publication repeated and in same typeface as on cover?
2. Is type large enough to be easily read?
3. Is it easy to find what page number an article is on?
4. Is the page divided into pleasing areas?
5. Would the use of grey screens or color help page be attractive?

Ask yourself about photos

Yes No ?

1. Are photos relatively large?
2. Are photos cropped well to eliminate unnecessary details and backgrounds?
3. Do photos look into copy, rather than off the page?
4. Are photos sharp rather than fuzzy?

How's your continuity?

Yes No ?

1. Is the same typeface that is used for journal name on cover also used on contents page, on page of first scientific article and on other pages?
2. Is certain type or symbolic artwork used throughout on all department headings?

COLOR

Color Pages

Over the years, a number of editors have begun to use color pages in addition to color covers. They have found that the decision to use color should not be based on cost, and that color should be considered for its functional values, just as any other typographic device. Basically, color must contribute to communication.

Following are some comments about color by Edward C. Arnold, a graphics art consultant, which appeared in an article he wrote for the *Ragan Report*.

Color is a spice and, just like culinary spices, it is most effective when used sparingly.

To follow this advice is extremely difficult. The cost of color does not increase as its area increases. The color surcharge is no greater for a whole page in color than for a single ornamental initial. So it is a common tendency to "get our money's worth" and use color lavishly.

Color is most effective when used to print non-verbal elements. Body type should never be printed in color; headlines should be printed in color only if that color has "enough guts" to provide high visibility.

The "gutsier" a color becomes—that is, the darker it becomes—the less obviously is it a color. The difference between robin's egg-blue and navy blue is that of "guts" or tonal value. The dark navy hue is easier to read. But it looks much more like black than like blue and so its chromatic values are diminished.

Colors with high "chroma"—brilliance or sheen—are easy to see. In fact, too easy. Some colors actually vibrate; the blinding orange helmets and vests worn by highway construction workers are a good example. So colors like shocking pink and peacock blue are almost physically hurtful to the reading eye, especially in body sizes.

Boxes, rules, tint blocks and large, loose areas of color are the best way to use this tool. Nameplates of magazines and trademarks or logos of organizations (after all, they're the same thing!) are good in color.

Don't print halftones in color; too much detail is lost. Line art—depending on the individual characteristics of each picture—usually is good in color.

Tint blocks are an area of color upon which type or art is surprinted. Except for yellow, colors used in tint blocks must be "screened down"—by peppering them with a Ben Day dot pattern—to lighten their tone. (A "tint" is produced by adding white to a color; adding black produces a "shade.") We can print a light pattern of black dots over an area of color and produce a shade.

Make sure that color used in a tint block has been lightened to provide maximum tonal contrast between it and the surprinted material. It is the difference in tonal value that makes the type visible and visibility is necessary, of course, to readability.

Don't surprint a black halftone on a tint block. The result is a flat, muddy reproduction that carries neither detail nor appeal.

A tint block should be regarded as "a little page." Just as we must have an adequate margin on a piece of paper, so there must be an adequate "margin" on the tint block. Don't run type right to the edge of the block.

Bleeding

Here are Edward Arnold's views on bleeding photos, a technique designed to expand a page, command attention and create excitement. The comments appeared originally in the *Ragan Report* and were reproduced in the *Medical Journalism* newsletter.

"Bleeding" is running a picture off the page. Actually that can't be done on a printing press. So a larger sheet is used; the picture is printed as close to the edge as possible; then the sheet is cut down, right through the picture to have it actually run off the new, smaller page.

There are two advantages of bleeds. The first is the ability to increase the size of the picture by using the margins. That's really not a great advantage. Except for a tiny picture, the marginal space is so small, in percentage, that the gain is inconsequential.

If only that much extra space is needed to display a photo properly, it is best obtained by judiciously cutting the length of the written copy.

The major advantage of a bleed is its "expanding effect."

A printed page is basically a rectangle. When that rectangle is enlarged by a picture breaking out into a bleed, not only that individual picture but the entire page expands. This creates a feeling of freedom, of being in a large, unrestricted area.

The only kind of art, then, that can bleed effectively is a photograph which has such limitless areas.

(It should be noted that type should never bleed; it is a finite element which requires precision of area to carry its message. Line art may bleed; but in all but a few instances, the expanding effect is negligible.)

Usually the areas for expanding are the sky and the foreground. In case the bleed is sideways, both these areas are involved.

If the sky in a picture is allowed to expand, it gives a feeling of a limitless firmament and of unrestricted freedom. The "Big Sky" phenomenon of our Western states is a perfect analogy. When you can see out to the limits of the universe, your spirit goes soaring off into outer space and the exhilaration is a physical one.

If the foreground area is bled, it moves into the reader. That moves other objects in the photo away from the reader. The effect is one of great space; but now a feeling of isolation sets in. The subject of the photo—separated from the viewer by the vast expanse of foreground—seems isolated and lonely. Often the reader feels a mood of solitary withdrawal. This may be either pleasant or disturbing . . . but the editor really doesn't know which effect it will have on the reader. In this case the captions carry the burden of conditioning the reader into the mood that the editor desires.

Portraits, then, should not bleed. There is no expansion factor in the human torso . . . speaking pictorially, that is. Would that those evening snacks didn't act on the waistline like a bled horizon!

There is no value to bleeding a picture into the gutter. While it is a technical bleed—the picture does run into the gutter margin—the fold of the page stops the expanding movement.

If the editor absolutely must bleed into the gutter, only one photo should be so treated. Especially to be avoided are bleeds into the gutter from both pages and the most horrendous sin is to have bleeds from facing pages bump into each other. The result of such collision is always confusion to the reader.

Note: We do not agree with the broad generalization that portraits should not bleed. Surely, that's true for most "head shots," which are dull, but occasionally a masterful portrait photographer produces a picture for a medical journal, perhaps of a key officer of the society, and the picture should be blown up to its fullest potential. Furthermore, medical journal editors tend to be timid about the use of large space for photos, and we encourage experimentation, with or without bleeding.

How To Use Color Effectively

The impact of color can be so important as to more than justify the added cost. However, the real problem is not the cost, but rather how to use color most effectively. Obviously, journals must not be garish, and there are lots of other obvious restrictions and rules. Journal editors can learn from the advertisements of pharmaceutical companies, which often are superbly designed by art directors, who use color so well that the ads sometimes dominate the editorial matter.

At our workshops, we often have urged those editors who are using Linotype and Letterpress to stick to these processes. However, it must be acknowledged that Letterpress printing plants sometimes are older, small operations which lack color sophistication.

If your printer functions as your art director or layout person, that may be a great bargain, but make sure that you're not forced to "accommodate" to the printer's facilities. In the days of the Model-T, Henry Ford used to say that buyers could have any color, as long as it was black. So don't let your printer sell you a Model-T.

O.K., you're sold on color. But which color or colors, where and how?

Al Hackl, president of Colortone Press, a major national printer in Washington, DC, gave some answers in an article he wrote for *pr reporter*. Excerpts from the piece, which was titled "Understanding the Hidden Meaning of Color," were reprinted in *Medical Journalism*.

Al Hackl's Advice

Disregarding your personal color prejudices and recommending the right one for the job at hand—the one that will bring the greatest return—is the dilemma. This is because color has meaning—hidden meaning that's hard to define.

Brighter colors get more attention than softer colors. Generally speaking, red and orange have a high visibility, and attention-getting power. This is partly because the warm colors appear to be advancing to the eye; cool colors seem to be retreating. Psychologically, nearness and attention are related, because in life greater attention is paid to things nearby.

But if everything were printed in red, there would be no contrast among the various parts, and all would be competing for attention on the same basis. So each case must be considered individually and built up accordingly.

Anything that tends to make copy more attractive will help sustain attention. However, any unfortunate color combination will repel readers. Greens and blues have a soothing effect and high-preference record in holding continuing interest.

Design must be balanced. For this reason, balance and weight factors of various colors should be kept in mind. The following scale is a handy guide:

3.1 _____ White
3.5 _____ Yellow
4.1 _____ Green

4.7 _____ Blue
4.8 _____ Purple, Gray
4.9 _____ Red

5.8 _____ Black

The amount of color in a design has to be considered along with the color itself and is largely a matter for the individual artist or designer to _feel._

Color can improve the legibility of copy when interspersed in the proper places. In black-and-white, boldface type, caps and italics are used with the same purpose in mind. However, color can do this job much more effectively.

Distance can be created by combinations (and the resulting interpretation) of colors. Cool colors recede; warm colors project themselves closer to the viewer.

This same principle can be applied to bring out the relative importance of the copy. Designers use cool colors as a background on which to superimpose type, since these recede and provide contrast.

For legibility, psychological tests rank the following colors, in this order. (The first is easiest to read, and each thereafter is somewhat harder to read.)

1. Black on Yellow paper
2. Green on White paper
3. Blue on White paper
4. White on Blue paper
5. Black on White paper
6. Yellow on Black paper
7. White on Red paper
8. White on Orange paper
9. White on Black paper
10. Red on Yellow paper
11. Green on Red paper
12. Red on Green paper

If colored stocks are required, it is generally safer to use black ink. Better results are obtained if pastel, light-colored stocks are used. By using two colors of ink on a light-colored stock, additional emotional factors may be packed into the message, and thus strengthen the basic appeal. In such a case, the body of the message should be printed in a color related to the color of the stock (very dark green ink on pastel light green stock) and the heads or highlights printed in the complementary color (red).

Sans-serif typefaces are most effective in color, particularly as heads. But in black-and-white, they are frequently hard to read because of the light absorption of the large black masses of type. Color can come to the rescue and enhance the legibility of the otherwise hard-to-read extra-bold faces. In color, they take on the added character normally provided by typefaces that have serifs.

Though we think we are creatures of reason, psychologists tell us that most decisions are emotionally inspired. If a color reminds the reader of some past experience, it may influence his or her attitude toward the particular printed piece. Anticipating this factor is probably the most intangible of all in forecasting a successful color combination.

The chart which follows, while partly unscientific, has some significance in daily life and may be used as a guide in choosing colors.

Psychological studies show that women prefer red, blue, violet, green, orange and yellow—in that order. Blue is the favorite color of men, followed by red, violet, green, orange and yellow. Children prefer bright colors; older people softer colors.

Red is the color of boldness and power. Too much becomes overpowering. Used sparingly, it gives lift to a page. Blue, with its sky and water association, denotes hope and patience. It is the favorite color of most people.

Yellow generates the buoyancy of a sunny day. It can light up a page when properly used. Orange, with its resemblance to gold, gives overtones of money and prosperity. Brown is a versatile color; men associate it with wood and leather, women with furs. Green suggests grass and foliage. Violet symbolizes robes of royalty, the dignity of church vestments and the pomp and splendor of high ritual.

The function of color is to capture attention, give information that words alone do not convey, guide the eye in reading and create a mood that makes the reader more perceptive to the printed message.

Color	Positive Factors	Negative Factors	Complementary Color
red	warmth	danger	green
(pink)	excitement	anger	
yellow	cheerful	dishonesty	purple
	light (sun)	sensational	(blue)
blue	cool	depressing	yellow
	serene	melancholic	(orange)
green	nature	envy	red
	youth	immature	(pink)
	(cool in the lighter hues)		

Color: A Dimension of Layout

The following article was excerpted from *impact*, the newsletter for editors:
"Color is layout's 5th Dimension," Cortland Gray Smith wrote in his book
Magazine Layout.

Certainly, it's a dimension of layout that we shouldn't have to miss
since the advantages of color far outweigh the disadvantages.

Let's take the negatives first. Number one—cost. Extra colors cost
money—there's no denying the fact—but technology and technique continue to whittle away at the tab. The second negative—the old "we've got it,
why not use it" approach. Function and purpose are incidental. Color is
splashed everywhere in reverse panels, tint blocks, headlines, dingbats.
When this mistake is made, color can actually detract from your message.

But even in the face of these negatives, the positives of color can be
overwhelming.

Color, statistics prove conclusively, if used judiciously and with purpose, *will* give you more readers. It will give you more *intense* readership. It
will give added longevity to your message.

Why is color more appealing and persuasive? Mainly because it is more
realistic. We live in a sea of vivid color as any stroll down a metropolitan
boulevard proves in a hurry. The drab hues are passe. And this holds for
publications as well as TV, packaging, advertising, graphics, design and the
like.

We, therefore, as editors have to do everything within our creative
power and limited budgets to make color work for us, even if our creativity
has to be restricted to one color of ink.

And how sad, in this era of wild and glowing hues, such a restriction
can be!

Back in 1955, the U.S. Bureau of Standards published a color dictionary that listed, between "abbey" (a strong violet) and "zuni" (a moderate
brown), exactly 7,455 different colors!

Few of us will deny that color has the power to increase our readership.
Every survey ever taken proves it.

It's the "in" way of reaching and accentuating the senses of modern-day readers. Color adds quality and prestige. It implies extra thought, extra
labor, extra creativity. It helps to create a mood unachievable with straight
type, and it can create optical affects or visual phenomena impossible to
create in any other way. For example:

Do you want a headline to "leap out" at your reader? Against the
proper color—a bright red for instance—a line of white type seems to leap

off the page, especially when close to and contrasted to a line of black type on the same background. There are many other ways to create the illusion of depth or add an extra dimension to your page with color.

Do you want to produce a multiplicity of brilliant effects with relative economy? It can be done simply by overprinting the new transparent colors.

Do you want a special report or a special section to *really* look special? A second color, or a different color paper stock for that matter, will definitely set such a section apart from the rest of your publication.

Do you want your colors to vibrate? Change the reality of a scene? Provide optical illusions? It can be achieved.

We as editors, it seems when all is said and done, had better opt for color in our publications. As the old saying goes: "Let us not gather corn if another path leads to a garden of orchids."

PUBLICATION COSTS

Keeping Costs Down

One of the first lessons an editor learns about printing is that changes cost progressively more as the job progresses. There are two basic types of errors. Author's Alterations (AA's) and Printer's Errors (PE's). Obviously, the goal is to aim for few of any type of error, but AA's are costlier than PE's.

Jaime Associates, a graphics design company in New York City, prepared the following list of simple ways to keep costs down.

Stages of possible changes

1. Manuscript—one person involved (author)
2. Typeset copy—about 6 people
3. Mechanical pasted up—artist—about 7 people
4. Blueprint made—add plate maker, stripper, pressman—about 12 people

Types of AA's

1. Cutting copy in the middle of a paragraph involves resetting entire paragraph and proofreading again.
2. Changing a semi-colon to a dash involves a reset.
3. Changing a period to a comma always means a reset. It's the next letter that is different. (Cap is wider.)
4. Fifteen years ago, it cost several dollars to change a period to a comma on the same line. And that was 15 years ago.

Clean Copy

Typewritten manuscript should be clean, double-spaced on one side of an 8½ × 11 inch sheet. Never send handwritten material to a typographer. The cleaner the copy, the less errors, the less time consumed.

Time is Money

If the job is a down-to-the-wire rush, do send a partial manuscript to the typographer (some shops will accept partial manuscripts) to get a head start on the job and avoid premium time costs, which can raise the price by 50 to 100%. (Better to have premium charge on only part of the job than on all of it.)

Late News

Save ¼ column of space to handle "Late News Flashes." Have an expendable photo, illustration or filler in case there isn't any last-minute news of significance. By allowing for late news, you will reduce the need for AA's after the blue has been made (the most costly type of change).

Don't Get Fancy

Justified copy is the least expensive to set (as opposed to flush left, flush right or centered), therefore, keep away from run arounds, and setting to a shape. Horizontal rules in tabulated columns are intrinsically expensive. Consult your typographer on alternate ways to set, e.g. boldface or italic type. Borders to make boxes can be costly. Expect to pay more for coupons. (They're hand-crafted and require separate leading—very time consuming).

Avoid Underlining

(Descenders get cut off.) Avoid using larger initial letters or any unnecessary change in typeface (not in family). If you must have these things, by all means order them—but be prepared to pay for them.

The Publication Budget

The following article appeared in the November 1981 issue of *Medical Journalism*. The prices cited, of course, have risen since that time, but the article is included here because it can serve as a rough guide to the relationship between one publication cost and another.

True or false:

1. Small-circulation publications have a much higher cost-per-copy than large-circulation publications.
2. Association publications cost more than the board of trustees, controller and other management think they should.
3. The production budget originally estimated by the designer/editor/ printer is considerably lower than the actual cost.

If your answer is true to one, two or all of the above, you're in good company—with most other editors!

Is it possible to produce an attractive publication, with color covers, artwork, photography and other features, and still keep costs within a reasonable budget? The answer is more likely to be in the affirmative if you are knowledgeable about production details, ranging from paper, typesetting and other fixed costs, to such variables as art and author's alterations.

Among the many newsletters for editors, one which is consistently useful, lucid and practical in its orientation to the needs of small-circulation publications is *Impact*, published monthly by Robert Leon Baker (203 N. Wabash Avenue, Chicago 60601, $18 a year). Following are excerpts from one of last year's issues of *Impact* about publication costs. 1981–1982 prices are generally higher than 1980, but this material can be extremely helpful.

To provide some common ground for pricing, we designed a mythical *Magazine "X"* using statistical averages of organizational publications. Thus, we described *Magazine "X"* to suppliers as a one signature book (16 pages); 8½ × 11 inches in size, printed on a 70-pound offset paper stock; about 50:50 art to text; two colors throughout; 10 on 12 body type; and self-cover. Circulation was set at 2,000 copies.

We solicited bids from several Chicago-area printers for the production of this mythical publication (explaining our purpose, of course). Their bids ranged from $1,915 to $2,410. Prices included typesetting, paste-up, keylining, offset plates, camera work, makeready, presstime, ink, paper, halftones, silverprints, bindery (fold, stitch, and trim) addressing, stuffing, sealing, typing, bagging, P.O. delivery.

We even considered costs of obtaining clearance from organizational executives, since such editorial procedures can be time-consuming and time can mean considerable expense to an organization when top executives are involved.

Here, then, is a breakdown of the figures. Please keep in mind that (1) they are based on metropolitan Midwest price averages, and (2) they represent what can be considered a *reasonable price* to pay for the various products and services required to produce a publication.

Offset Prep

Offset negatives for our *Magazine "X"* average out at about $27 a page or $432. This includes halftones, assuming an average of three to the page. Few printers (if any!) provide silverprints free. Most tack on a fat fee, and this is something to find out before ordering. Minimum charges for silverprint corrections range from $10 to $20.

For the few die-hard publishers still printing letterpress, halftone engravings in metropolitan centers run from 12 to 14 cents a unit (minimum of 73 units). Copper is no longer used.

Typesetting

Most publications are now paying from $45 to $65 a page for hot type. (Based on a 10-point type with a 2-point lead.) Cold type is running in the range of $40 to $55 for an 8½ × 11 page.

As you reduce type size and decrease leading you increase your typesetting costs per page by almost 20 percent. For example, where the range is $55 to $60 a page for 10 on 12, it becomes $66 to $72 when set 8-point solid.

Other factors to consider in typesetting charges:

1. The expense for setting a tabloid size page (circa 11¼ × 15½) is almost double that of the regular 8½ × 11 size.

2. Use of pictures on a page does not necessarily reduce your typesetting costs proportionately. In other words, where a full page of type costs you $60 to set, a half page of type (with a half page of pictures) will not cost $30. You have additional make-up, and cutline type to consider. In this situation, the cost would more likely average out to $40 or more.

AWARDS

1976

The winners of the first Sandoz annual Medical Journalism contest were *The Journal of the Indiana State Medical State Association,* the *Journal of the Iowa Medical Society,* the *Harris County Physician,* and the *Bulletin of the Medical Society of the County of Monroe.*

Edited by Frank B. Ramsey, M.D., the *Journal of the Indiana State Medical Association* had a circulation of about 4,600. Its distinctive covers were part of an extremely attractive overall design, its clinical articles were concise and readable, and its news content was varied and practical, according to the judges.

The *Journal of the Iowa Medical Society* had a circulation of about 2,800. The use of summaries at the beginning of each article and concise endings were among the outstanding features commended by the judges. Marion E. Alberts, M.D. was its scientific editor.

The editor of *The Harris County Physician* was L. Rodney Rodgers, M.D., of Houston. The publication's circulation was 4,200. One of its laudable features was the extensive use of good-quality photos and drawings produced with a very low production budget.

The *Bulletin of the Medical Society of the County of Monroe* was edited by David A. Sherman, M.D., of Rochester. This attractive, low-budget publication was produced with an electronic-type composer and other equipment at the medical society's office.

Honorable mentions were given to the *New York State Journal of Medicine, Delaware Medical Journal, Chicago Medicine* and *The Bulletin of Onondaga County Medical Society* in Syracuse, New York.

The judges who selected the winners used the following criteria in their judging; these criteria remain to this day as the guidelines for choosing the publications to be honored.

Layout

1. Publication achieves order at no sacrifice of interest, is simple but never dull, interesting but never precious, placing ease of the reader over gratification of the designer (e.g., limited reverses, overprints). Publication has a graphic identity achieved through practice of echoing graphic effects spread to spread within the issue, and issue to issue; that is, there is a recognizable graphic character.

2. Publication is sequenced in the interests of the reader. Professional articles (the "editorial well") are clustered in non-interrupted layout. Ideally, articles are self-containing (no "continueds") though they may flow through advertising matter. Departments and general news flow through the front and back of the publication as advertising dictates.
3. Major parts—articles, departments, news and advertising—are given sharp graphic separation (usually through choice of typeface and/or size). The reader knows instantly what page he has turned to.
4. Publication avails itself of the possibilities of the spread in horizontal sweeps (breaks across gutter of titles, photos) and vertical accents.
5. Unrelated pages on the spread are graphically defined by opposing horizontal versus vertical layouts, rule, color, double-burns, etc. against absence of same on facing pages.
6. Back-of-the-book pages and/or others forced to carry many disparate items show reductions in parts wherever possible for simplicity (i.e., in head styles, sizes, composition styles).
7. Wide expanses of text are relieved by such devices as subheads, boldface leadins, capitals, interior blurbs.
8. Cover is effective (basic criteria as in No. 1; e.g., order without sacrifice of interest). Title design distinctive, identifying.
9. Contents page is easy to find, easy to scan, achieving separations through uses of space (e.g., indentions) rather than in wide range of type sizes or, worse, faces. Deletes or subdues distracting elements (e.g., symbols of associations, awards).
10. Color uses are functional; e.g., used to accent not ornament.
11. Quality of advertising is commensurate with (or superior to) editorial layout. Advertising is so positioned as not to intrude on editorial layouts unnecessarily.
12. Basic column width is appropriate to the format, is in the interest of readability and cohesion.

Typography

Display choice

13. Title type faces are in character with the publication as established by the editorial content and the identity sought for it. Whether choice is varied or restricted, approach to usage remains constant issue after issue to achieve identification value for the publication.
14. Where contrasts of type faces are attempted (e.g., title to title, title to blurb) they are decisive in choice of face and/or size.
15. Weight and interest qualities of the display face(s) are such as to

carry yet not dominate the spread; they gain—but not thru obvious striving—attention.

16. Where varied sizes must appear on a given spread (as on news pages possibly), they are employed with restraint (three considered a practical maximum).

17. Faces are contemporary in spirit or classic (timeless), not dated, not of the fashion of a few years past.

18. Photographic enlargements of type have not disturbed fitting of the letters.

Text face choice

19. A typesetting system of reasonable quality has been used (as evidenced by letter fit, alignment, hyphenation range, *hairspacing* when required).

20. Size is large enough for easy reading; 10-point would appear minimum for most fonts.

21. Width of face is in harmony with basic column width employed (i.e., relatively narrow to relatively wide).

22. Face maintains tonal harmony (grey to black) with tonal intensity of photography.

23. Face is contemporary or classic, not so antiquated or stylized as to invite attention to the design.

24. Leading seems in best interests of the reader and the "color" of the face chosen.

Cutline choice (captions)

25. Type is of a size, weight, and design that clearly separates cutline from text line while showing no tendency to dominate the text.

Photography

26. Photographs add to or at least sharpen understanding of text; they do not appear to be thrown in simply to embellish or fill space.

27. Photography is properly laid out, not simply strung through the text; e.g., it is positioned to continue or sharply interrupt lines of movement or force.

28. Photographs do not appear posed, stiff; they stress activity; they minimize head shots, pictures of buildings, etc.

29. Photographs are properly cropped to avoid waste areas; no series of heads in dissimilar sizes).

30. Tone and style of photography is consistent through publication (no shapshot to studio range).

31. Choice of screen seems in interests of the photography.

Artwork

32. Style is consonant with character of the publication; i.e., no clip-art, no vague, bland, meant-for-many-uses illustration.
33. Clashes with halftones have been avoided. (Usually meaning art and halftones are not combined on a given spread.)

Production

34. Inking is consistent, solidly black. Contrast with the sheet is firm.
35. Paper is sufficiently opaque to avoid strike-through of backup pages.
36. Imposition does not waver; e.g., margins do not waver.

1977

In 1977, prizes were awarded to 12 medical, pharmaceutical and hospital publications. The first prize recipients were *Virginia Medical; Nebraska Medical Journal; Atlanta Medicine; The Bulletin of the Orange County Medical Association,* Orange, California; *Ohio Pharmacist,* and Memorial Sloan-Kettering Cancer Center *Clinical Bulletin,* New York. Each was awarded $500 and a plaque.

Honorable mentions went to *Texas Medicine; Journal of the Mississippi State Medical Association; St. Louis Medicine; Westchester Medical Bulletin,* Purchase, New York; *The Journal of Kansas Pharmacy,* and *Bulletin of the Mason Clinic,* Seattle.

The following are profiles of some of the winning journals, highlighting their outstanding features:

Virginia Medical, published in Richmond by The Medical Society of Virginia, has a circulation of about 7,000. It was edited by W. Taliaferro Thompson, M.D., of Richmond, and Ann Gray, managing editor. The monthly publication was cited for its excellent writing, crisp editing, variety of content, with an emphasis on news and a simplified format with a strong organization of departments.

Texas Medicine, published in Austin by the Texas Medical Association, has a circulation of about 12,000. Don G. Harrell, M.D., of Dallas, was chairman of the board of publications; Joseph M. Abell Jr., M.D., of Austin, was chairman of the scientific publication committee, and Marilyn Baker was managing editor. The attractive covers, the use of large-size type, white space and other features which make the monthly publication extremely readable were among the assets cited by the judges.

The **Nebraska Medical Journal**, published monthly in Lincoln by The Nebraska Medical Association, has a circulation of 1,900. The editor was Frank Cole, M.D., of Lincoln. The candid, informal editorials and other features, including humorous and nostalgic items, are combined with original scientific articles and extensive news. Information services include listings of Nebraska offices of governmental and voluntary agencies in the health and related fields.

The **Journal of the Mississippi State Medical Association**, published in Jackson, has a circulation of 2,000. W. Moncure Dabney, M.D., of Crystal Springs, was editor and Nola Gibson was managing editor. The monthly publication concentrates on original scientific papers and articles about state medical subjects and is uncluttered with "fillers."

Atlanta Medicine, the bulletin of the Medical Association of Atlanta, was edited by S. Robert Lathan, M.D., and Eleanor M. Sumerville, managing editor. The 6 × 9-inch, 40-page monthly publication is tightly edited and easy to read.

St. Louis Medicine, the bulletin of the St. Louis Medical Society, is published 20 times a year. George Bohigian, M.D., was editor in 1976 and Theodore L. Paletta, M.D., was editor in 1977. The publication publishes a great deal of material on a very low budget and is extremely responsive to the interests of its readers, as indicated by an annual survey.

The **Bulletin of the Orange County Medical Association** was edited by Arthur D. Silk, M.D., of Orange, Calif. The monthly publication is equal in appearance and content to any regional or state medical journal, and Dr. Silk was given a special commendation.

Westchester Medical Bulletin, published 10 times a year by the Westchester County Medical Society, Purchase, N.Y., was edited by Ira J. Gelb, M.D., of New Rochelle, and Vincent R. Zingaro, managing editor. The publication has changed its format several times since its inception in 1935, including enlarging the typeface and other design revisions for easier reading. The cover article generally salutes the local chapter of a health organization.

Ohio Pharmacist, the monthly publication of the Ohio State Pharmaceutical Association, Columbus, was edited by Gerard Fee, executive director, and Mary Bonelli. The importance of the publication to the Association is indicated by its budget, which is its biggest item, with the exception of staff salaries.

The **Journal of Kansas Pharmacy**, published since 1880 by The Kansas Pharmaceutical Association, Topeka, was edited by Douglas P. Johnson, R.Ph., and Ellen M. Francis, managing editor. The monthly, 1,200-circulation publication, is designed to help Kansas pharmacists and covers a variety of professional subjects.

Clinical Bulletin is published quarterly by Memorial Sloan-Kettering Cancer Center, New York. The staff was headed by Harry Grabstald, M.D., editor-in-chief; Denise D. Wood, editor, and Walter Anderson, managing editor. The journal is distributed to 10,000 physicians and researchers throughout the world and is highly regarded as a useful source of information about current methods of cancer diagnosis and treatment. Every aspect of the publication is exemplary, particularly the photos and artwork which are an integral part of the scientific articles.

The Bulletin of the Mason Clinic is published quarterly at the Virginia Mason Medical Center in Seattle, Wash. It was edited by David G. Fryer, M.D., with the assistance of Bettye Carson. Each issue features several significant scientific articles and brief clinical notes about recent cases. There are no personnel news or features.

The awards were in six categories, in accordance with the circulation and type of publication. The editors or managing editors of eight of the 12 publications were women. The judges gave special commendation to Ann Gray of *Virginia Medical* and Denise Wood of the Memorial Sloan-Kettering Cancer *Clinical Bulletin.*

1978

In the 1978 competition, seven journals won first prizes and 12 received honorable mention.

First Prize Winners

The largest number of entries was from the large-circulation state medical journals. The first-prize recipient, **Michigan Medicine**, is the official journal of the Michigan State Medical Society, East Lansing. Published monthly, with a circulation of 8,200, *Michigan Medicine* was edited by Herbert A. Auer, deputy director of the Society, and Judith Marr, managing editor. Major changes in the format were made every year in order to stimulate current and new readers. Duotone photos on the covers, convenient location of contents page on inside front cover, line drawings, cover and special articles printed on colored paper, effective use of several colors for headlines, efficient use of boldface type, crisp editing, omission of jump articles, and other innovations were indicative of great effort and creativity. *Michigan Medicine* was unusual in its omission of research and clinical reports, and instead concentrated on medical and related news of interest to physicians in the state.

The **Journal of the Oklahoma State Medical Association**, published monthly in Oklahoma City, with a circulation of 2,700, includes scientific articles, together with a variety of news and features. The lively editorials by

Editor Mark R. Johnson, M.D. are extremely candid and often are reprinted in other publications. The readability is enhanced through effective use of white space between the lines and elsewhere, "blurbs" and other quotations as breaks within long articles and repetition of the cover within the issue to introduce the feature article.

The **Greater Kansas City Medical Bulletin**, the monthly publication of the Jackson County Medical Society, was edited by Andrew McCanse, M.D. The circulation of 2,500 is for physicians in Jackson and Clay Counties in Missouri and Johnson County in Kansas. Each issue included photos and biographies of all applicants for membership. Other useful features were a two-page monthly calendar of seminars and personal commentaries by medical school and society officers.

Tulsa Medicine, edited by Jack Spears, executive director of the Tulsa County Medical Society, has a monthly circulation of 775. The 6¼ × 9½-inch size is smaller than the 8½ × 11-inch size of most medical journals. The small size and circulation do not diminish the high quality of the color covers, paper, typesetting, printing and other design and production features.

The second-largest number of entries was from state pharmaceutical associations. The first-prize recipient, **California Pharmacist**, is the monthly, 6,400-circulation publication of the California Pharmaceutical Association, Sacramento. Editor Robert C. Johnson and managing editor Martin M. Stevenson paid attention to many details. For example, the neatly ordered text is not strewn about, color is used on the cover and throughout, photo sizes and layout vary and are treated with flair and logic, studio head shots and static and cliche photos are avoided, and the writing style is clear and crisp.

The two hospital award recipients are quarterly publications. The **Henry Ford Hospital Medical Journal** features scientific and clinical articles by staff members and alumni of the Henry Ford Hospital in Detroit. Edited by John W. Rebuck, M.D., Ph.D., the 7,200-circulation journal published significant research and clinical reports in a highly readable and attractive 7 × 10-inch format. A recent issue, for example, was devoted to papers by former residents of Robert S. Knighton, M.D., chairman of the department of neurology and neurosurgery at Henry Ford Hospital. Photos of the alumni reunion brightened and supplemented the papers by eminent physicians who now are located throughout the world.

Saint Raphael's, published by The Hospital of St. Raphael, New Haven, Connecticut, is unique among the winners. It is published for the general public and has a design and editorial approach which presents health care information in a manner similar to general magazines. Edited by Paul J. Taylor, the large-sized (9 × 12 inches) magazine recently doubled its circulation to 55,000, while maintaining a relatively small budget. A recent issue featured articles on annual physicals, artificial bone joints, short-term surgery (titled, "In at Morning, Out by Afternoon") and a description of the pathology department (imaginatively titled, "No Quincys or Jekylls").

Honorable Mentions

Among the honorable mentions, three state medical journals with a circulation in excess of 3,000 were cited. **The Journal of the Medical Association of Georgia,** published monthly in Atlanta, with a circulation of 4,700, was edited by Edgar Woody Jr., M.D. Imaginative covers and well-written boldface excerpts within articles were helpful to scanning readers.

New York Family Physician, published quarterly by the New York Sate Academy of Family Physicians in Binghamton, New York, is one of the few journals of a state specialty medical society. Edited by Martin Markowitz, M.D., of Brooklyn, New York, with a circulation of 4,500, the 6 × 9-inch, 28-page magazine omits scientific papers and information available from other sources. A very low budget does not inhibit its attractiveness.

The Journal of the Iowa Medical Society, with a circulation of 3,100, has been redesigned since it received the Sandoz award in 1976. Marion E. Alberts, M.D., of Des Moines, noted that the cover drawings and other design changes resulted from his attendance at Sandoz journalism workshops. The publication was a neat mixture of scientific articles, editorials, news, features and departments.

Among the smaller-circulation state medical journals, honorable mentions were awarded to **Arizona Medicine** and the **Journal of the Mississippi Medical Association.**

Arizona Medicine, published monthly by the Arizona Medical Association, Phoenix, with a circulation of 2,900, was edited by Marshall B. Block, M.D. Contents, which are listed on the front cover include scientific articles and a variety of news and features. Though photos and artwork are rarely used, the use of large-sized type, white space and simple layout make the journal pleasant and useful to read.

The Journal of the Mississippi State Medical Association, published monthly in Jackson, with a circulation of 2,000, was edited by W. Moncure Dabney, M.D., of Crystal Springs. The publication includes, in the same position in each issue, a typed newsletter and other departments, as well as scientific papers. Nola Gibson was managing editor.

The Cincinnati Journal of Medicine, with a circulation of 2,150, was edited by George X. Schwemlein, M.D., medical editor, and William J. Galligan, managing editor and executive director of the Academy of Medicine of Cincinnati. In addition to scientific articles and news, the *Journal* publishes public relations and perspective columns about local socioeconomic medical issues.

Honorable mentions were awarded to three county medical journals with circulations under 2,000. **The Bulletin,** published monthly in Bakersfield, California, by the Kern County Medical Society, has the smallest circulation, 640, of any of the award recipients. Charles Ashmore, M.D., editor, and Myron R. Corbett, managing editor and executive director of the Society, were not restricted by the small size of the circulation and budget. The 6 × 9-inch publication has a full range of departments, including scientific articles, society news, editorials and other features. Color covers are of local scenes.

News Capsule, published 10 times a year by The Fairfield County Medical Association, Fairfield, Connecticut, was edited by Leonard R. Tomat, executive secretary. The budget, one of the smallest of any medical society publication, inhibits use of color and artwork, but this is compensated by simplicity, timeliness and good taste. Circulation is 1,500.

Worcester Medical News, published bimonthly by the Worcester District Medical Society, Worcester, Massachusetts, has a circulation of 2,000 and was edited by Samuel Bachrach, M.D. The contents page, on the inside front cover of the 8½ × 11-inch publication, indicates the variety of departments, including editorials, medical news, society notes and book reviews.

The honorable mention recipient among pharmaceutical publications was **Arizona Pharmacist**, published monthly, with a circulation of 950, by the Arizona Pharmaceutical Association, Phoenix. The editor was H. Juanita Servatius. The 8½ × 11-inch colorful publication has been redesigned by Richards & Associates, a design firm in Phoenix.

The two honorable mention recipients among hospital publications were the **Nassau County Medical Center Proceedings** and the **Bulletin of The Mason Clinic**. The *Proceedings*, published quarterly by the Nassau County Medical Center, East Meadow, New York, has a circulation of 5,200, primarily on Long Island. Editor Carl Pochedly, M.D., was assisted by V.T. Maddaiah, Ph.D., and Mable Pochedly. The 7½ × 10-inch format features extremely readable 10-point type, sharp photos, bold headlines and colorful covers. Clinical and news articles are tightly edited.

The Bulletin of the Mason Clinic, published quarterly in Seattle, Washington, has a circulation of 4,000. David G. Fryer, M.D., was editor and Bettye Carson was managing editor. The 6 × 9-inch, compact format is uncluttered, clean and well-balanced in design and content. Most of the articles are clinical and research reports, which are illustrated by photographs and drawings by clinic staff members.

1979

First Prize Winners

Pennsylvania Medicine, the monthly publication of the Pennsylvania Medical Society, Lemoyne, has a circulation of 15,000. The staff was headed by David A. Smith, M.D., medical editor, and Mary L. Uehlein, managing editor. The magazine has a good combination of medical, legal and socio-economic articles. One of its most popular features is Medigram, a newsletter which appears on the first few pages.

Among the smaller-circulation state journals, the first prize was awarded to **The West Virginia Medical Journal**, published monthly by the West Virginia State Medical Association in Charleston. Circulation is 2,440. Stephen D. Ward, M.D., of The Wheeling clinic, was editor; Charles R. Lewis was managing editor, and Custer B. Holliday was executive assistant. High-quality paper and printing help to make the well-structured layout easy to read. The scientific and news sections are clearly defined, and recently were improved with new headings.

Among the larger-circulation local medical journals, first prize was given to **Cincinnati Medicine**, the quarterly, 2,800-circulation publication of the Academy of Medicine of Cincinnati. Dianne Bricker was director of communications, and her predecessor, Linda J. Phelps, was managing editor in 1978, when the publication was launched.

Cincinnati Medicine replaced the *Cincinnati Journal of Medicine*, which had shown a progressive decline in readership. The exciting new format omits scientific articles and features such relevant subjects as "Drop-In Medicine," about the increasing use of emergency rooms as clinics.

The Worcester Medical News, the bimonthly, 2,000-circulation publication of the Worcester District Medical Society, Worcester, Massachusetts, was edited by Samuel Bachrach, M.D. Highlights were candid editorials and controversial features. The November–December, 1978 issue, for example, featured editorials by Dr. Bachrach about jail medicine and Federal standards on hospital beds, articles by University of Massachusetts medical students titled "Should Hitler Be My Patient" and "Medical Ethics," and a personal report by a former Worcester County jail physician.

The top prize for a pharmaceutical journal was given to **The Maryland Pharmacist**, the monthly 1,450-circulation publication of the Maryland Pharmaceutical Association in Baltimore. David A. Banta was editor and Sharon Spies was assistant editor. Many photographs were used, mostly taken by Abrian Bloom, staff photographer, and reproduced on a good quality paper.

The first prize in the hospital category went to **Vita**, the quarterly magazine of Medical Center Hospitals in Norfolk, Virginia. Started in 1978 and produced by Graffic Traffic Studios in Norfolk, *Vita* is a free magazine sent to 40,000 potential contributors and others in the eastern Virginia area. J. Michael Keating, public relations director of the Hospitals, was editor and David F. Thomas of the Studios was contributing editor. A recent issue featured illustrated articles about patent medicines, arthritis and kidney transplants.

Honorable Mentions

Maryland State Medical Journal, the official monthly publication of the Medical and Chirurgical Faculty of the State of Maryland, is published in Baltimore and has a circulation of 6,000. James G. Zimmerly, M.D., was editor and Blaine Taylor was managing editor. Regular features include a radiological case history, county medical society, auxiliary and committee reports, original articles by and various prominent government officials, lawyers, judges and others, including Neil Solomon, M.D., Ph.D., a syndicated health columnist who is Maryland State Secretary of the Department of Health and Mental Hygiene. Since 1975, the *Journal* has been publishing a series of articles by Blaine Taylor which describe how health has played a significant part in international political and historical events.

The Journal of the Medical Association of Georgia, published in Atlanta with a circulation of 4,700, was edited by Edgar Woody Jr., M.D. The managing editor was Susan J. Dillon. Sections were neatly grouped for scientific articles, features, editorials and news.

The Journal of the Medical Association of Alabama, published in Montgomery with a circulation of 4,000 was edited by William L. Smith, M.D. William H. McDonald, director of communications of the Association, received a special commendation for creative layout and graphics techniques, particularly the annual Christmas card and other imaginative, colorful covers. Whereas most editors strive for orderliness and predictability, Mr. McDonald intentionally heightens expectations and awareness by variety.

Cooperation, the bimonthly publication of the Missouri Association of Osteopathic Physicians and Surgeons, is published in Jefferson City, with a circulation of 1,300. Edward H. Borman was editor and Bruce A. Barth was publications director. Scientific articles are omitted and the emphasis is on news, editorials, features and photos, produced competently with an extraordinarily small budget. This was the first osteopathic publication to receive a Sandoz award. Another outstanding publication in this year's competion was *Buckeye Osteopathic Physician*, the monthly journal of The Ohio Osteopathic Association, edited by Jon F. Wills.

Chicago Medicine, the 9,300-circulation semi-monthly publication of the Chicago Medical Society, was produced by a hard-working staff headed by William J. Monaghan, editor, and Kathy McEwen, managing editor. Recent improvements include more photographs, shorter news items and a cover format which highlights the contents in a colorful, dignified manner.

LACMA Physician, which also is published semi-monthly, is the Bulletin of the Los Angeles County Medical Association. Circulation is 10,500, one of the largest of any medical journal. Arthur J. Riesenfeld, M.D., was chairman of the editorial board and Sharon Brown was managing editor.

In August, 1979, the publication, which previously was titled the *Bulletin*, underwent considerable plastic surgery, with the assistance of designer Lou Falcone. From the page-one contents to the last-page calendar, the orientation has been on clarity and readability.

Among the small-circulation medical journals, an honorable mention certificate was presented to **The Bulletin of the Marion County Medical Society**, a 1,400-circulation monthly magazine published in Indianapolis, Indiana. Harold W. Hefner was executive director of the Society and editor of the *Bulletin*. In 1978, in its 70th year, the publication was redesigned, with larger headlines and body type, increased use of art and summaries of meetings instead of verbatim reports.

The Utah Pharmacy Digest, the monthly publication of the Utah Pharmaceutical Association, Salt Lake City, has a circulation of 600, the smallest of any of the winners. Paul W. Muller, a pharmacist, is managing editor. Large-size type with wide spacing between the lines makes the two-column format very readable.

The Nassau County Medical Center Proceedings, published quarterly by the Nassau County Medical Center, East Meadow, New York, has a circulation of 5,400, primarily on Long Island. Editor Carl Pochedly, M.D., is assisted by V.T. Maddaiah, Ph.D., and Mable Pochedly. The 7½ × 10-inch format features extremely readable 10-point type, sharp photos, bold headlines and colorful covers. Clinical and news articles are tightly edited. A redesign in 1978 strengthened the cover, so that it is one of the most attention-getting, readable and informative of any medical publication.

Special Awards

Special prizes of $250 each were presented to medical journals in Indianapolis, Houston and Sacramento.

The Journal of the Indiana State Medical Association, published monthly in Indianapolis with a circulation of 5,330, received first prize in the 1976 competition and has attained a continued level of excellence. Last year, the publication was redesigned, and it now has brighter and more colorful covers and interior pages, standardized department heads, larger headlines and bolder use of white space, boxes and other graphics techniques. The judges praised Frank B. Ramsey, M.D., the long-time editor, and Martin T. Budger, the new managing editor, for "adding impact to quiet conservatism."

Harris County Physician Newsletter, published semi-monthly by the Harris County Medical Society in Houston, was cited because it is one of the few publications which uses the newsletter format. The four pages are easy to scan and read, with boldface lead-ins for each item. Laura Reesby was editor of the 4,700-circulation publication, which, along with the medical magazines in Chicago and Los Angeles, is one of the few to be published 24 times a year.

Perhaps the most unusual format is maintained by **Sacramento Medicine**, a monthly tabloid newspaper published by the Sacramento County Medical Society. The 1,200-circulation covers Sacramento and El Dorado Counties in California. D. Gilbert Wright, M.D., was editor; William E. Dochterman, executive director of the Society, was assistant editor, and Joleane M. King was managing editor. As a result of a format change in 1978, the 11 × 16-inch, 12- to 16-page newspaper now features short articles on a variety of subjects.

The judges also commended Paul S. Kamleiter, editor of the **Dallas County Pharmaceutical Society Newsletter,** monthly circulation 800. The annual total cost to the Society is about $300! Pharmacist Kamleiter writes it and then does the complete camera-ready layout during his spare time at home. A Dallas drug wholesaler pays for the printing. More important than the extraordinary budget, which probably is a national record, is the quality of the publication. Almost all of the articles are originals, and not rehashes or pickups from state and national publications, and the stress is on local news.

1980

Over 100 journals entered the 1980 annual Medical Journalism competition and 15 of these received awards. The first prize of $500 was given to the *Journal of the Medical Association of Georgia, Portland Physician* (Oregon), *Illinois Pharmacist* and the *Magazine of the American Association of Medical Society Executives.*

Special prizes of $250 each were presented to the *Maryland State Medical Journal, Connecticut Medicine*, the *Bulletin of the Los Angeles County Medical Association* and the *Harper-Grace Hospitals*, Detroit.

Honorable mentions were credited to the *Journal of the Tennessee Medical Association;* the *Bulletin of the Marion County Medical Society*, Indianapolis; *The Imperial Medical Bulletin of Polk County Medical Asso-*

ciation, Lakeland, Florida; *Chicago Medicine; California Pharmacist; Georgia Pharmaceutical Journal* and the *Bulletin of the Mason Clinic*, Seattle. Following are descriptions of the winning journals:

The top award among the state medical journals went to the **Journal of the Medical Association of Georgia**. Published in Atlanta, with a circulation of 4,700, the monthly magazine was produced by Edgar Woody Jr., M.D., editor, and Susan J. Dillon, managing editor. Reflecting a trend among local journals, most of the issues were devoted to a theme of general interest.

A recent issue on teenage pregnancy featured data, articles and editorials, plus regular departments about association activities. The cover was an original drawing of the poignant expression of a pregnant teenager. The artist, Richard Lyons of Richard Heiman Advertising, was responsible for the striking covers, which include old woodcuts.

Special awards were given to two other state medical monthly journals, *Maryland State Medical Journal* for editorial excellence, and *Connecticut Medicine* for scientific merit.

Maryland State Medical Journal, with a circulation of 6,000, was produced in Baltimore by James G. Zimmerly, M.D., editor, and Blaine Taylor, managing editor. Though the publication has excellent graphics, particularly its photography, the judges cited the extraordinary range of subjects, notably well-researched historical features and distinguished coverage of socio-economic issues and commended Mr. Taylor for his creative, vigorous writing.

Connecticut Medicine, with a circulation of 5,300, is published by the Connecticut State Medical Society in New Haven. The editor, Fred Fabro, M.D., of Torrington, stressed scientific content. A typical issue of over 70 pages has about six clinical, research and scientific articles, each with an introductory abstract, plus a variety of editorials, general news and department reports.

The Journal of the Tennessee Medical Association, which received an honorable mention, has a circulation of 5,200. Produced in Nashville, the staff included John B. Thomison, M.D., editor, and Jean Wishnick, managing editor. Miss Wishnick was cited for simplifying and enlivening the graphics.

Local Medical Journals

The top award among the county and city medical journals was to **Portland Physician**, the 2,100-circulation publication of the Multnomah County Medical Society, Portland, Oregon. Editor Stacey Graham Wilson, who was responsible for one of the nation's most attractive and readable medical publications, produced the monthly magazine within an extremely small budget. Designer Douglas Osborn also was credited for the major changes made in 1979.

LACMA Physician, the Bulletin of the Los Angeles County Medical Association, received a special $250 award for continued excellence, particularly the dramatic cover photos and other graphics. The semimonthly publication has a circulation of 10,500, one of the largest of any medical journal. Arthur J. Riesenfeld, M.D., was chairman of the editorial board, and Sharon Brown was managing editor. In 1978, the publication underwent considerable plastic surgery, including a name change and major design improvements. Graphics and editorial strengthening continued in 1979.

Three local journals received honorable mentions: *The Bulletin of the Marion County Medical Society*, Indianapolis; *The Imperial Medical Bulletin of the Polk County Medical Association*, Lakeland, Florida, and *Chicago Medicine*. Circulation ranges from 1002 in Lakeland to 9300 in Chicago!

The Marion County Bulletin was produced by Harold W. Hefner, editor, and Jackie Freers Stahl, assistant editor. The monthly magazine, with a circulation of 1,450, was totally redesigned in 1978, and improvements have continued. Alternate issues salute a local hospital, with a cover drawing by K.P. Singh, a native of India who is an architect in Indianapolis.

The Imperial Medical Bulletin is a small-size monthly publication produced in Lakeland, Florida, by Ronald W. Case, M.D., editor; John W. Glotfelty, M.D., photographer, and Elsie M. Trask, managing editor and executive director of the Polk County Medical Association.

Chicago Medicine, the 9,300-circulation semi-monthly publication of the Chicago Medical Society and The Medical Society of Cook County, was produced by William J. Monaghan, editor, and Kathy McEwen, managing editor. The editors continued to maintain an appearance which is clean, simple, attractive and a pleasure to read.

Pharmaceutical Journals

The top award among the state pharmaceutical journals was to **Illinois Pharmacist**, the 3,700-circulation publication of the Illinois Pharmacists Association, Chicago. The editor was Alan L. Granat, executive director of the Association. The monthly magazine was published jointly with the Illinois Journal of Pharmacy from 1977 to 1979. In September 1979, the two publications separated, and the Illinois Pharmacist emerged in a completely new format, which is well organized, attractive and lucid.

Honorable mentions were presented to *California Pharmacist*, the monthly publication of the California Pharmacists Association, Sacramento, and *Georgia Pharmaceutical Journal*, the monthly publication of the Georgia Pharmaceutical Association, Atlanta.

California Pharmacist has a circulation of 7,000, one of the largest of any pharmaceutical publication. Editor Nancy Martini concentrated on writing style, and the news articles were among the best of any medical or pharmaceutical publication.

Georgia Pharmaceutical Journal, with a circulation of 2,000, was edited by Larry Braden, a pharmacist who also was executive vice president of the Georgia Pharmaceutical Association. Major design and editorial changes were made in 1979, with a new orientation to objective, third-person reporting, rather than the views of the Association.

Other Publications

A first prize was awarded to **The Executive**, the quarterly publication of the American Association of Medical Society Executives, Chicago. The 1,000-circulation magazine was edited by Dennis L. Breo and published by one of the Association's members, the Harris County Medical Society in Houston. The judges noted that "a haphazard publication was completely overhauled in late 1979 with exciting photos, judicious use of color, timely articles and other major changes."

A special award of $250 was presented to **Harper-Grace Hospitals of Detroit** for its collection of publications, ranging from a weekly bulletin to an annual report, produced under the auspices of Frank F. Bredell, director of public relations. Mr. Bredell edited *Pacemaker*, a general magazine sent free three times a year to 14,000 physicians and donors. Joan Baldwin edited the *Harper-Grace Medical Bulletin*, a weekly newsletter distributed to 1,500 physicians and others.

An honorable mention was given to the **Bulletin of The Mason Clinic** in Seattle, Washington. The 4,000-circulation quarterly journal, which also received honorable mentions in 1977 and 1978, has been redesigned to reduce costs, improve picture quality and maintain the dignified appearance. The staff included David G. Fryer, M.D., medical editor, and Mary B. Wieckowicz, editor.

1981

Prizes were awarded to 17 medical, pharmaceutical and hospital publications in the sixth annual medical journalism competition conducted by Sandoz Pharmaceuticals.

The four recipients of first prizes of $500 each were *Virginia Medical, The Bulletin of the Orange County Medical Association* (California), *Pennsylvania Pharmacist* and *Albany General Hospital* in Albany, Oregon.

Honorable mentions were credited to 13 publications, including seven published by state and local medical and pharmaceutical associations: *Pennsylvania Medicine, Michigan Medicine, The Western Journal of Medicine, Bulletin of the Los Angeles County Medical Association, Cincinnati Medicine, Georgia Pharmaceutical Journal* and *Florida Pharmacy Journal.* The two honorable mentions to hospitals are *Pacemaker Magazine* of Harper-Grace Hospital, Detroit, and *St. Francis Life,* of St. Francis Medical Center, La Crosse, Wisconsin. Special category honorable mentions were *The Internist,* published by the American Society of Internal Medicine, Washington, D.C.; *Synergy,* published by The Ohio State Medical Association, Columbus; *The Ohio D.O.,* published by Ohio University College of Osteopathic Medicine, and *The Long Island Pediatrician,* published by the Long Island chapter of the American Academy of Pediatrics, East Meadow, New York.

Medical Journals

The top award among the state medical journals was to **Virginia Medical,** the monthly publication of The Medical Society of Virginia. Published in Richmond, with a circulation of 7,000, the magazine is produced by W.T. Thompson Jr., M.D., editor; Duncan S. Owen Jr., associate editor, and Ann Gray, managing editor. *Virginia Medical* also received the Sandoz first prize award in 1977, and the judges expressed special commendation to Ms. Gray, whose editorial resourcefulness has produced such delightful features as reproductions of physician signatures with a discussion of their hieroglyphics.

Among the state medical honorable mentions, *Pennsylvania Medicine* and *Michigan Medicine* previously received first prizes, and both were commended for continued excellence.

Pennsylvania Medicine is published monthly by the Pennsylvania Medical Society, Lemoyne, with a circulation of 15,000. David A. Smith, M.D., was medical editor and Mary L. Uehlein was managing editor. The covers have been consistently the most attractive and inviting of any state or local journal. During the last year, the publication changed paper stock and effected other economies without diminishing its outstanding appearance.

Michigan Medicine, the monthly journal of the Michigan State Medical Society, East Lansing, has a circulation of 9,000 and was edited by Judith E. Marr. Since changing its format in 1976, *Michigan Medicine* has been a leader in the trend to socioeconomic reporting. Each issue features a special report, with four to six articles on such topics as election issues, medical students, hospices and Indochinese refugees.

The Western Journal of Medicine is published monthly in San Francisco by the state medical associations of California, Idaho, Nevada, Utah and Washington. Its circulation is 44,000. The staff included Malcolm S.M. Watts, M.D., editor; Lloyd H. Smith Jr., M.D., associate editor, and David Greer, managing editor. The publication combines clinical case reports and scientific articles with editorials and features, and is presented in a traditional format, including the complete contents page as the cover.

The top award among the county and city medical journals went to **The Bulletin of the Orange County Medical Association,** which received the same honor in 1977. The monthly publication, with a circulation of 2,300, is published in Orange, California, and edited by Arthur D. Silk, M.D., of Garden Grove. The clarity of design and writing made this publication one of the most outstanding in any category.

LACMA Physician, the Bulletin of the Los Angeles County Medical Association, is published 20 times a year, with a circulation of 10,500. The editorial board was headed by Arthur J. Riesenfeld, M.D., and Sharon Brown was managing editor. Interviews with government officials and others are lively and timely.

Cincinnati Medicine, published quarterly by the Academy of Medicine of Cincinnati, has a circulation of 2,350 and was edited by Leslie D. Laine. Started in 1978, the publication received a first prize in 1979 and has continued to experiment with graphics changes, including excellent use of photography.

Pharmaceutical Journals

Pennsylvania Pharmacist, the monthly journal of the Pennsylvania Pharmaceutical Association, Harrisburg, received first prize in the pharmaceutical category. Stanley T. Singer, executive director of the association was editor, and circulation was 2,400. Printed on glossy stock with a two-column format, the publication has an uncluttered layout which is easier to read than many others in this category.

Honorable mentions were given to the monthly publications of the Georgia Pharmaceutical Association and Florida Pharmaceutical Association.

Georgia Pharmaceutical Journal has a circulation of 2,200 and was edited in Atlanta by Larry L. Braden, R. Ph., executive vice president of the association. The use of color and artwork has been increased since the publication was launched in 1978.

Florida Pharmacy Journal has a circulation of 3,200 and was edited in Tallahassee by Editor Jim Powers and his wife, Managing Editor Pat Powers. The cover colors are well-designed invitations to read the feature articles.

Hospital Publications

Albany Journal Hospital, Albany, Oregon, received first prize for its *Life Line,* a quarterly magazine for about 3,000 employers, volunteers, patients and community leaders. Christine Craft of Chris Craft Photography, Albany, was responsible for the publication—which features a greater quantity and quality of photography than almost any other publication of this type.

Pacemaker, a three-times-a-year magazine of Harper-Grace Hospitals, Detroit, received an honorable mention. Edited by Frank F. Bredell, the attractive magazine is sent to 15,000 employees, volunteers and community leaders. The public relations department of Harper-Grace Hospitals was commended for its array of publications, particularly the bulletins and brochures edited by Joan M. Baldwin.

St. Francis Life, the quarterly magazine of St. Francis Medical Center, La Crosse, Wisconsin, also received an honorable mention. Thomas L. Sunde, director of public information, was editor of the 25,000-circulation, color tabloid, which is sent to donors and community leaders.

The fourth miscellaneous category also produced honorable mentions to four unusual publications. **The Internist**, the 17,000-circulation, monthly publication of the American Society of Internal Medicine, Washington, D.C., was edited by William Campbell Felch, M.D., and Connie Schantz, managing editor. The publication is not a research or clinical journal and makes excellent use of photographs and visual techniques to report news of its meetings and relevant issues.

Synergy is an offbeat monthly tabloid published for patients by The Ohio State Medical Association. Carol Wright Mullinax was editor. Circulation is 14,000 and distribution is to association members for placement in their waiting rooms. Easy to read, the four-pager has as its motto, "You and your doctor working together to keep you healthy."

The Ohio D.O., the quarterly publication of Ohio University College of Osteopathic Medicine, Athens, was edited by Carl Jon Denbow, Ph.D., and has a circulation of 4,000. The first issue, which was published last summer, featured a color cover photograph of a couple kissing, to highlight the article on the first graduation of osteopaths at Ohio University.

The Long Island Pediatrician, which also received an honorable mention, is published semiannually by the Long Island chapter of the American Academy of Pediatricians. The editors were Carl Pochedly, M.D., and his wife, Mable Pochedly, of the Nassau County Medical Center, East Meadow, New York. Though the circulation is only 800, the magazine is as well produced and written as any medical magazine.

1982

In 1982, the seventh annual *Medical Journalism* competition was held and 22 medical, pharmaceutical and hospital publications won awards. First prize recipients were *Texas Medicine, MSDC News*, the monthly newspaper of the Medical Society of the District of Columbia, *Ohio Pharmacist* and *Horizon*, the magazine of the Hospital for Special Surgery in New York.

Special awards of $250 were given to the *Bulletin of the Orange County Medical Association* in California, *Quality Review Bulletin*, the journal of the Joint Commission on Accreditation of Hospitals and the *Journal of Biocommunication.*

Honorable mentions were credited to 15 publications including seven medical, five pharmaceutical and three hospital publications: *Pennsylvania Medicine, Michigan Medicine, Colorado Medicine, LACMA Physician* (Los Angeles County Medical Association), *San Francisco Medicine, Detroit Medical News, Sombrero* (published by Pima Country Medical Society in Tucson, Arizona), *Florida Pharmacy Journal, Alabama Pharmacy, Missouri Pharmacist, Georgia Pharmaceutical Journal, Nevada Pharmaceutical Association News, St. Francis Life* (St. Francis Medical Center, La Crosse, Wisconsin), *Innerview* (La Crosse Lutheran Hospital, La Crosse, Wisconsin) and *Pacemaker* (Harper-Grace Hospitals, Detroit, Michigan).

Following is a breakdown of the journals into their respective categories—medical, pharmaceutical and hospital—and a brief description of the features which made them prize winners:

Medical Journals

The top award among the state medical journals is to **Texas Medicine**, the monthly journal of the Texas Medical Association in Austin. Edited for many years by Marilyn Baker this 21,000-circulation publication combines scientific articles with news, features and editorials. The superbly designed magazine has extraordinary covers which generally are dramatic photos or art related to the articles. For example, the October 1981 cover of *Texas Medicine* was an abstract painting of a blue sky to symbolize the bright outlook as a result of the Medical Practices Act. Several articles discussed the new law. The designer was Ed Triggs, who has designed many of the covers.

Among the three honorable mentions in the state medical journal category, two—Pennsylvania and Michigan—previously received awards, and they were commended for continued excellence.

Pennsylvania Medicine is the 16,000-circulation monthly publication of the Pennsylvania Medical Society in Lemoyne, Pa. The managing editor is Mary L. Uehleim, and the medical editor is David A. Smith, M.D. The covers, which are unusually varied, were among the best of any medical journal, and the articles also were stimulating, including many on such controversial topics as toxic waste management, nuclear energy, health-care costs and malpractice risk management.

Michigan Medicine, the 9,000-circulation, monthly publication of the Michigan State Medical Society, E. Lansing, has been edited for many years by Judith E. Marr. The publication is an outstanding example of service to members, with a large number of departments and features. Research articles and clinical reports are not published in this news magazine. Excellent graphics include four-color covers and bold headlines.

Colorado Medicine, the 5,000-circulation, monthly publication of the Colorado Medical Society, Denver, was edited by William S. Pierson. A new format, introduced in 1980, combines scientific articles, news and features in an attractive, easy-to-read manner. The managing editor was R.G. Bowman, executive vice president of the Society.

The first prize among the county and city medical publications is to **MSDC News**, the 3,400-circulation, monthly newspaper of the **Medical Society of the District of Columbia**, Washington, D.C. The staff was Carlos Silva, M.D., editor; F.P. Ferraraccio, executive editor, and Dianne L. Bricker, managing editor. The tabloid newspaper size, which was redesigned in 1981, is unusual among medical publications. The three-column format is highly readable, with considerable white space, bold headlines, photos, charts and artwork. Emphasis is on lively, late-breaking news, rather than committee reports and other archival material. The judges were especially impressed by such bold changes as switching from two colors in the old format to one color in the new version, with no loss of attractiveness and some savings in printing cost.

Honorable mentions were presented to four local medical publications, published in Los Angeles, San Francisco, Detroit and Tucson.

LACMA Physician, the bulletin of the **Los Angeles County Medical Association**, is published 20 times a year. Arthur J. Riesenfeld, M.D., was editorial board chairman; Sharon Brown was executive editor, and Howard Bender was managing editor. The 10,500-circulation magazine is exceptionally well edited in its clear writing and design.

San Francisco Medicine, the 2,400-circulation, monthly magazine of the San Francisco Medical Society, combines a large amount of news, features and departments. Sheldon Gross, M.D., was editor and Carole M. Warner was managing editor.

The Detroit Medical News is published weekly by the Wayne County Medical Society. With a circulation of 3,400, the prodigious project was supervised by Susan Adelman, M.D., editor; Sidney D. Kubernick, M.D., co-editor, and Roger F. Mecum, executive director. Essentially a three-column, 12-page newsletter, the publication concentrates on membership news and local events.

Sombrero is the 900-circulation, monthly magazine of the **Pima County Medical Society**, Tucson, Arizona. Eloise R. Clymer was editor and Constance D. Wry was associate editor. They are physicians' wives who did everything—writing, editing, layout, photography, advertising and mailing.

The $20-annual subscription and the advertising revenue makes the low-budgeted publication self-sustaining, with no subsidy from the Society.

Pharmaceutical Journals

Ohio Pharmacist, the 4,200-circulation, official publication of the Ohio Pharmaceutical Association, Columbus, received first prize in the state pharmaceutical category. Edited by Amy Bennett, R. Ph., the monthly magazine included scientific articles, as well as news, features and departments.

The judges noted that the greatest overall improvement, particularly in covers, content pages and other design, was shown among the entrants in this category. The first prize winner and several of the honorable mentions were as attractive as award-winning state medical journals, in spite of budgets which often were lower.

Honorable mentions were credited to publications of the state pharmaceutical associations in Florida, Alabama, Missouri, Georgia and Nevada.

Florida Pharmacy Journal, the 3,000-circulation, monthly publication of the Florida Pharmacy Association, Tallahassee, has been edited for many years by Jim Powers, editor, and his wife, Patsey J. Powers, managing editor. In 1981, the editors continued to improve the magazine, which has received awards in past years, and made several design and production changes. Paper was changed from 60-pound opaque cover and 50-pound inside to coated stock. Type style was changed from 10-point souvenir to melior, with romic-bold headlines. The color cover often uses a dramatic black-and-white photo.

Alabama Pharmacy, the 2,000-circulation, monthly publication of the Alabama Pharmaceutical Association, Birmingham, was edited by Jon D. Baranier. The magazine was extensively redesigned in 1981, with additional color, photographs, text "blurbs" and other graphic devices. In addition to the "face-lift," extensive editorial changes, including a reduction of technical articles and the addition of guest editorials, added to the liveliness. Black-and-white covers, which often are exceptionally dramatic and attention-getting, provide proof that additional colors can be important but are not essential.

Missouri Pharmacist, the 1,800-circulation, monthly magazine of the Missouri Pharmaceutical Association, Jefferson City, was edited by Deedie K. Bedosky. Design changes in 1981 included a new nameplate and format. Clarity is enhanced with a single typeface.

Georgia Pharmaceutical Journal, the 2,200-circulation, monthly publication of the Georgia Pharmaceutical Association, Atlanta, was edited by Larry L. Braden, R. Ph., executive vice president. A relatively new publication (started in 1979), the magazine continues to reflect design and editorial changes.

Nevada Pharmaceutical Association News, the 500-circulation, quarterly publication of the Nevada Pharmaceutical Association, was edited by Nancy Martini. The only winner with a traditional newsletter format, the three-column publication ranges from six to eight pages. The *News* has the smallest circulation and budget of any winner. Though the Association office is in Reno, the editor's office is in Sacramento, California.

Hospital Publications

Horizon, the 13,000-circulation magazine of The Hospital for Special Surgery, New York, was awarded first prize in the category for hospital and miscellaneous publications. The oldest orthopedic hospital in the country, The Hospital for Special Surgery publishes *Horizon* three times a year as part of an external public relations program to attract patients, staff and donors. The editor-in-chief was Andrew J. Dvosin, who also was director of public relations. Art Director John Yadrick and Photographer James Prince were commended for the magnificent color, and black-and-white photographs which are used profusely. The Spring 1981 issue (which was the first issue) featured a cover photo of the upper end of a femur and included photo essays on Roosevelt Island (as seen from the Hospital, which is on the East River of Manhattan), ballet (Mikhail Baryshnikov performed at a benefit for the Hospital), interviews with staff members and an article on bone formation (written by Joseph R. Hixson, a prominent medical freelancer). Horizon is one of those rare publications which is a delight to look at, as well as to read. The contents page, for example, is a perfect model of thoughtful, careful design and writing.

Of the three honorable mentions, two are hospitals in the same city, La Crosse, Wisconsin, which is not nationally renowned as a medical or journalism center. **St. Francis Life,** the 20,000-circulation, quarterly magazine of St. Francis Medical Center was edited by Thomas L. Sunde, who also was director of public information and marketing communications. Redesigned in 1981 from a newspaper to a magazine, the new format encourages many large-size photos. For example, the Fall 1981 issue featured a cover photo of a helicopter to illustrate a four-page article about the Medical Center's heliport. The five photos with the article were tightly cropped, dramatic accents to the action. Other recent cover articles, also vividly written and illustrated, were about the involvement of a staff cardiologist with the U.S. Olympic Ski Team and the visual options of contact lenses.

Innerview, the 10,000-circulation quarterly publication of La Crosse Lutheran hospital, was edited by Luanne Sorenson. Each issue is devoted primarily to a specific medical service, such as renal dialysis and obstetrical care. The 24-page magazine is 8½ × 12, an offbeat size which enhances its distinctiveness and permits a three-column format with large-size photos, many full-paged or framed in the center of a large area. The liberal use of white space, the wise selection and placement of excellent black-and-white photos, the use of large-type blurbs and captions in a second color, and other sophisticated design techniques were a credit to Illustrator Kathy Troyanic, Medical Media Director Joe Mengel and others, including the La Crosse Printing Company.

Pacemaker, the 15,000-circulation publication of Harper-Grace Hospitals, Detroit, is published three times a year for employees, volunteers and community leaders. Editor was Frank F. Bredell and Assistant Editor Joan Baldwin. Mr. Bredell, who also was director of public relations, and Ms. Baldwin, assistant director, also were responsible for a weekly *Medical Bulletin*, a beautifully illustrated Annual Report and other publications. *Pacemaker* and *St. Francis Life* also received honorable mentions last year.

Special Awards

Special awards were presented to three publications, each of which is unique and thus prompted the judges to add these extra prizes.

The Bulletin of the Orange County Medical Association, a 2,300-circulation, monthly magazine, is published in Orange, California, and edited by Arthur Silk, M.D., of Garden Grove. Last year, the magazine received first prize among local medical publications. This year's prize was in recognition of such extraordinary continued excellence that the *Bulletin* simply sets a standard for any editor to learn from and appreciate. Everything about the magazine, including its 7 × 10-inch size, is distinctive. The number of pages—generally well over 100—was indicative of the extraordinary efforts of Dr. Silk, and his staff, notably Managing Editor John J. Rette and Associate Editor Ann Ricketts. One of the many unusual features is the humor and whimsy in some of the articles, editorials and graphics. The high level of sophistication is reflected in the lovely typeface (Trump Medieval) and intelligent use of borders, ruled lines, white space and other graphics.

Quality Review Bulletin, The Journal of Quality Asurance, is published monthly by the Joint Commission on Accreditation of Hospitals, Chicago. Maryanne Shanahan was editor-in-chief and Barbara Wendorf was executive editor of the 8,000-circulation magazine for health-care professionals and administrators. The goal is to improve patient care by providing information about quality care. High editorial standards are maintained by the editors, who work closely with physicians, hospital administrators, nurses and other quality-assurance profesionals who are the authors and readers. Tables, figures, charts and other graphics are indicative of their hard work and strong commitment to untangle and simplify abstract and overly technical concepts. The magazine was redesigned in September 1981 to display the contents page and other sections with greater clarity and efficiency. "Pull-out quotations" are used effectively to break up all-text pages and highlight key points.

The Journal of Biocommunication is published three times a year by The Association of Medical Illustrators, The Health Sciences Communications Association and the Association of Biomedical Communications Directors. The board of editors, representing the three organizations, was Frank Allan, M.D., of George Washington University Medical Center, Washington, D.C.; Sue Seif, of Medical College of Virginia, Richmond, and Paul Perles of Northbrook, Illinois. The circulation is 1,900, Basically a scientific journal, the two-column articles are superbly enhanced with pen-and-ink drawings, and other illustrations, including the signatures of authors.

1983

Prizes were awarded to 20 medical, pharmaceutical and hospital publications in the eighth annual medical journalism competition conducted by Sandoz Pharmaceuticals.

The four recipients of first prizes of $500 each are *The Journal of the Florida Medical Association, Portland Physician*, (Oregon), *Florida Pharmacy Journal* and *La Crosse General Hospital* in La Crosse, Wisconsin.

Florida received two first prizes, which was unprecedented for any state in the eight years of the competition.

Special awards of $250 each were presented to the *Journal of the Iowa Medical Society, Michigan Medicine, Pennsylvania Medicine, Virginia Medical* and *St. Joseph Medical Center* in Burbank, California.

Honorable mentions were credited to nine publications: *Colorado Medicine, the Journal of the Medical Society of New Jersey, Journal of the Oklahoma State Medical Association, Journal of the Tennessee Medical Association, The Bulletin of the Orange County* (California) *Medical Association, Cincinnati Medicine, Missouri Pharmacist, Connecticut Pharmacist* and *Harper-Grace Hospitals* in Detroit.

Medical

The Journal of the Florida Medical Association, with a circulation of 15,500, is published monthly in Jacksonville. Daniel P. Nunn, M.D., editor, supervised a large staff of full- and part-time editors and contributors, including Robert C. Fore, Ed.D., executive editor; Judith Hill Constantin, managing editor; four other editors, and a consulting editorial staff of about 50 people. The *Journal* generally featured several scientific articles, followed by several special articles and a variety of departments. A discussion of the *Journal's* annual history issue was to appear in this Newsletter.

The Journal of the Iowa Medical Society, with a circulation of 3,400 is published monthly in Des Moines. Marion E. Alberts, M.D., was scientific editor; Eldon E. Huston was executive editor. This publication is a good mix of professional feature articles and departments. It is not flashy or visually striking, and is simply a solid piece of work. Screens and different color stock add variety without increasing costs. All of the writing and layout are designed to sensibly facilitate easy reading. The end result was consistently successful.

Michigan Medicine, the 9,000-circulation monthly magazine of the Michigan State Medical Society, E. Lansing, was edited by Judith Marr. More than any other state medical journal, *Michigan Medicine* has skillfully succeeded in an all-news magazine format, with no scientific or technical papers. Here was the rationale, according to Miss Marr.

"Readership studies demonstrated that our members did not look to our magazine as a prime source of new and significant medical developments. Instead, they asked for more information which would help them on a day-to-day basis in their medical practices. They wanted to read more about legislation, economics, practice management and news about medicine. That is what we try to provide them in a balanced and readable fashion."

Each issue of *Michigan Medicine* has a four-color bleed photograph on the cover, related to a special report which provides detailed information. The magazine was one of the best demonstrations of professional photography, drawings, graphic elements (many in color) and other very pleasing visual features. For these reasons, *Michigan Medicine* has received many awards, including an honorable mention in last year's competition.

Pennsylvania Medicine, the 15,800-circulation monthly publication of the Pennsylvania Medical Society, Lemoyne, Pa., has received many awards, including honorable mention in last year's competition. David A. Smith, M.D., was medical editor, and Mary L. Uehlein was managing editor. Each isue was crammed with news and useful information.

Michigan Medicine and *Pennsylvania Medicine* are similar in their news orientation. Both have a three-column format. *Pennsylvania* separates the columns with ruled lines and uses a slightly smaller typeface.

Virginia Medical, the 6,800-circulation monthly publication of The Medical Society of Virginia, Richmond, also has received several awards. Edwin L. Kendig Jr. was editor and Ann Gray was managing editor. The journal is traditional only in its emphasis on medical and scientific reports and articles, presented in a conventional two-column format.

The design, editing and even the subject matter of *Virginia Medical*, however, are quite unconventional. Ann Gray is one of the most creative editors in this field. She and her associates consistently produce an extraordinarily bright magazine.

Colorado Medicine, the 5,100-circulation monthly publication of the

Colorado Medical Society, Denver, was produced by William S. Pierson, executive editor; R.G. Bowman, managing editor, and Shiela Swan, editor. Woody Colahan, production assistant, deserved special commendation for his many functions as staff artist and designer. His covers were delightful and the layout was particularly clean, with disciplined typography, supplemented with a few simple, strong effects.

The Journal of the Medical Society of New Jersey, a 10,500-circulation monthly in Lawrenceville, N.J., was edited by Arthur Krosnick, M.D. Geraldine R. Hutner was managing editor and Dorothy J. Griffith was assistant managing editor.

America's first medical society (founded July 23, 1766) publishes a traditional journal, with emphasis on scientific articles and case reports, supplemented by general articles and news. The New Jersey *Journal* is completely contemporary, however, particularly in its attractive covers; well-designed contents page; clean, uncluttered layout and tight editing. The leisure interests of physicians also are recognized, such as with a feature on medical philately by Joseph H. Kler, M.D., of New Brunswick.

The Journal of the Oklahoma State Medical Association is a 3,000-circulation monthly publication. Mark R. Johnson, M.D., was editor-in-chief, and the staff included Anita H. Delaporte, director of communications, and Louise Martin, editorial assistant.

The Oklahoma *Journal* combines scientific articles and a variety of news in a traditional two-column format. Boldface subheads and blurbs, additional white face and other improvements during the last year gave the *Journal* a quiet, clean look. Its typography, boxed tables, wide margins, mood-seasonal covers and other features were outstanding.

The Journal of the Tennessee Medical Association, Nashville, is a 5,500-circulation monthly publication. John B. Tomison, M.D., was editor, and Jean Eishnick was managing editor. The *Journal* combined scientific articles and case reports with news and departments in a neat, easy-to-read, two-column format. A somewhat rectangular outline of the state of Tennessee appears on the cover of the *Journal* and also is used to indicate the end of each article.

Portland Physician, the 2,100-circulation magazine of the Multnomah County Medical Society, Portland, Oregon, is published 10 times a year. Arlene Wagar Tiland, communications director of the Society, was editor. A native of Portland, she received a journalism degree from the University of Oregon in 1978 and started editing *Portland Physician* in 1981.

Cincinnati Medicine, the 2,700-circulation quarterly publication of the Academy of Medicine of Cincinnati, was edited by William J. Galligan, executive editor, and Leslie D. Laine, managing editor.

Several striking design changes in 1982 made this past award-winner more attractive. The covers now are four colors instead of two. Trump Medieval Roman is a contemporary replacement for the sans serif body type previously used. Photo captions are in bold Helvetica. A three-column format is broken up with 14-point blurbs in one and two columns. A two-column format sets aside the letters and other special pages, including an op-ed page titled "Second Opinion."

The **Bulletin of Orange County Medical Association**, Orange, Calif., is a 2,600-circulation monthly publication. Arthur D. Silk, M.D., was editor, John J. Rette was managing editor and Cheryl Pruett was assistant editor. The *Bulletin* is unique in its page size—9¾ × 6¾—and unique in many other ways, notably extremely high-quality standards for the paper, typography, layout, printing and every other element. What is really extraordinary, though, are the irreverence, wit, modern approach to controversial subjects and variety of innovations which reflect considerable effort and care by the staff.

Pharmaceutical

Florida Pharmacy Journal, the 3,200-circulation monthly publication of the Florida Pharmacy Association, Tallahassee, was edited by James B. Powers. His wife, Pat Powers, was managing editor. The publication, which received an honorable mention in last year's competition, recently was redesigned. Headlines, previously too heavy, were screened back 3 percent to produce a softer, yet sharply distinguished effect. Brief synopses have been added to the contents page, expanding on the article titles. The cover designs are unique and colorful, with emphasis on journal content.

The nameplate has been slightly changed. The tail of the F in Florida has been removed to provide unity and give better graphic effect. Romic type is used for department heads, and melior type is used for the text, which is slightly larger than the 10-point souvenir used prior to 1981.

Connecticut Pharmacist, the 1,900-circulation bimonthly publication of the Connecticut Pharmaceutical Association, Wethersfield, was edited by Daniel C. Leone, executive director, and Harlan L. Kimball, editorial coordinator. Good contrast photos were reproduced well on quality paper, with a three-column grid format.

Missouri Pharmacist, the 1,600-circulation monthly publication of the Missouri Pharmaceutical Association, Jefferson City, was edited by Deedie K. Bedosky. One of the best edited pharmaceutical journals, *Missouri Pharmacist*, used boldface lead-ins, subheads and blurbs to accent and break up its three-column news format.

Hospitals

Innerview, the 10,000-circulation, quarterly magazine of **LaCrosse Lutheran Hospital**, LaCrosse, Wisconsin, is edited by Luanne T. Sorenson. The unique size—8½ × 12 inches—lends itself to extraordinary layouts, generally featuring big, bold photos. A second color is used on the cover and throughout the magazine in a most effective manner, such as a frame for black-and-white photos, circling a part of a drawing, blurbs and for specific words (e.g., a list of do's and don'ts in which the first word on each line appears in red). A ruled line across the top of the page helps to frame the layout and adds to the harmonious appearance of continuity. Special praise also to LaCrosse Printing Company for its superb reproduction, especially of the many bleeds, reverse type on solid black and other qualities.

Saint Joseph Medical Center in Burbank, California, publishes *On Call*, a quarterly 11 × 14 tabloid, and other publications. *On Call* (15,000 circulation) is a fascinating blend of a newspaper and magazine, with lots of black-and-white action photos and layouts which are always different, in accordance with the text and art. The staff was mainly Rhoda Weiss, director of publications, and Andrea Rosenwein, assistant director. The special award is for the hospital's annual report, a unique publication in the form of a calendar.

Harper-Grace Hospitals, Detroit, publishes *Pacemaker* (a 25,000-circulation, three-times-a-year magazine), *Harper-Grace Medical Bulletin* (a 3,000-circulation, weekly four-pager for the staff) and an annual report. *Pacemaker* is produced by Frank F. Bredell, director of public relations, and Joan M. Baldwin, assistant director. Ms. Baldwin also is editor of the *Medical Bulletin*. Harper Hospital in the Detroit Medical Center and Grace Hospital in northwest Detroit have a total of over 1,400 beds.

1984

Many special awards were presented in the 1984 annual Medical Journalism competition. We believe this was because of the greatly improved quality of many low-budget health publications. In all, 21 prizes were awarded in this ninth annual competition for outstanding appearance and editorial quality.

First Prize Winners

Michigan Medicine, the 9,000-circulation monthly publication of the Michigan State Medical Society, E. Lansing is edited by Judith Marr. The purpose was stated in each issue: "to provide useful information for Michigan physicians about actions of the Michigan State Medical Society and contemporary issues, with special emphasis on socioeconomics, legislation and news about medicine in Michigan."

Each issue of *Michigan Medicine* has a four-color bleed photograph on the cover, related to a special report which provides detailed information. The magazine is one of the best demonstrations of professional photography, drawings, graphic elements (many in color) and other very pleasing visual features. For these reasons, *Michigan Medicine* has received many awards, including a special award in 1983 and an honorable mention in 1982.

Portland Physician Scribe, the 2,200-circulation monthly newspaper of the Multnomah County Medical Society, Portland, Oregon, was edited by Arlene Wager Tiland. The 16-page tabloid (11½ × 17½) was started in January 1983 to provide timely news, as an additon to the bimonthly *Portland Physician*. Mrs. Tiland edited both publications and she deserved wondrous praise. Last year, *Portland Physician* received first prize and this is the first time that an editor has received two consecutive first prizes.

The newspaper was written by professional reporters, under the direction of Mrs. Tiland and managing editor Anita Weier. Columns were written by Brad Davis, executive director of the Society, and John Tamasky, M.D., president. The five-column ruled line format was punctuated with photos on every page, color on page one, headlines ranging from one to five columns and other professional features, such as large-size Cheltenham type, unjustified right margins, italic captions and boldface blurbs and subheads. Production time (typesetting, pasteup and printing) generally was three days! Scribe indeed was breathtaking!

California Pharmacist, the 7,100-circulation monthly magazine of the California Pharmacists Association, Sacramento, was produced by Robert C. Johnson, editor (also executive vice president of the Association), and Hal Silliman, managing editor. Mr. Silliman started in late 1983 and his predecessor, Nancy Martini, also deserved recognition, as well as designer Lisa Bacchini.

Pharmaceutical publications generally operate with modest budgets for graphics and *California Pharmacist* was no exception. It compensated with an orderly three-column layout, liberal use of white space and, most important, sharp writing and editing.

Dimensions, the 15,000-circulation quarterly publication of Hutzel Corporation of America, Detroit, was edited by Pamela A. Young. Hutzel operates two not-for-profit health care facilities in southwestern Michigan, Hutzel Hospital in Detroit and Hutzel Hospital-Warren in Warren. Started in 1983, Dimensions is for patients, staff and benefactors. One of its virtues is the extensive use of many dramatic large-size photos which do not require captions.

Special Awards

Special awards of $250 each were presented to the following publications:

The Western Journal of Medicine, the 50,000-circulation monthly publication of the California Medical Association, San Francisco, was produced by Malcolm S.M. Watts, M.D., editor; Lloyd H. Smith Jr., M.D., associate editor, and David Greer, managing editor. Mr. Greer deserved particular congratulations for superbly combining clinical and other scientific papers with news and other features.

Until 1973, the publication was solely for the members of the California Medical Association and was called *California Medicine*. Since then, it has been a unique regional publication for the members of the medical associations in Idaho, Nevada, New Mexico, Utah, Washington and Wyoming. Recent affiliations were established with the Western divisions of clinical investigation societies in dermatology, pediatrics, research and other fields. In addition, many individuals are subscribers and the circulation revenue has been used to enhance the *Journal's* quality.

The Journal of the Medical Society of New Jersey is a 10,500-circulation publication with 13 issues a year. The editor, Arthur Krosnick, M.D., and managing editor, Geraldine Hunter, received an honorable mention last year. Outstanding design features include four-color covers generally produced by professional illustrators, color used on contents page, easy-to-read Times Roman typeface, charts and tables enhanced with 10 percent screens, perfect-style binding and strong organization of departments.

The Journal of the Iowa Medical Society, with a circulation of 3,400, is published monthly in Des Moines. Marion E. Alberts, M.D., was scientific editor; Eldon E. Huston was executive editor, and Donald L. Neumann was managing editor. Last year, when the *Journal* also received a special award, we stated that this "publication is a good mix of professional feature articles and departments. It is not flashy or visually striking and is simply a solid piece of work."

That statement still is accurate, except that the *Journal* now is exceptional in its special inserts and theme issues, particularly those about health education for patients. The *Journal* recently changed its name to *Iowa Medicine*.

The Bulletin of Orange County Medical Association, Orange, California, is a 2,500-circulation monthly publication. Arthur D. Silk, M.D., was editor and Gail Bularo associate editor. Last year *The Bulletin* received an honorable mention. This publication really is in a class by itself.

The Bulletin is unique in its page size—9¾ × 6¾—and unusual in many other ways, notably extremely high-quality standards for the paper, typography, layut, printing and other elements. What is really extraordinary, though, is the irreverence, wit, modern approach to controversial subjects and a variety of innovations which reflect considerable effort and care by the staff.

Cincinnati Medicine, the 3,000-circulation quarterly publication of the Academy of Medicine of Cincinnati, was edited by William I. Galligan, executive editor, and Leslie D. Laine, managing editor.

The publication has received many awards, including an honorable mention last year. In 1983, Miss Laine introduced a new, cleaner contents page and continued to make other refinements in design and writing style. One of the many pleasing features was the running of articles intact with no jumping to the back pages. More important, the articles were carefully written, with a rhythm which included short sentences and colorful quotations.

Michigan Pharmacist, the 4,800-circulation monthly journal of the Michigan Pharmacists Association, Lansing, was edited by Louis M. Sesti, editor, and Tami McClaren, managing editor. In 1983, the publication was redesigned as part of the Association's centennial celebration. Covers generally used drawings which also are used to illustrate articles. About 30 photos are used in each 46-page issue.

The Internist is the 20,000-circulation publication of the American Society of Internal Medicine, Washington, D.C. It is published 10 times a year and edited by William Campbell Felch, M.D., editor, and Susan J. Reinsel, managing editor.

The Sandoz awards competition does not include national medical journals. *The Internist* was considered to be eligible as it is a magazine with each issue devoted to a single health care topic from the socioeconomic-political view. Thus, its orientation, circulation and format are akin to several state medical journals and hospital publications. The simple three-column grid layout works well, with Century Type for text, avant-garde headlines, broad vertical margins, unjustified right margins, tint boxes and boldface blurbs.

Controversial topics are discussed by physicians, legislators, hospital administrators, insurers and patients. Started in 1959, *The Internist* has evolved from a two-color, 20-page magazine to a four-color, 36-page magazine. More important, its quality reflects the creativity and care of its staff. For example, comments in articles refer to previous or forthcoming issues, so that there is a continuity.

Private Practice, the 185,000-circulation monthly publication of the Congress of County Medical Societies, Oklahoma City, was edited by Karen Cason Murphy. The publication has been vastly improved in design, editorial features and writing quality. Though it has a sizeable budget for printing and mailing (note the circulation!), *Private Practice* operates with a frugal budget for writing, design and production. The end result looks as attractive as publications with much larger budgets.

1985

Prizes were awarded to 20 medical, pharmaceutical and hospital publications in the tenth annual *Medical Journalism* competition conducted by Sandoz Pharmaceuticals.

The four recipients of first prizes of $500 each were *The Journal of the Medical Society of New Jersey, San Francisco Medicine, Journal of Kansas Pharmacy* and *The Mount Sinai Journal of Medicine* in New York.

Special awards of $250 each were presented to *Pennsylvania Medicine, Harris County Physician* (in Houston), *Michigan Pharmacist, Canadian Hospital Association, Harper-Grace Hospitals* in Detroit and the *Joint Commission on Accreditation of Hospitals* (in Chicago).

A special prize of $500 was awarded to *The Bulletin of the Orange County Medical Association* in Orange, California for "such continued excellence that it is in a class by itself."

Honorable mentions were credited to nine publications: *Iowa Family Physician, Virginia Medical, Dallas Medical Journal, Denver Medical Bulletin, Sombrero* (the magazine of the Pima County Medical Society in Tucson, Arizona), *Ohio Pharmacist, Palmetto Pharmacist* (Journal of the South Carolina Pharmaceutical Association), *Texas Pharmacy* and *Roanoke Memorial Hospitals* in Roanoke, Virginia.

First Prize Winners

The Journal of the Medical Society of New Jersey is published 13 times a year in Lawrenceville, NJ. The editor is Arthur Krosnick, M.D., and the circulation is 10,700. Each issue is a "treat." For example, the September 1984 issue celebrated 300 years of medicine in New Jersey. The December 1984 issue featured two articles on compulsive gambling. The covers by Frank Cecala are original works of art worthy of gallery exhibition.

Each issue, which generally is well over 100 pages, includes a collection of scientific and general articles, as well as many departments—membership newsletter, legal bulletin, editorial, meeting minutes, calendar, book reviews, obituaries, new members and other features.

The outstanding qualities of this modern, professional publication are its clarity, legibility and distinctiveness, strong origination of departments, original and timely articles and careful editing. Among the design and production qualities are:

- Perfect binding gives the magazine an attractive, finished look.
- Four-color commissioned covers are attractive and informative, highlighting a scientific article.

- Three-color table of contents page is well designed, engaging and complete.
- Bookman typeface is readable and distinct.
- Photographs and drawings are crisp and clean.
- Charts and tables use a playful 10 percent screen.
- Color screens highlight socioeconomic articles.
- Pages utilize white space, creating an uncluttered look.
- In-house advertising is distinctive and eye catching.

The managing editor is Geraldine R. Hutner, the assistant managing editor is Dorothy J. Griffith and the graphic artist is Frank Cecala. A publication committee of seven people is headed by Paul J. Hirsch, M.D., and an editorial board includes over 30 specialists. The 8 × 11 magazine is printed by Hughes Printing Co. in East Stroudsburg, PA.

San Francisco Medicine, the 3,000-circulation monthly magazine of the San Francisco Medical Society, combines a variety of feature articles with editorials and news departments. R. Eugene Tolls, M.D., is editor and Michelle B. Rodrigues is managing editor. The judges also credited Carole Warner, who was managing editor until late 1984. Many issues are devoted to a single theme, such as alternative medicine, disasters and medical marketing. Excerpts from recent articles will appear in future issues of this newsletter.

The Journal of Kansas Pharmacy is published five times a year, with a circulation of 1,250, by The Kansas Pharmacist Association, Topeka, KS. Ken Schafermeyer, executive director of the Association, is editor, and Jeanne Pangrac is managing editor. Each issue is quite extensive, and varies from about 28 pages to over 50 pages. The weight and type of paper, colorful covers and other features give a quality look, though, in fact, it's a low-budget production.

The Mount Sinai Journal of Medicine is published nine times a year by The Mount Sinai Medical Center, New York. Circulation is 6,000 and subscribers pay $25 a year, which is a bargain since each issue has over 100 pages of text. Started in 1934, the *Journal* has evolved from a collection of case reports to a general medical journal of international esteem.

David A. Dreiling, M.D., has been editor-in-chief since 1974. Lester R. Tuchman, M.D., who was assistant editor for five years and editor for 20 years, still functions as a consultant, with the title of editor emeritus. Clair Sotnick is managing editor. Five physicians are associate editors, and over 50 physicians are contributing editors or members of the editorial board.

From 1968 to 1984, the *Journal* was the publication not of one hospital, but of a large medical complex, including five hospitals and a medical school. In 1984, the *Journal* became affiliated with three other institutions, Cedar-Sinai Medical Center in Los Angeles, Mount Sinai Medical Center in Chicago and Mount Sinai Medical Center in Miami, FL.

Many of the issues are devoted to proceedings of meetings at the institutions, such as a symposium on recent advances in monitoring during anesthesia and a series of symposia on medical ethics.

Special Awards

Pennsylvania Medicine, established in 1897, is published monthly by the Pennsylvania Medical Society, Lemoyne, PA. David A. Smith, M.D., is medical editor, Mary L. Uehlein is managing editor and Karen K. Davis is assistant managing editor. The 17,000-circulation magazine was one of the first state medical journals to switch from clinical and research articles to a news format. However, each issue generally includes one or more medical features, such as "Diagnosing multiple personality disorder" (September 1984) and "Subcutaneous venous access for chemotherapy" (November 1984).

The emphasis on news is indicated by the front section, appropriately called Newsfronts. A two-page late-news Medigram, written in crisp newsletter style, is followed with several news articles. Departments, which always start on a new page, include editorials by the editor and members, legislative and legal counsel reports, and a variety of features.

Harris County Physician Newsletter is the 6,000-circulation semimonthly six-page newsletter of the Harris County Medical Society, Houston, TX. The editor is James Hickox, executive director of the Society, with the assistance of Dan Finch, associate director, and Beth Tucker, director of communications. A three-column format permits articles and photos, as well as news briefs.

Michigan Pharmacist is the 4,250-circulation monthly journal of the Michigan Pharmacists Association, Lansing, MI. Louis M. Sesti is editor, Larry D. Wagenknecht is associate editor and Mary Jo Buday is managing editor.

The publication was redesigned in 1984, with a new cover format, and an arrangement of contents to encourage reading throughout the 36 pages. For example, the cover feature article always appears on pages 4 and 5 and the second feature article always appears on pages 22 and 23. Every other month, the first lead feature provides continuing education credits.

Dimensions in Health Service is the 11,000-circulation monthly journal of the Canadian Hospital Association, Ottawa, Ontario. Ruta Klicius is managing editor and Jean-Claude Martin is executive editor. In each issue, the editorial appears in English and French. The other articles, which are in English only, are about a variety of services, programs and management techniques for health care professionals.

Harper-Grace Hospitals in Detroit produce a variety of free publications about activities at these institutions (total of 1,400 beds). Frank F. Bredell, director of public relations, edits several of the publications, including the semi-annual *Pacemaker*, of which Joan Baldwin is assistant editor. *Pacemaker* is a lay magazine with magnificent full-page and large-size photographs.

VIM is a four-page booklet sent quarterly to about 3,500 older people at nursing homes and private residences. Upbeat advice is sprinkled with humor and delightful art. The promotional section describes health education programs at the hospitals.

Quality Review Bulletin is the 7,400-circulation monthly publication of the Joint Commission on Accreditation of Hospitals, Chicago. Karen Gardner is executive editor and Maryanne Shanahan is director of the department of publications. An article about the 238-page blockbuster 10th anniversary issue of *QRB*, published in December 1984, will appear in the next issue of this newsletter.

Honorable Mentions

The Iowa Family Physician is the quarterly journal of the Iowa Academy of Family Physicians, Des Moines. It is edited by Charles E. Driscoll, M.D., of the department of family practice at the University of Iowa College of Medicine, Iowa City, and mailed to all (2,600) physicians in the state, regardless of specialty. The 6 × 9 two-column format features many short items and small-space photos, generally totaling 28 pages. However, the Bookman typeface, liberal use of white space and ruled lines, good quality printing and other features make the magazine easy to read.

Virginia Medical, the 7,200-circulation monthly magazine of The Medical Society of Virginia, Richmond, is almost in a class by itself because of its outstanding feature articles and many other assets. The creativity of the editors is demonstrated by the types of subjects (often controversial), sparkling quality of writing, dramatic covers and other features. Edwin L. Kendig Jr., M.D. is editor and Ann Gray is executive editor.

Denver Medical Bulletin is the 1,500-circulation monthly four-page newsletter of the Denver Medical Society, Denver, CO. James L. Kurowski, M.D., is editor and Ann Stoenner is managing editor. Using a three-column format, the editors generally run front-page features and page-two editorials as two columns and then combine a collection of one-column articles and news briefs.

Dallas Medical Journal is the 2,800-circulation bimonthly publication of the Dallas County Medical Society, Dallas, TX. In 1982, Mrs. Richy Sharshan was employed and directed to improve the publication's appearance. Mrs. Sharshan, who recently was promoted from assistant editor to managing editor, indeed has succeeded in changing the old-fashioned format. For example, she moved the drab contents page from the cover to inside and now uses original art on the covers. She continues to make changes, and fortunately, still uses letterpress.

Sombrero, the 1,050-circulation monthly magazine of the Pima County Medical Society, Tucson, AZ, is a low-budget publication produced by Eloise R. Clymer, editor, and Constance D. Wry, associate editor. The judges noted that the design changes reflected several suggestions made at the Sandoz workshops, though, of course, this is not a criterion for the awards.

Ohio Pharmacist is the 4,000-circulation monthly publication of The Ohio State Pharmaceutical Association, Columbus. Amy Bennett, R.Ph., is editor. The very attractive color covers are inexpensive, as the editor often uses stock photos and clip art. In fact, other features, such as an excellent non-gloss paper, connote quality without extravagance.

Palmetto Pharmacist is the 1,700-circulation monthly journal of the South Carolina Pharmaceutical Association, Columbia, SC. M. Sharon Fennell who is executive director of the Association, is editor, and K.B. Day is managing editor. The use of color on inside pages, commissioning of original articles and stress on tight editing and lucid writing are features which make this publication superior to many other low-budget state pharmaceutical journals.

Texas Pharmacy is the 4,000-circulation monthly magazine of the Texas Pharmaceutical Association, Austin, TX. Luther R. Parker, who is executive director of the Association, is editor, Tom Kleinworth is managing editor and Sara Parzen is editorial assistant. The judges try to study the publication and not be influenced by the entry letter. However, in this case, the letter from Mr. Kleinworth was so comprehensive (Texas-style) that we are reprinting it in entirety for the guidance of other editors.

On Call, the 15,000-circulation quarterly magazine of Roanoke Memorial Hospitals, Roanoke, VA, is edited by Vance B. Whitfield, director of public relations. The generous use of white space and large-space drawings and photographs help to make this a very relaxed, upbeat magazine.

Special Prize

The Bulletin of the Orange County Medical Association is the 2,500-circulation monthly publication of the Orange County Medical Association, Orange, CA. So many qualities of the *OCMA Bulletin* are extraordinary, including its unique size (6⅞ × 10), that the judges awarded it a special prize. Arthur D. Silk, M.D., of Garden Grove, is the long-time editor, John J. Ratte is managing editor and Gail Bucaro is associate editor. Qualities include a simple, elegant design style, spacing between lines and other easy-to-read features, purity of layout and typographic balance, clarity of writing and editing and everything else which reflects the careful attention and impeccable standards of the editors. Reading the *OCMA Bulletin* indeed is a treat!

Paul Fisher's Comments

Paul Fisher, professor of journalism at the University of Missouri, Columbia, MO, has been one of the judges of the Sandoz Medical Journalism Awards since the inception of the project 12 years ago. The following are some of his personal comments after this year's judging session.

Some of the publications seem to have hit a plateau, after years of steady, noticeable climb in their graphic appearance.

Publications that early on recognized the value of graphics continue to work at design, such as to consider:

• Titles as more than labels to be centered above text in small, nondescript, serifless design,

• text as matter for easy reading, rather than a dull, unrelieved report,

• photos as useful beyond showing a face or filling out a column.

And, just as surely, publications perceiving no value in graphics continue to duplicate a look on their pages unchanging now over a decade or more.

As ever, the range of submissions is extremely broad. Extensive, immaculately designed research journals from hospitals—their discipline reflecting professional editing and graphic talents—join newsletters produced on word processors. There are publications dominated by photography, some of it four-color process, and others without any illustration.

The best of the traditional journals now recognize that in the coverage of the annual meeting, a museum showing of ancient tools of the art, and other events, there exists the possibility of inserting into their orderly, highly predictable pages a spread or sequence of spreads capable of introducing an invaluable change of pace, a relief from the business at hand.

Nowhere is appreciation of graphics more apparent than in the hospital external magazines. While the content of the photography is run of the mill —often no more than posing of people—the quality of the photography, and its reproduction in exciting layouts that recognize the importance of size, is very much not run of the mill.

But it's the research journals of the hospitals that win hands down the award for best typography. Here the typesetting is often flawless, though probably more expensive, and control of space and display is beyond reproach.

Decay in text. Overall, the Sandoz Competition entries have not escaped the increased tawdriness the new, cheaper typesetting systems have generally produced on printing everywhere. So long as economies are sought, crude hyphenation and justification programming must be expected. More than ever, there is a need to be as generous in sizing text, now commonly too small. (*Flat out: it's got to be at least 9-point on shorter measures, 10- and 11-point on longer.*)

It's accepted that whatever the authorities arrayed against sans serif design in text settings, its admirers in this competition will continue to specify it. They do wrong and delight in their sinning.

Inking. Overall, the presswork is surprisingly poor. It's a rare publication that comes through with a consistent color—even inking—on all pages. Frequently, pages come up densely black only to be followed by grey dropoffs.

Scrappiness. Publications that do not run fairly extensive editorial pieces—say, two pages and more—across a substantial portion of their issues hazard a scrappy appearance. Some publications dominated by small elements project more the appearance of a scrapbook, with elements seeming to have been pasted onto the page as they chanced to come to hand and as space allowed.

Consider this. On a single page, are a short feature, a news story, a runover concluding an earlier item and several ads of various sizes. Each item presents its own typographic display. It's a terrible situation from the viewpoint of graphic order and interest. And it occurs frequently.

There are no easy answers and, such as they are, they are the responsibility of the editor. An editorial plan/sequence must be established and typographic effects reduced. To these ends compartmentalization of contents —departmentalization—probably is the first step.

Thank you, Paul Fisher! Here are a few final comments from one of the other judges.

Awards were given to two newsletters—*Harris County Physician Newsletter* and *Denver Medical Bulletin.* Obviously, it's difficult to compare newsletters with magazines. Perhaps a separate category for newsletters will be created. Certainly, more local associations should consider switching to the newsletter format, as a way to save money, and more important, communicate news more efficiently.

As with other competitions, the entrants generally are restricted to those who are top quality. This makes it harder for the judges, particularly if they do not want to give awards year after year to the same people.

Is it possible that several excellent publications are not entered in the Sandoz competition because the editors are too modest? Or too busy? Or maybe they believe they are "above" our winners. Or different. Wait a minute. Maybe the non-entrants don't care about the Sandoz awards, or worse, never heard about them! Well, we'll see—next year.

1986

In 1986, prizes were awarded to 24 medical, pharmaceutical and hospital publications. California received more prizes than any state in the history of the project—two first prizes, one special award and five honorable mentions.

The four recipients of first prizes of $500 each were *The California Physician, Cincinnati Medicine, California Pharmacist* and New York Medical Quarterly (New York Medical College, Valhalla, NY).

Special awards of $250 each were presented to *New York State Journal of Medicine, Missouri Medicine, Western Journal of Medicine* and *Hutzel Hospital* in Detroit.

A special prize of $500 was given to *Pennsylvania Medicine*, a monthly news magazine which has become self-supporting from its advertising and circulation revenues.

Honorable mentions were credited to 15 publications: *Texas Medicine, Wisconsin Medical Journal, Orange County* (California) *Medical Association Bulletin, San Francisco Medicine, The Bulletin of the Medical Society of Monroe County* (Rochester, NY), *Portland* (Oregon) *Physician Scribe, Sacramento Medicine, Sonoma County Physician* (Santa Rosa, CA), *College of Pharmacists of Puerto Rico, Michigan Pharmacist, Palmetto Pharmacist* (Columbia, SC), *Texas Pharmacy, Harper-Grace Hospitals* (Detroit), *Hennepin County Medical Center* (Minneapolis) and *St. Joseph Medical Center* (Burbank, CA).

First Prize Winners

California Physician is the monthly magazine of the California Medical Association, San Francisco. Started in 1984, the magazine is sent to 32,000 physician members to provide practical socioeconomic material not found in other publications. Kelly F. Guncheon is managing editor and David B. Horner, M.D., past president of the Californai Medical Association, is chairman of the editorial board.

Since it is competing fiercely for reader attention, *California Physician* vies for prose that is clean and straightforward. The intent is to provide a publication that has the credibility of a journal, the urgency of a newspaper and the graphic presentation of a weekly news magazine.

The format, which strives for readability, is consistent where familiarity and identity are required (department heads, cover and table of contents elements, body faces) and varied where freshness and imagery are key (feature article heads, article graphics, editorial layouts). The emphasis is on clean presentation, complementary typefaces, design balance and fresh approaches to article layout.

Mr. Guncheon also emphasizes cost efficiency. He notes, "In our first 18 issues, we paid for only two photographs and a cartoon. The rest of our photography is done by staff. Our artwork is done by a freelance design consultant, who is contracted to assist us with layout and graphics. The design is a team effort, with all of our staff contributing ideas and assisting with the magazine's presentation," stated Mr. Guncheon.

Cincinnati Medicine, a previous Sandoz Award winner, is the 3000-circulation quarterly magazine of the Academy of Medicine of Cincinnati. The staff is William J. Galligan, executive director, Susan J. Clarke, executive editor, Cullen Clark, managing editor, William C. Miller, M.D., consulting medical editor, Margaret J. Schneider, M.D., "In Remembrance," editor and Pamela G. Fairbank, column editor.

Last fall, Dr. Miller replaced Gary Podolny, M.D., as consulting medical editor. Dr. Podolny was instrumental in transforming the old journal into its bright magazine format.

Mr. Clark appended the following comments to his entry:

"Our readers, like all physicians, have incredible demands on their time. Every issue of *Cincinnati Medicine* must compete intensely for the time and attention of our readers. This competition has forged some great strengths in our magazine. Striking covers grab our readers' attention and draw them into the cover story. Good design makes the book easy to read. An excellent editorial package provides information our readers need, and also information they won't get anywhere else—by putting a local focus on the big issues, by covering significant local developments, and by keeping our readers informed about major Academy projects.

"Another strength of *Cincinnati Medicine* has been our ability to attract columnists and guest writers who are experts in their field—lawyers with an in-depth knowledge of health care issues, business consultants who specialize in practice management, even the governor of Ohio.

"Like every county medical journal, we sometimes feel like David in a world of Goliaths. But with effort and a commitment to good journalism, I believe that we produce an excellent publication."

California Pharmacist is the 7100-circulation monthly magazine of the California Pharmacists Association, Sacramento. Robert C. Johnson is editor and Mary Peppers-Johnson is managing editor.

The judges commended Hal Silliman, who was primarily responsible for the publication's redesign last year. The new look is equal to outstanding state medical magazines and general interest publications with sizeable budgets.

New features of **California Pharmacist** include a four-color photo on the front cover, coated non-glossy paper stock and a heavier paper weight to make reading easier, and a streamlined organization of the editorial copy.

The editorial copy is divided into sections (association news, professional affairs, legislative news, drug reviews, features, people, drugs in the news), with each section attractively labelled at the top of the page.

The quantity and quality of articles in **California Pharmacist** is indicated by its contents page. Here's a part of the contents page of the November 1985 issue.

Cover Story: Join CPhA in San Francisco for the 1986 Annual Meeting —a special time for pharmacists to make policy for the profession and socialize. Details on the meeting, the schedule and hotel and event registration forms are inside.

CPhA keeps pace: New law allows Schedule II oral scripts for hospices

Responding to changes in health care practice, CPhA secured legislation to allow terminally ill patients to more speedily receive medication for the relief of pain.

Can physicians' assistants prescribe and dispense?

The regulating authority over PAs—the Division of Allied Health Professions—says "no!"

Challenges for pharmacy! . . Rebuilding national unity, redirecting education:

In the second article of three, CPhA Executive Vice President Robert C. Johnson points out the work ahead for pharmacy as it moves into the 21st century.

How to build more productive relations with physicians:

Hospital and community pharmacists can easily increase communication with physicians. Doing so further integrates the pharmacist into the health care team—and can bolster pharmacy profits.

Trustee profile: Terry Grant.

District 12 encompasses a vast chunk of California and more than 800 pharmacists. Read how this trustee has been representing the area.

CPhA's academies prepare pharmacists for the future:

Getting pharmacists ready for the 21st century and educating them about current practices are two important functions of the association's academies.

In addition, the issue included these departments: Association News, Coming Attractions, Dickinson's Pharmacy, Building Fund, People, Classified Ads, CE Registration Form and Journal CE test.

The New York Medical Quarterly is published by New York Medical College, Valhalla, New York. It is distributed free to students and sent to health professionals and other paid subscribers. Arthur H. Hazes, M.D., is executive editor, Robert E. Madden, M.D., is editor-in-chief, Renee M. Cohen is managing editor, six physicians are associate editors and 25 physicians are on the editorial board.

The 7 × 10 inch size is distinctive and the two-column layout is very easy to read, particularly because of the pleasant use of white space between articles. The clinical reports and scientific articles include excellent photographs, drawings and tables, as well as cogent abstracts. Ms. R. Cohen often intersperses poetry and essays.

Special Awards

Missouri Medicine is the 7200-circulation monthly publication of the Missouri State Medical Association, Jefferson City. Jordan W. Burkey is editor, Donald G. Sessions, M.D., is associate editor and Laurel Ellison is managing editor.

Miss Ellison, who became managing editor in December 1984, is primarily responsible for the total redesign of the magazine. Here's her report, which is reprinted verbatim as a compliment to her and also its usefulness to others:

I began the redesign by changing the typeface from a dated-looking Caledonia to a more open face, Palatino. In addition, for interest and contrast, I chose Optima for headlines and department heads.

The major change in the area of scientific articles was made by a cleaner, easier-to-read layout on the cover page of each scientific article for the readers' convenience.

Each department head was redesigned for quick recognition and identification. The use of closed, square bullets was incorporated to set off copy and to add an easy graphic element to the pages.

Progress Notes, which had been printed separately and then tipped into the front of the journal, was redesigned to be a part of the regular pages of the journal to save both time and money. Progress Notes, which recaps news of the state medical association, now begins every month on the right hand page following Contents and is set apart from the rest of the journal by its 10 percent bleed gray screen. Copy is set unjustified to give the stories a more informal, inviting appeal.

Regular columns by the president, editor and Auxiliary president were redesigned to incorporate a "blurb" to entice more readers into these pages. In addition, all text is set ragged right to make the copy more conversational. White space has also been used more effectively than in the past. Where before these pages had been set on a measure of 30 picas, I have shortened these to columns of 12.5 picas for easier readability.

The final task was redesigning the cover. My budget was so limited that I could not afford a monthly fee for an artist or other creative services. I believed publishing the contents on the cover would be dull and especially unattractive to advertisers who want readers to have to open up a journal to see what's in it. My solution was to use artwork and photography by Missouri artists of Missouri scenes or, even more desirable, artwork or photography created or owned by our own members.

Since my first appeal to our members to solicit such works for our cover, I have been amazed by the talent and the diversity of submissions by our members. Each month the physicians seem to enjoy seeing the artwork of one of their own colleagues on the cover of the journal. Our entire medical association staff may be the smallest in the nation for the size of our association and each area of responsibility, including our state medical journal, is somewhat understaffed.

New York State Journal of Medicine is the 27,000-circulation monthly publication of Medical Society of the State of New York, Lake Success. Alan Blum, M.D., who was editor since 1983, was succeeded in February 1986 by Pascal J. Imperato, M.D., who had been deputy editor.

The Journal has received international attention for its theme issues, particularly the April 1985 issue on "Minorities and Medicine" and the July 1985 issue on "The World Cigarette Pandemic," which was a sequel to the December 1983 issue on the same subject.

In his introduction to the *189 editorial pages* (plus front and back advertising), Dr. Blum thanked his staff and over 200 other contributors. Here's his report:

"Each of these theme issues took more than a year to coordinate. The minorities issue may be the first of its kind to be published by any medical society and represents the work of nearly thirty authors from throughout the United States. The issue on smoking is the most comprehensive examination of the problem ever published by a medical organization. An emphasis on illustrations—nearly 250 are included in the 200-page publication—was created to stimulate greater awareness of the omnipresent imagery of cigarettes in our society.

"The design of the two theme issues (two other theme issues were produced in 1985) is identical to that of regular issues. In 1983 I selected the typeface, redesigned the nameplate, introduced an editorial well (with various medical society news and information items throughout the advertising pages), and placed the table of contents on the cover as a way of reinforcing a simple, uncluttered format. I reduced the number of category headings, and these are now limited to major ones (e.g., Research Papers, Case Reports, History) that are clearly noted on the table of contents."

The Western Journal of Medicine is published monthly by the California Medical Association, San Francisco, as the official journal of the medical associations in Arizona, California, Idaho, Montana, Nevada, New Mexico, Utah, Washington and Wyoming and also the California Society of Internal Medicine and the western regions of several clinical investigation societies. Its 52,000-circulation is the largest of any local medical publication, and each issue is extremely comprehensive, with an average of 140 pages. The emphasis is on clinical and case reports supplemented by local news. The publication, which has been published since 1902, increasingly receives international recognition. Malcolm S.M. Watts, M.D., is editor,

Lloyd H. Smith Jr. is associate editor and David Greer is managing editor.

An example of Dr. Watt's editorial innovation is the Epitomes section, which each month highlights the major advances in a different specialty with 15 or 20 brief "epitomes" (two or three paragraphs per item) by experts in the field.

The annual special issues, published in December, often are purchased for use as text and reference books. The 1981 issue on cross-cultural medicine was reissued as a hardcover book by Praeger. The 1984 issue on personal health maintenance was written by experts in public health, epidemology and clinical medicine.

The 1985 issue on high-tech medicine opened with an introduction by Dr. Watts and an article, Star Wars in Medicine, by R. Paul Robertson, M.D., of the University of Colorado School of Medicine, who was guest editor for this issue. Here are the titles of part of the extraordinary collection of articles:

Lasers in Ophthalmology

Endoscopic Gastrointestinal Laser Therapy

Cutaneous Laser Therapy

Cardiac Positron Emission Tomography

The Current Status of Magnetic Resonance Spectroscopy—Basic and Clinical Aspects

Basic Principles of Magnetic Resonance Imaging—An Update

Clinical Applications of Magnetic Resonance Imaging—Current Status

Strategies for Treating Autoimmune Disease With Monoclonal Antibodies

Monoclonal Antibodies—Therapeutic and Diagnostic Uses in Malignancy

The New Biomedical Technology

The Molecular Biology of Chromosome Alterations in Myelogenous Leukemia

Combined Heart and Lung Transplantation

Hutzel Hospital, a 394-bed facility in the Detroit Medical Center, publishes **Dimensions**, a quarterly magazine for patients, staff benefactors and others. Pamela A. Young is editor of the lively 32-page magazine. Here's part of her extraordinarily detailed report:

Dimensions magazine is a quarterly magazine that is designed to provide solid medical information to the public and the news media. Its purpose is to get Hutzel Hospital's name out in a subtle manner and to educate our audience regarding current medical topics, technology, research and breakthroughs at Hutzel and the Detroit Medical Center.

With the number of magazines on the market, we felt that we had to attract our audience's attention and to keep them interested in reading *Dimensions.* By using a more consumer-oriented approach, we have found that our readers actually look forward to receiving each issue in the mail. It is not just a typical hospital publication.

One way to sustain our readership is to provide our audience with new and useful information that they can apply to their own lives. There are usually three major feature stories, one "wellness" article that we buy and illustrate with our own photos and several smaller features.

Writers are required to interview patients, their families, members of the professional staff and outside experts. We also try to mix the types of stories, in order to appeal to all readers. Although we are Michigan's largest obstetrical hospital, we also deal with concerns such as male infertility or alcoholism. For example, one issue dealt with penile implants while another talked about balloon angioplasty. We do not use the "theme" type of magazine as many other hospitals do. We feel that a mix of stories is more likely to appeal to our readership. If there is one story that they don't want to read, they may want to look at another.

Our designer uses both contemporary and classic elements when designing each issue of *Dimensions*.

Many magazines use the traditional san serif headlines such as Avant Garde, Futura or Helvetica. We feel that the san serif Gill Sans appears cleaner. It is an unusual but readable typeface and, when used for headlines, the reader is treated to a friendlier look. *Dimensions* is not slick, but it is professionally done and is pleasing to look at. We don't want to overwhelm our readers and make them feel that our stories are too technical to read.

For our Winter, Spring and Summer 1985 issues, the body copy is set in 10/11 pt. Century Schoolbook. This was chosen for its easy readability. Our Fall 1985 issue is set in 10/11 pt. Caslon 224, a new typeface that sparkles on the page. We changed typefaces when we changed typesetters and felt that Caslon would give a fresh look to the pages without confusing our readership.

Blurbs are taken from the main story and are used in the traditional manner—to complement pictures and draw the reader's attention to the story.

Initial capital letters are used in either black or in color. They set off the beginning of most major stories and have become a recognizable *Dimensions* trademark.

Dimensions features a four-color cover and each has attracted a lot of attention. We specifically set up our cover shots and they are carefully planned by members of the editorial team. This team approach has been very effective.

Each shot is carefully staged with studio lighting and we dare to be different. It is an experimental type of creative photography because we know we need something that accurately portrays the main story, yet doesn't turn our readers away.

We try to balance the type of photo used in each issue. For example, one issue may feature a hi-tech shot such as a bone with a joint implant. Another shows a family peering at their newborn baby—but the shot is seen from the baby's crib.

To accent the cover, we use a two-color format in the inside of the magazine. This has been very effective for us because we get that four-color effect with only two colors and the magazine looks bright and clean. The color can also be used to highlight photos and these duotones also add a feeling of warmth and friendliness which is found throughout the magazine.

Other added features include the use of side rules, shadow boxes around blurbs and pictures, and large photos. The three-column layout allows for more versatility in cropping pictures and in designing attractive layouts to complement each story.

Response to our magazine has been wonderful. Readers call to request copies of articles for their friends; others have recommended patients to our staff doctors. Some persons even call to suggest future story ideas. The media also has picked up story ideas and used them to generate other stories. For example, one of the local television reporters read the menopause story in our summer issue and she arranged to do a two-part series on menopause and osteoporosis. Not only did women learn that Hutzel recently opened a menopause clinic, but we received over 200 calls from prospective patients.

Special Prize

Pennsylvania Medicine, the 17,500-circulation monthly news magazine of the Pennsylvania Medical Society, Lemoyne, has received many awards for its editorial excellence. David A. Smith, M.D., is medical editor. Mary L. Uehlein is managing editor, Karen K. Davis is assistant managing editor and Jean Beatty is advertising manager.

The judges added the special prize, which is rare in the history of the competition, because of the many years of excellence of *Pennsylvania Medicine* and also because of an unusual business aspect. The total annual cost to publish *Pennsylvania Medicine* is about $300,000, which is moderate in view of the number of pages (about 70 per issue) and the production and editorial quality. The advertising and circulation income of *Pennsylvania Medicine* has increased every year for the last ten years and *the publication now is self-supporting.* Noteworthy is the increased space sold to non-pharmaceutical advertisers, which is a compliment to Miss Uehlein's editorial skills, as well as to Miss Beatty's success.

At last year's Sandoz workshop, Miss Uehlein described her use of skilled freelance writers who help the small staff to include several dozen articles and news reports in each issue. The conversion of the August issue into a membership directory has had a positive impact on readers and advertisers. Advertising revenue for this issue was about $39,000, higher than any other issue in the history of the magazine.

We congratulate *Pennsylvania Medicine*, and thank them for revealing extensive details about their business:

Pennsylvania Medicine

	1982	1983	1984	1985
Total income	$205,700	$223,500	$255,000	$315,000
Advertising pages	480	495	528	568
Advertising income	195,329	207,470	239,030	300,210
Production expenses	163,340	179,880	199,690	203,000
Pharmaceutical adv.*	100,157	108,295	104,520	142,380
Local adv.**	95,172	99,175	134,510	157,230

*net income
**display and classified

Pennsylvania Medicine operates like a business, with annual budgets and goals. The projected income in 1984 and 1985 was $240,000 and $270,000. The actual income excluded the projections. In 1986, the projected income is $320,000. We hope that *Pennsylvania Medicine* surpasses this projection. You deserve it!

Honorable Mentions

Texas Medicine is the 24,510-circulation monthly publication of the Texas Medical Association, Austin. Mrs. Rae Rajgert is managing editor and Richard D. Cunningham, M.D., is chairman of the editorial committee. The staff includes Jim Busby, articles editor, Donna B. Jones, news editor, and Shari Henson, production manager/editorial assistant.

All covers are prepared by artist Edward Triggs. The cover illustration and color vary considerably, but the sophisticated style is immediately recognizable. The cover design is based on one article, though several others are cited on the cover.

The format is a mix of news, editorials, features, departments and scientific articles (largest number of pages). The monthly column on medicine and the law is quite popular with readers.

Wisconsin Medical Journal is the 7000-circulation monthly publication of The State Medical Society of Wisconsin, Madison. Victor S. Falk, M.D., is medical editor and Mary Angell is managing editor.

A new format, introduced in January 1985, featured several major changes, including the elimination of advertising on front covers, which had been a tradition for over 40 years.

The contents and publication information appear on the inside front cover and first page. Classified ads and meeting announcements are on yellow pages. Annual special issues include a Blue Book, with reference material on medicolegal, socioeconomic, legislative and governmental data, and a Green Book, which is a membership directory.

The Bulletin of the Orange County Medical Association is published monthly in Orange, California. The 2500-circulation publication has received many awards, including a Special Prize last year. However, its many qualities are so extraordinary the judges deemed it necessary to call attention again to the *Bulletin*. It's really in a class by itself and you have to see it to really appreciate the careful attention and impeccable standards of the editors.

Arthur D. Silk, M.D., of Garden Grove is the long-time editor, John J. Ratte is managing editor and Gail Bucaro is associate editor. Qualities include a simple, elegant design style, spacing between lines and other easy-to-read features, purity of layout and typographic balance, clarity of writing and editing and a unique size (6⅞ × 10).

San Francisco Medicine is the 3200-circulation monthly magazine of the San Francisco Medical Society. R. Eugene Polls, M.D., is president (he was editor last year), Arthur E. Lyons, M.D., is the new editor and Shelly B. Rodrigues is managing editor. Each issue features several articles on the same subject, such as computers in the office, insurance, AIDS, as well as news, features and departments.

San Francisco Medicine was a first prize winner last year and therefore was ineligible for any of this year's top prizes.

The Bulletin is published 11 times a year in Rochester, NY, by the Medical Society of the County of Monroe, Rochester Academy of Medicine and the Seventh District Branch of the Medical Society of the State of New York. Philip P. Bonanni is editor and Donna Crossed Bodewes is managing editor of the 1800-circulation magazine. The *Bulletin* combines special articles, features and news in a bright, crisp, lively, pleasant format.

The total cost to the owners is $1,000 a year! The explanation for this feat is that the printer is responsible for all advertising and receives the revenue. Ms. Bodewes negotiated this unusual arrangement three years ago with a local newspaper publisher, Your Brighton-Pittsford Shopper in Rochester. Rochester.

Portland Physician Scribe, a 2200-circulation tabloid newspaper, is published semi-monthly by the Multnomah County Medical Society, Portland, Oregon. Madonna DeLacy is editor of a publication which is unique in several ways, including its 17½ × 11⅜ size. The four-column format is useful for lengthy articles on socioeconomic and other issues, with photos all on one page. The newspaper is published in two eight-page sections. The *Scribe* flag is in color atop of page one, which enables full-color advertising on page eight.

Sacramento Medicine is the 1500-circulation monthly magazine of the Sacramento-El Dorado Medical Society, Sacramento, California. Richard Johnson, M.D., is editor and Joleane King is managing editor.

In 1979, *Sacramento Medicine* received a Special Award for its excellent 12-page format. However, the printing costs became too great and, in October 1985, the publisher switched to a 24-page, one-color, 8½ × 11 format. In fact, it was the first county medical society publication to switch to electronic desk top publishing. Here is their report:

"All composition, from typesetting to camera-ready pages, is accomplished on a Macintosh computer and Apple Laser Writer. No hard copy is given to an outside typesetter. The staff no longer dummies up the galleys. Scissors, tape and wax no longer are used to compose *Sacramento Medicine*. Its crisp uncluttered news magazine format can be produced on the Macintosh computer (including graphics) in half the time of the former tabloid and at nearly half the cost. In fact, in less than one year, the capital investment costs will be recovered and composition costs will be nearly non-existent.

"For readers with a discriminating eye for photo-typesetting, the Laserwriter type with its 1,500 dots per inch is "fuzzier" than the sharp 2,500 dots per inch of other type. We hope to increase the resolution with the arrival of a state-of-the-art laser printer sometime this year. Other than that minor drawback, we're very satisfied with our newfound technology."

Sonoma County Physician is published 11 times a year by the Sonoma County Medical Association, Santa Rosa, California. David J. Quenelle, M.D., editor, and Pamela L. Ronconi, managing editor, produce a first-rate magazine, which is particularly commendable in view of the small circulation (900) and low budget.

In harmony with the magazine's community orientation, its graphic design emphasizes a friendly, open feeling. The warm informal face of Souvenir type was selected for the magazine's banner and standing heads. The traditional, but always-current look, of Times Roman was chosen for the text. Both editorially and graphically, the magazine strives to preserve its link to traditional medical journals. It has achieved its goal of editorial and design excellence.

Revista Farmacéutica de Puerto Rico (Pharmacy Review of Puerto Rico) is the 3000-circulation quarterly magazine of the Colegio de Farmacéuticos de Puerto Rico (College of Pharmacists of Puerto Rico), San Juan. Sandra M. Fabregas is editor.

Revista is the first U.S. publication from outside the continental United States to receive a Sandoz award. Felicitas!

Each 36-page issue is filled with articles (a few are in English), news, photos and advertisements.

Michigan Pharmacist is the 4300-circulation monthly magazine of the Michigan Pharmacists Association, Lansing. Louis M. Sesti is editor, Cheryl L. Robinson is managing editor and Larry D. Wagenknecht is associate editor. *Michigan Pharmacist* received a Special Award last year and thus was ineligible for a prize this year. The Honorable Mention is a recognition of its continued excellence. It is one of the best pharmaceutical publications and compares favorably with many larger-circulation medical publications. The new cover format, developed in 1985, features a color photo or artwork plus easy-to-read highlights.

Paladium is the text typeface. For contrast, tables are set in Helvetica Light. The editorial text content is justified and opinion columns are set ragged right with hairline rules between columns. Departments are identified by the use of standing heads which were redesigned for a cleaner, more readable look.

The editorial coverage follows a formula which complements the design qualities. The first lead feature always appears on pages 4–5, and the second lead appears on pages 22–23.

The four-page "Insider" is a late-news section on different color paper, bound in the center. It is the last item sent to the printer.

Palmetto Pharmacist is the 1700-circulation monthly magazine of the South Carolina Pharmaceutical Association, Columbia. Robert H. Burnside Jr. is the new editor (M. Sharon Fennell was editor in 1985) and K.B. Day is managing editor.

The printer, Professional Printers of Columbia, helps in the cover art and other design and production.

Texas Pharmacy is the 3900-circulation monthly magazine of the Texas Pharmaceutical Association, Austin. Luther Parker is editor and Tom Kleinworth is managing editor. The 36-page publication has a greater variety of articles than in many other pharmaceutical magazines.

In addition to news and columns, each issue includes personality profiles and special articles, all of which require additional time and effort by the small staff.

The clean, orderly consistent design uses 10-point Baskerville for body copy and large size (generally 30 to 36-point) headlines in Eusebius bold.

Harper-Grace Hospitals, a 1400-bed facility in Detroit, publishes *Pacemaker*, a three-times-a-year magazine sent to about 40,000 people in the community. Frank F. Bedell, director of public relations, is editor, and Joan Kolodzies is assistant editor.

The imaginative colors, first-class photography (often full-page or large-space at the beginning of each article), large-size headlines and subheads, and other design and editorial features enable this 24-page publication to compete with paid-circulation consumer magazines. Photos are used on the contents page to illustrate the four major articles. The lead articles in 1985 were titled "New Hope for Cancer" (about a Harper first—a superconducting cyclotron), "Emergency" (a six-page article with large-size type and over 10 photos) and "Window to the Body" (about the center for magnetic resonance imaging being built).

Hennepin County Medical Center, Minneapolis, publishes *Alumni Quarterly*, which is sent to 2800 staff, alumni and friends. Lynn Abrahamsen is executive editor and Monette Johnson is managing editor.

Founded in 1887, Hennepin County Medical Center started the *Alumni Quarterly* in May 1985 to keep in touch with its medical alumni. Like college alumni magazines, the 24-page publication includes considerable news of staff and alumni. The well-written articles feature top-notch photography.

Saint Joseph Medical Center, Burbank, California, publishes a quarterly tabloid newspaper, *On Call*, and an annual report in the form of a unique, magnificent calendar. Both have received considerable recognition, including Sandoz awards. Rhoda Weiss, who is the renowned director of marketing and community relations of Saint Joseph Medical Center, is the editor, assisted by Andrea Rosenwein, Susan Solomon and Gail Fox. *On Call* is an 11 × 14, eight-page mini-magazine. The three-column format permits a variety of photo layouts which is very clean and easy-to-read.